MESON SPECTROSCOPY

A Note from the Publisher

This volume was printed directly from a typescript prepared by the editors, who take full responsibility for its content and appearance. The Publisher has not performed his usual functions of reviewing, editing, typesetting, and proofreading the material prior to publication.

The Publisher fully endorses this informal and quick method of publishing conference proceedings, and he wishes to thank the editors for preparing the material for publication.

MESON SPECTROSCOPY

A Collection of Articles

Edited by

CHARLES BALTAY
Columbia University

ARTHUR H. ROSENFELD
University of California, Berkeley

W. A. Benjamin, Inc.

New York   Amsterdam

1968

MESON SPECTROSCOPY: A Collection of Articles

Library of Congress Catalog Card Number 68-57421
Manufactured in the United States of America
12345K321098

W. A. Benjamin, Inc.
New York, New York 10016

Preface

This volume of collected papers, concerned mainly with mesonic resonances, is based on reviews presented at the Conference on Meson Spectroscopy held at the University of Pennsylvania, Philadelphia, April 26-27, 1968. It is not, however, intended to be the proceedings of the conference. Some of the talks were not written up, while others have been expanded beyond what was presented at the conference. However, we hope that we have assembled a useful volume on the properties of mesons, seen mainly from an experimental point of view.

Since the field is a rapidly changing one, we have placed much emphasis on speedy publication. We hope that the reader will put up with non-uniform typing and some hand-drawn figures in the interest of timeliness.

C. BALTAY
A. H. ROSENFELD

July 1968

Contents

viii   Contents

Opening Remarks

In the name of the Organizing Committee: Charles Baltay, Gerson Goldhaber, Jules Halpern, Art Rosenfeld, Peter Schlein, Walter Selove, and myself, I welcome you heartily and enthusiastically to this meeting.

This meeting enjoys the sponsorship of the University of Pennsylvania whose president, Gaylord Harnwell, is a physicist. The entire physics department with William Stephens, its Chairman, have given enthusiastic support, and I should especially mention our welcoming committee with Henry Primakoff, Sherman Frankel, Al Mann, and others. We are particularly thankful to Mr. Leonard Dill, Assistant to the President of the University, for his invaluable aid in the organizing of our social events done with Jules Halpern who is also our dinner chairman.

Preparations could not have been made without the superb organization of Mirko Nussbaum, the invitations secretary, who computerized the administration and correspondence for the meeting. For the excellence of many technical aspects of the conference, we are grateful to Vaskin Hagopian. I would like to thank Messrs. Manny Doxer and John Rappolt, our departmental administrators, for their most able organizational work; and I especially thank our charming and prodigious secretaries.

It is perhaps not unnatural that the first meson spectroscopy meeting be held here. It is in this building, far from any large accelerator laboratory, that the f-meson was discovered by Selove, Hagopian, Brody, and others. Also, one of the most difficult problems of meson spectroscopy, that of the low energy $\pi\pi$-scattering, is being pursued by several groups of this department, today.

This place is far from a large accelerator but not far from a small Princeton-Penn Accelerator where a number of experiments are carried out by the members of this department. The directorate of Princeton-Penn Accelerator asked me to convey to you their greetings and the following message: the participants of the meson spectroscopy meeting are welcome to submit proposals for new experiments to the program committee at PPA.

The meeting is envisaged to be informal: Discussion participants will not be asked to announce their names and their affiliations before they speak, unless they want to. The *reviewer's* duty is to give a review of the experimental situation and his opinions on a very specific problem or topic, rather than a complete summary of the whole field; for almost every reviewer we have a *commentator* who will express a different point of view or supplement the reviewer. The speakers will not be asked to write the texts of their talks; however, we welcome the initiative of Baltay and Rosenfeld to issue collected papers to which the contributions can be made within terms of slides, or pictorial atlases, or short texts in either telegraphic style or a full text—in all, on a voluntary basis—all left to the speakers to decide. We are inviting free opinions, not only established facts. We have introduced even the rumors to be reviewed in the program. We would like to hear free-style interpretations of data.

We would like to learn which experiments are being done or intended to be done with new experimental methods; but we do not like the practice of stating some very preliminary, insignificant data, of defining these "effects", and of then discussing them as established facts—for no matter how much we like to hear preliminary data we must not forget the hard truth said by Pablo Picasso (conversations about modern painting with Marius de Zayas, 1923):

> *In my opinion to search means nothing*
> *...to find is the thing.*

BOGDAN MAGLIC

ππ Scattering Information from $\pi N \to \pi \pi N$ [*]

W. Selove

University of Pennsylvania

For a meson spectroscopy conference, information on $\pi\pi$ scattering is relevant primarily with respect to known or suggested resonances which couple to the $\pi\pi$ system. The subject of $\pi\pi$ scattering, and $\pi\pi$ phase shifts, has a broader interest, both on general grounds and for a number of specialized reasons that have recently been receiving considerable attention. This report deals primarily with recent attempts to determine $\pi\pi$ phase shifts from the single-pion-production process.

$$\pi N \to \pi \pi N, \tag{1}$$

using the Chew-Low extrapolation procedure.[1]

Much of what I report here is based on data from a multi-laboratory collaboration.[2,3] This report is a strictly preliminary one; the tentative conclusions have for the most

[*] Supported in part by the U.S. Atomic Energy Commission.

part not yet been discussed with the collaboration experimenters.

      I shall first summarize the principal results reported
here.

      1) Baton, Laurens, and Reignier[4] have recently
found using the $\pi^- \pi^0$ system that a very simple form of
Chew-Low extrapolation seems to work well. More recent
evidence indicates that the particularly simple extrapolation
used by Baton et. al. does not always work that well. To
obtain accurate $\pi\pi$ phase shifts it will probably be necessary
to make more complicated extrapolations, requiring considerably more data.

      2) An extrapolation study of the $\pi^- \pi^+$ system indicates
that the T=0 $\pi\pi$ s-wave phase shift, δ_o^0, increases through
90° at a mass of about 720 MeV.

      3) Available evidence concerning the possibility of a
"sharp" resonance (Γ<50 MeV) in δ_o^0 at about 700 MeV is still
insufficient to settle the question.

      4) In the $\pi^- \pi^+$ system, there is a sharp change in the
F-B (forward-backward) asymmetry at about 1000 MeV. The
evidence suggests this is probably a $K\bar{K}$ threshold effect
rather than a new resonance.

      5) Data from reaction (1) is very meager for $\pi\pi$
masses below 400 MeV or so, and so low-mass $\pi\pi$ phase shifts
cannot be well determined at present from this reaction.

      I now discuss these points in more detail.

      The data for the ρ region provide an excellent test
for the extrapolation method. First we note that even
without extrapolation, the physical-region data for the ρ
from reaction (1) have a Δ^2-dependence and angular dependence
that strongly support the OPE model. $d\sigma/d\Delta^2$ is somewhat
smaller than predicted by OPE and falls off more rapidly

with Λ^2. These features, and the decay correlations of the
charged ρ, are well predicted by the absorption-modified
theory, OPEA[5].

Although OPEA works well for the ρ, our objective is
to study the feasibility and consistency of the extrapolation
method. In fact, however, we shall see that the OPEA model
provides some useful guidance regarding the extrapolation
method.

Baton et. al. found that an extrapolation determination
of $\sigma(\pi^-\pi^0)$ at the ρ peak gave good agreement with the unitarity limit $12\pi\chi^2$. The statistical uncertainty in the
extrapolated σ was about 20% at the ρ peak. Baton et. al.
also examined the effect of assuming that

$$d\sigma/d\Lambda^2 \to 0 \quad \text{at} \quad \Lambda^2 \to 0 \tag{2}$$
("Pseudo-peripheralism")

They call this the assumption of "pseudo-peripheralism".
The statistical uncertainty in the extrapolated σ is then
much reduced, to about 7% at the ρ peak. They found that
the agreement with the unitarity limit remained very good.

Constraining the extrapolation according to the
pseudo-peripheralism assumtpion obviously sharply narrows the
statistical error in the extrapolated σ. As explained below,
however, it turns out that this assumption gives inconsistent
results. In general, therefore, one will have to carry out
the extrapolation without the pseudo-peripheralism assumption.
In order to explain this conclusion, we start by considering
some general features of the extrapolation procedure.

Chew and Low pointed out that if the experimental
cross section $d^2\sigma/d\Lambda^2 dm$ for reaction (1) is extrapolated to
$\Lambda^2 = -\mu^2$ then the result should be simply related to the $\pi\pi$

cross section:

$$\left.\frac{\partial^2 \sigma}{\partial \Delta^2 \partial m}\right)_{\Delta^2 \to -u^2} \xrightarrow{\hspace{1cm}} \frac{\Delta^2}{(\Delta^2+u^2)^2} \frac{pm^2}{k^2_{lab}} \sigma_{\pi\pi} C_I \qquad (3)$$

Here Δ^2 is the square of the 4-momentum transfer, u is the
pion mass, m and p are the mass and momentum in the dipion
rest system, k_{lab} is the laboratory beam momentum, and C_I
is a factor including the pion-nucleon coupling constant
and an isotopic-spin Clebsch-Gordan coefficient. [6]

In an idealized "pure OPE" model the relationship
in (3) would hold as an exact equality even in the physical
region. Extrapolation will be particularly simple and un-
ambiguous if the experimental Δ^2-dependence of $\partial^2 \sigma/\partial \Delta^2 \partial m$
differs from this pure-OPE form only by some simple function
of Δ^2. This idea suggests two functional forms which have
been tried for the extrapolation. For pure OPE both would
give straight-line extrapolation. Writing $dN/d\Delta^2$ for the
number of events per unit Δ^2 (in a given interval Δm), these
two functions can be written

$$(\Delta^2+u^2)^2 \frac{dN}{d\Delta^2} \equiv F \qquad (4)$$

and

$$\frac{(\Delta^2+u^2)^2}{\Delta^2} \frac{dN}{d\Delta^2} = \frac{F}{\Delta^2} . \qquad (5)$$

Ideally--i.e., for pure OPE-- one would expect both F and F/Δ^2
to give straight-line plots (Fig. 1).

Experimentally, F/Δ^2 for the ρ region is not constant,
but falls with increasing Δ^2. Baton et. al. found that for
each mass bin in the ρ^- region, in their experiment at

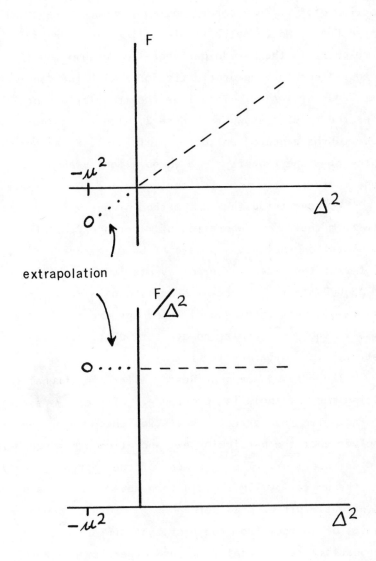

Fig. 1 Idealized extrapolation functions. The extrapolated
values of F and of F/Δ^2, multiplied by known constants,
give $\sigma_{\pi\pi}$.

2.77 GeV/c, F/Δ^2 is consistent with a linearly decreasing function of Δ^2. They correspondingly made a straight-line fit to F/Δ^2. Note that a straight-line fit for F/Δ^2 corresponds to the pseudo-peripheralism assumption (2), and is equivalent to a quadratic fit for F with the constraint that F=0 at $\Delta^2=0$. This linear extrapolation for F/Δ^2 gives the results shown in Figure 2, with $\sigma_{\pi\pi}$ going very close to the expected unitarity limit of $12\pi\chi^2$ at the peak of the ρ. (One expects $\sigma_{\pi^-\pi^0}$ to go slightly above $12\pi\chi^2$ since there is also some scattering in the T=2 s-wave.)

   We have tried the same method of analysis for the data from the $\pi\pi$ collaboration of reference 2. This collaboration includes π^-p data at beam momenta from 1.9 to 3.0 GeV/c; the total number of events is about 30,000 $\pi^-\pi^+n$ and 20,000 $\pi^-\pi^0p$. The results are shown in Figure 3. The $\pi^-\pi^0$ results are in reasonably good agreement with Baton et. al. The $\pi^-\pi^+$ results however are distinctly in disagreement with the unitarity limit.

   The ρ resonance provides a calibrating signal for testing the extrapolation procedure. If the $\pi^-\pi^+$ system does not give the correct results for the ρ we are led to conclude that the particular extrapolation procedure being used is incorrect. The agreement of the <u>charged</u> ρ results with the unitarity limit would then have to be regarded as fortuitous. Differences between $\pi^-\pi^0$ and $\pi^-\pi^+$ could readily result, of course, from the fact that different exchanges are possible; specifically, ω^0 and other isospin-zero exchanges can contribute to the $\pi^-\pi^0$ final state but not to the $\pi^-\pi^+$ state.

   We have examined the available data to test further the reliability of the extrapolation procedure used thus far.

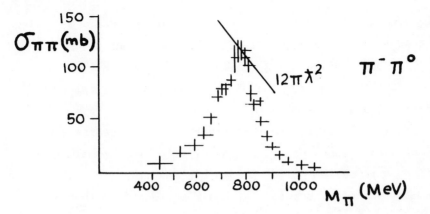

Fig. 2 $\sigma_{\pi\pi}$ extrapolated, from reference 4, using linear F/Δ^2.

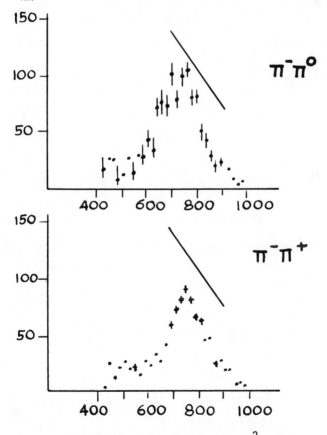

Fig. 3 $\sigma_{\pi\pi}$ extrapolated, using linear F/Λ^2, from data of reference 2.

We find evidence that the linear extrapolation of F/Λ^2
is in fact incorrect, at least for $\pi^-\pi^+n$ events.

One example of this evidence is shown in Figure 4.
This shows $dN/d\Lambda^2$ for the ρ^0 at 8 GeV/c[7]. At that energy
data are available down to Λ^2 values much less than μ^2 --
this is not true for the 2-3 GeV/c data. It can be seen
that $dN/d\Lambda^2$ shows no indication of going to zero at $\Lambda^2=0$.
(The $\pi^-\pi^+$ system at the ρ mass, in reaction (1), is well
known to include substantial contributions from the T=0
s-wave $\pi\pi$ interaction; detailed study indicates that the
finite non-zero value of $dN/d\Lambda^2$ at Λ^2 near zero is not due
purely to this s-wave interaction[8].)

If $dN/d\Lambda^2$ is roughly constant at $\Lambda^2 \to 0$, then

$$F/\Lambda^2, = \frac{(\Lambda^2 + \mu^2)^2}{\Lambda^2} \frac{dN}{d\Lambda^2} \quad ,$$

varies like $1/\Lambda^2$. The linear extrapolation of F/Λ^2 used
in Figs. 2 and 3 is then incorrect. We make several remarks
on this matter: 1) Even with $dN/d\Lambda^2$ non-zero at $\Lambda^2 \to 0$
one can extrapolate the function F; this function, unlike
F/Λ^2, will not have any spurious singularities at $\Lambda^2=0$.
2) Extrapolating F, without the constraint F=0 at $\Lambda^2=0$,
gives results consistent with the unitarity limit, both for
the data of Baton et. al. and for the 2-3 GeV/c collaboration.
Results for the $\pi^-\pi^+$ data from the collaboration, using a
quadratic extrapolation for F, unconstrained at $\Lambda^2=0$, are
shown in Figure 5. Of course this unconstrained extrapolation
gives considerably larger statistical uncertainty in the
extrapolated $\sigma_{\pi\pi}$ than one gets with the constrained extrapolation, larger by a factor of 5 to 7. 3) If $dN/d\Lambda^2$ as a
function of Λ^2 has approximately OPE shape for $\Lambda^2 > \mu^2$ and at
the same time has a shape very different from OPE for $\Lambda^2 < \mu^2$,

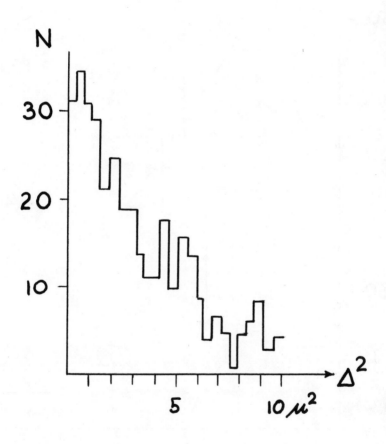

Fig. 4   dN/dΔ^2 for ρ^0 production at 8 GeV/c.

W. SELOVE

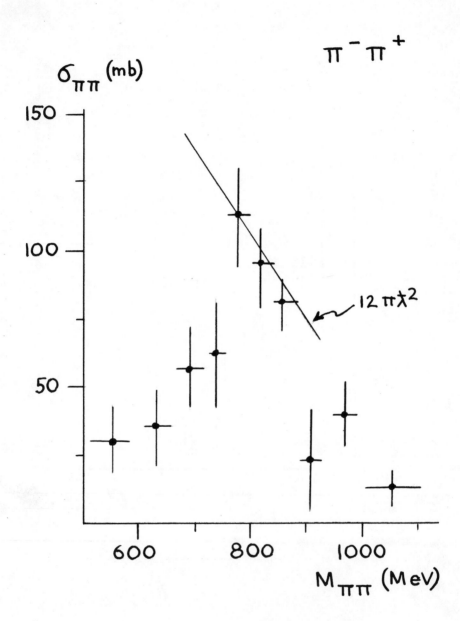

Fig. 5 $\sigma_{\pi\pi}$ extrapolated, using unconstrained F, from data
       of reference 2.

there is no reason to believe that a quadratic extrapolation
for F is adequate for obtaining highly accurate results.
(In order to make internal self-consistency checks for the
adequacy of quadratic extrapolation a great deal more data
would be necessary, at beam momentum high enough to provide
events with Λ^2 much less than μ^2.)

It should be noted that the apparent non-zero value
of $dN/d\Lambda^2$ at $\Lambda^2 \to 0$ is predicted by OPEA theory, which gives
a rather simple physical explanation of this difference
from pure OPE. In effect, absorption is accompanied by
diffraction scattering ("distorted waves"), which fills in
the zero in the primitive OPE Λ^2-distribution.

Up to this point we have discussed only the determination of the total $\sigma_{\pi\pi}$. We turn now to the problem of
determining $\pi\pi$ angular distributions, and phase shifts, by
extrapolation.

To obtain information on the individual $\pi\pi$ phase
shifts δ_ℓ^I one would like to subdivide the data still further,
into distributions in θ, the $\pi\pi$ scattering angle (defined in
the dipion rest system). I.e., we would like to extrapolate
$dF/d\cos\theta$, and not just F. From Figure 5 it is clear that the
present amount of data is statistically inadequate for such
an extrapolation. In an attempt to obtain some information
on the phase shifts we have made an analysis corresponding
to the constraint condition (2)--i.e., we have extrapolated
$\dfrac{d}{d\cos\theta}\dfrac{F}{\Lambda^2}$ as a low order power series. While we have
just seen that extrapolation of F/Λ^2 gives a value of $\sigma_{\pi^-\pi^+}$
which is incorrect by about 20%, we may still hope that this
extrapolation with constraint (2) may at least indicate the
general behavior of the phase shifts. Although this method
may not give perfectly precise numerical values for the phase

shifts, it should be capable of giving the algebraic sign, and should show evidence of any sharp resonances present, for example in δ_o^0.

In Figure 6 we show the cos θ distribution of $\pi^-\pi^+$ data in different Δ^2 bins for one mass interval, for the "$\pi\pi$ collaboration"[2]. We fit these distributions with a power series in cos θ, saving only s and p wave terms, and write

$$\frac{(\Delta^2 + \mu^2)^2}{\Delta^2} \quad \frac{dN}{d\cos\theta} = A_o + A_1 \cos\theta + A_2 \cos^2\theta \quad (6)$$

where $\dfrac{dN}{d\cos\theta}$ is used as an abbreviation for $\dfrac{\partial^3 N}{\partial\Delta^2 \partial m \, \partial\cos\theta}$.

In this s-p approximation, the extrapolated values of A_2, A_o, A_1 should be related respectively to pure p wave, pure s wave, and s-p interference.

Figure 7 shows approximately the behavior of the extrapolated values of the A_n as functions of $m_{\pi\pi}$. What is actually plotted are the A_n multiplied by a factor u, = p/m^2, which according to the OPE relation (3) should give quantities simply related to the s and p phase shifts. We write the resulting relations:

$$A_o u = C\left[\frac{4}{9}\sin^2\delta_o^0 + \frac{1}{9}\sin^2\delta_o^2 + \frac{4}{9}\sin\delta_o^0 \sin\delta_o^2 \cos(\delta_o^0 - \delta_o^2)\right]$$
(extrapolated A_o, etc.)   (7a)

$$A_1 u = C\left[4\sin\delta_o^0 \sin\delta_1 \cos(\delta_o^0 - \delta_1) \\ +2\sin\delta_o^2 \sin\delta_1 \cos(\delta_o^2 - \delta_1)\right]$$
(7b)

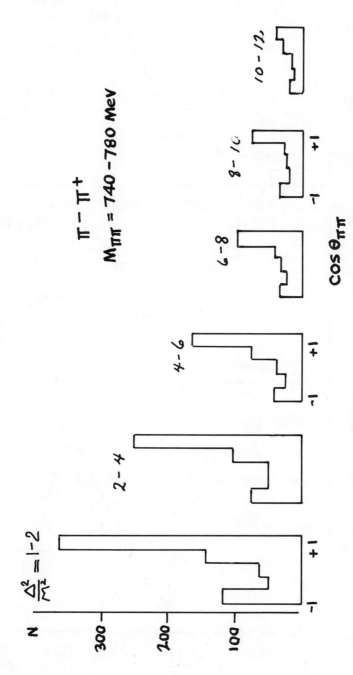

Fig. 6 dN/dcosθ, from data of reference 2.

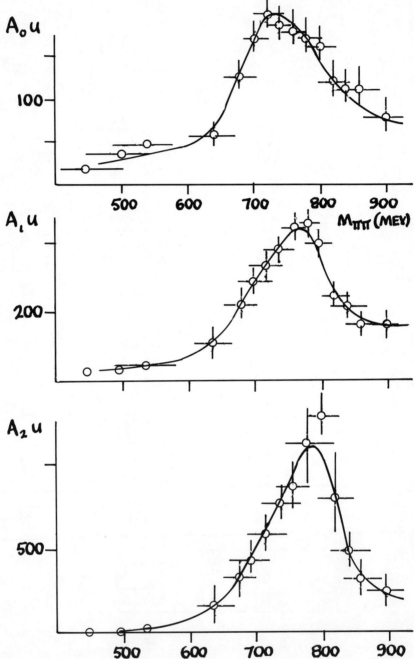

Fig. 7   Extrapolated values of $A_n u$ (see equs. 6,7)
         from data of reference 2.

$$A_2 u = C \left[9 \sin^2 \delta_1 \right]$$

Here C is a common constant. There is some basis for believing that even if, due to incorrect extrapolation, the extrapolated A_n do not have the correct values (see Figure 3), the
ratios of the A_n may still be approximately correct[9]. It
is actually from these ratios, and more specifically from the
ratio A_1/A_2 (see below), that we believe we do get some useful information on the s-wave $\pi\pi$ phase shifts.

A brief remark on the method of extrapolation. For
A_o and A_1 the extrapolated values shown in Fig. 7 were obtained by a linear extrapolation. For A_2, a quadratic extrapolation
was used for most bins; a linear extrapolation was used for a
few mass intervals, in which the numbers of events were
relatively small. The choice of linear or quadratic extrapolation was made simply on the basis of the appearance of the
plots of the A_n vs Δ^2. In general the extrapolated values are
not very different for linear and quadratic extrapolations.

Figure 7 shows that $A_2 u$, which should correspond to
the pure p wave, has a resonance shape, quite similar to that
found for $\sin^2 \delta_1$ (for the other charge state, the $\pi^-\pi^o$) by
Baton et. al.[4] (Figure 8).

We now discuss the information which this analysis can
give on the s-wave phase shifts, δ_o^0 and δ_o^2. First, as to
δ_o^2. Baton et. al., from analysis of the $\pi^-\pi^o$ system, determined the behavior of δ_o^2 (Fig. 8). Our analysis of the
collaboration data[2] gives a similar result, though less
precise--we cannot carry the physical-region points to as low
a value of Δ^2 as Baton et.al., because the experimental biases
at low Δ^2 for the $\pi^-\pi^o p$ final state are less well known for this
collection of data from many laboratories than they were for
Baton et. al. We therefore take δ_o^2 from reference 4.

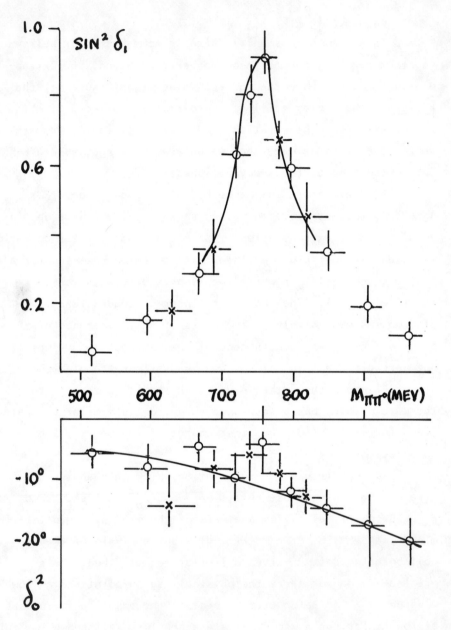

Fig. 8 δ_1 and δ_0^2 from reference 4.

We obtain δ_1 from the collaboration data by taking A_2u to be proportional to $\sin^2 \delta_1$ and by normalizing our curve for A_2u to give $\sin^2\delta_1 = 1.0$ at the ρ peak. We can then in principle use either A_0 or A_1, for the $\pi^-\pi^+$ data, to obtain $\delta_0^{\,0}$. In fact A_0 and A_1 together should give an overdetermined value for $\delta_0^{\,0}$ and should therefore give a consistency check.

Unfortunately, however, A_0 (or A_0u) cannot be used directly to give unambiguous values for the s-wave phase shifts. The reason is best seen by considering the nature of the power series expansion (6) for the case of a pure p wave--i.e., for the case of a pure ρ. For this case ideally A_0 and A_1 should be zero. However, OPEA predicts that as $\Delta^2 \to 0$, A_0 will <u>not</u> go to zero. In fact OPEA predicts that for this case of a pure p wave A_0 (as well as A_2) will diverge at $\Delta^2 \to 0$. If the data do not extend to Δ^2 much less than μ^2 (this is the case for the 2-3 GeV/c collaboration data, at the ρ mass) this divergence may not be at all evident. But even so the prediction of OPEA is still that as Δ^2 goes below μ^2 A_0 as defined in (6) will be positive and increasing. Consequently one expects from OPEA that the linearly extrapolated A_0 will not be zero. Thus one expects that this extrapolated A_0 will have a mass dependence which mirrors the p wave resonance, even if there is no true s-wave scattering at all.

This expectation is borne out when we examine the $\pi^-\pi^0$ data from the collaboration. That is, we find that A_0u does mirror the ρ resonance, even though we believe that $\delta_0^{\,2}$, which is the only s-wave term present for the $\pi^-\pi^0$ system, does not have a resonance, and in fact A_1u, which can also be analysed to give $\delta_0^{\,2}$, does not show any evidence of a

resonance. (Our results for $A_o u$ for the $\pi^- \pi^o$ system appear
to be somewhat different from the results obtained by Baton
et. al. They used a slightly different method of analysis,
however, using a Legendre polynomial expansion instead of a
power series expansion for $dN/d\cos\theta$. Upon examining their
method and result, we believe there is no serious discrepancy
between their results and ours for the $\pi^- \pi^o$ system.)

We therefore believe that $A_o u$ cannot easily be used
to give direct information on the s-wave phase shifts, because, as predicted by OPEA, the very strong p wave effects
near the ρ appear to contribute substantially to the value
of A_o at the edge of the physical region even though in
principle these p wave effects should contribute nothing
to the value of A_o at the pole. Insofar as OPEA is a useful
guide, however, we can expect that $A_1 u$, and particularly
the ratio A_1/A_2, will be much less influenced by absorption
effects, and may therefore give useful information on the
s wave phase shifts.

Before completely leaving A_o, it is worth noting
that the shape of $A_o u$ shown in Figure 7 is substantially
different from the shape of $A_2 u$. We remark that this
difference in shape is present for the $\pi^- \pi^+$ system but <u>not</u>
for the $\pi^- \pi^o$ system. The difference in shape therefore
suggests that there may be a rapidly changing T=0 s-wave
phase shift, δ_o^0, near 700 MeV.

We have determined values for δ_o^0 as a function of
$M_{\pi\pi}$, from the ratio A_1/A_2, obtained from Figure 7. As first
pointed out by Gutay et.al.$^{(10)}$, this method produces in
general a pair of possible solutions, δ_o^0 and $\delta_o^{0'}$, where
$\delta_o^{0'}$ equals $(\pi/2) + \delta_1 - \delta_o^0$. These two values of δ_o^0 are
degenerate if δ_o^0 happens to equal $(\delta_1/2) + (\pi/4)$.

The value of $\delta_0{}^0$ determined in this way is plotted
in Figure 9. The two solutions for $\delta_0{}^0$ are degenerate in
the vicinity of 700-750 MeV. Away from that region, there
are two separate possible curves for $\delta_0{}^0$. According to
Figure 9, one could draw four different curves giving a
smooth variation of $\delta_0{}^0$. These could be called, following
Malamud and Schlein[19], the up-up, up-down, down-up, and
down-down solutions.

The 4 branches for the $\delta_0{}^0$ curve (2 at low mass and
2 at higher mass) shown in Fig. 9 are in good agreement with
other analyses that have been made, without extrapolation,
by Gutay et. al.[10], by Malamud and Schlein[11], and by
Walker et. al. [12]. The present analysis gives one new
piece of information, and that is the indication, from the
behavior of A_0u, that $\delta_0{}^0$ goes through $90°$ more or less
rapidly near 700 MeV. This rules out the high-mass "down"
branch, and leaves only the down-up and up-up solutions. The
sharpness of the rise in A_0u near 700 MeV suggests that the
down-up solution is to be preferred.

The down-up and up-up solutions are shown in Fig. 10.
It must be realized that the wings shown on these points
represent only one standard deviation, of statistical error
only. Before drawing any deep-ranging conclusions from
these results one should remember that the entire theoretical
analysis has a somewhat shaky base, because the extrapolation
procedure we have used is a crude one, and may lead to
significantly incorrect results.

In Fig. 10 we also indicate a few points which have
been suggested as giving information on $\delta_0{}^0$ from other types
of experiments. The K_{e4} results[13], as of the date of
this talk, appear to be uncertain as to sign as well as
magnitude,[14] but the rough upper limit on magnitude is

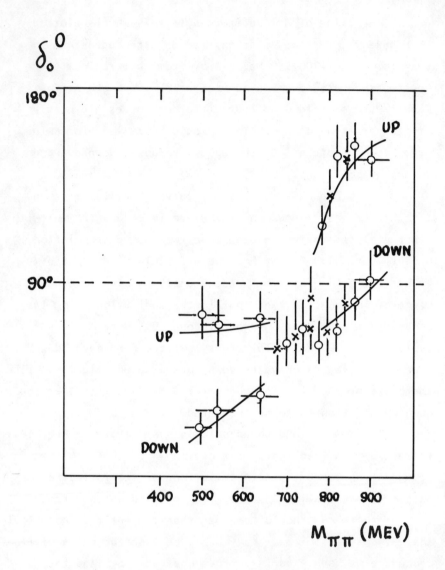

Fig. 9 δ_0^0, determined from data of reference 2.

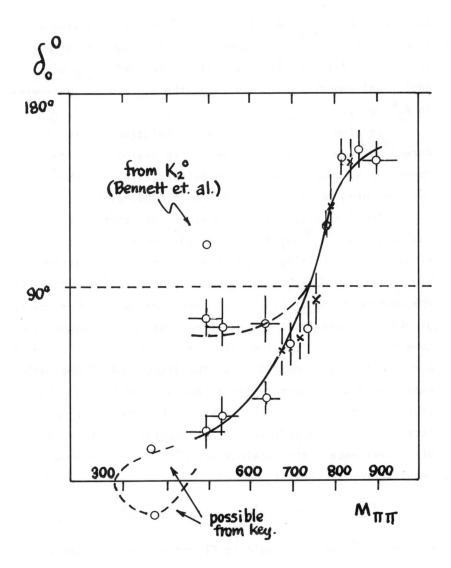

Fig.10 Preferred solution for δ_0^0 (solid line).
Heavy dashed line gives "up-up" possible
solution.

compared to the true width of such an ϵ^0 resonance, then
the height of the ϵ^0 bump compared to the height of the f^0
bump should be ideally about 1/8 (see (3) and footnote (6)).
Since the f height in the $\pi^-\pi^+$ mode is however somewhat
smaller relative to the ρ^0 than simple OPE would predict,
one might expect instead to find

$$\text{height } (\epsilon^0 \rightarrow \pi^0\,\pi^0) \text{ /height } (f^0 \rightarrow \pi^0\,\pi^0)$$

to be about 1/6. But Fig. 11b indicates, for the η, that
the mass resolution is of the order of 100 MeV. Hence a
narrow ϵ^0 would be reduced further in height. If this
reduction were to be about a factor of 2, then the ϵ^0
signal in Fig. 11b would be only about 1/12 the height of
the f^0 signal, and perhaps two bins (50 MeV each) wide. Such
an ϵ^0 signal cannot be ruled out by the data of Fig. 11b.
Moreover, it should be noted that the Δ^2 dependence of ϵ^0
production might well be narrower than for f^0 production;
that would make the true ϵ^0 signal smaller still.

From this type of analysis, applied to all the
experiments which have reported searches for the ϵ^0, I
believe one must conclude that there is still no compelling
evidence one way or the other as to whether there is a
<u>narrow</u> resonance (i.e., $\Gamma \lesssim 50$ MeV) in $\delta_0^{\,0}$ near 700 MeV.

Finally I comment briefly on the behavior of the
forward-backward asymmetry $(F-B)/(F+B)$ in $\pi^-\pi^+$ scattering,
for masses up to 1000 MeV and higher. Veillet's compilation,[18] reported at the Berkeley conference, shows that
$(F-B)/(F+B)$ remains positive and large over the entire mass
range from 500 to about 900 MeV, and then drops suddenly to
a new level, near zero, at 1000 MeV. The persistent positive
value, first of all, indicates that the magnitude of $\delta_0^{\,0}-\delta_1^{\,1}$

remains less than 60° or so throughout the mass range of
500 to 900 MeV[19]. Secondly, at about 1000 MeV the
forward-backward asymmetry does not simply go through
a narrow deviation from which it _returns_ but instead makes
a permanent excursion. The simplest interpretation of this
effect is probably that the T=0 s-wave $\pi\pi$ amplitude
rather suddenly changes from elastic to heavily inelastic.
Such a change, together with a small value of δ_1, would
produce just the observed shift in F-B. And there is reason
to believe, from the $\overline{KK}$ threshold enhancement in $\pi^- p$
collisions, that the T=0 s-wave $\pi\pi$ channel does suddenly
increase in inelasticity just at 1000 MeV.

   To summarize the evidence on δ_0^0: There _is_ evidence
that δ_0^0 does increase through 90° near 700 MeV. It is not
clear that the δ_0^0 curve indicated in Fig. 10 has the
characteristics normally thought of as going with a
"resonance", though it may. For a resonance one would have
expected to see an excursion at the resonance involving a
change of δ_0^0 by 180°--Fig. 10 does not show clear evidence
of such a change.

   One would be more ready to call the δ_0^0 behavior
"resonant" if one saw clear evidence of a very _sharp_
excursion in δ_0^0. Although the available evidence cannot
rule out a narrow resonance near 700 MeV, Fig. 10 shows a
"width" (45° to 135°) of about 100 MeV, for the preferred
down-up curve; and the results shown in Fig. 10 are even
consistent with a reasonably smooth steady ("non-resonant")
increase in δ_0^0 from threshold on up. As one goes past
1000 MeV, the evidence suggests that the T=0 s-wave $\pi\pi$
amplitude becomes heavily inelastic.

   My summary of the situation on extrapolation
determinations of $\pi\pi$ scattering is given in the first few

paragraphs of this report. The data show evidence that at Λ^2 less than μ^2 or so absorption effects cause substantial deviations from the predictions of the primitive OPE theory. These deviations complicate the problem of making correct extrapolations. Even rather crude procedures seem to give $\sigma_{\pi\pi}$ at the ρ peak correct to 20% or so; but it is not clear how reliably one can get the magnitude of non-resonant phase shifts from the amount of data presently available. Theoretical suggestions for improved methods of extrapolation would be very welcome.

References and Footnotes

1. G.F. Chew and F.E. Low, Phys. Rev. <u>113</u>, 1640 (1959).

2. The collaborating laboratories are: Argonne National
    Lab., Univ. of California at Berkeley, Univ. of Colorado,
    Univ. of Michigan, Purdue University, Univ. of Pennsylvania,
    C.E.N. Saclay, Univ. of Toronto, and Univ. of Wisconsin.
    The data used range over beam energies from 1.9 to 3.0 GeV/c.

3. Most of the detailed work of analysis of the combined
    data has been done by S. Marateck, V. Hagopian, and me;
    discussions with experimenters from all the collaborating
    laboratories have been very helpful, and particularly
    important help has been obtained from L. Gutay.

4. J. Baton, G. Laurens, and J. Reignier, Nucl. Phys. <u>B3</u>,
    349 (1967) and Phys. Letters <u>25B</u>, 419 (1967).

5. See J.D. Jackson, Proc. XIII Int'l Conf. on High-Energy
    Physics, Univ. of Calif. Press, 1967, pp. 149 ff, for a
    review and references.

6. This form predicts, e.g., that if the ρ and f^o couple only
    to the 2π system then the ratio of heights of the f^o and
    ρ^o peaks on a plot of $\Delta N/\Delta M(\pi^-\pi^+)$ should be $h_f/h_\rho \approx 5/4$.
    The experimental value, integrated over the physical
    region, is about 3/4 at 5 to 8 GeV/c.

7. Notre Dame--Penn collaboration, J.A. Poirier et. al.,
    Phys. Rev. <u>163</u>, 1462 (1967).

8. H. Yuta, F. Forman, and W. Selove, private communication.

9. According to L. Durand (private communication) it is
    reasonable to expect that absorption effects will have
    less effect on the ratio of s and p wave amplitudes than
    on either one separately. See also M. Bander, G. Shaw,
    and J. Fulco, Phys. Rev. <u>168</u>, 1679 (1968).

10. L.J. Gutay et. al., Phys. Rev. Letters <u>18</u>, 142 (1967).

11. E. Malamud and P.E. Schlein, Phys. Rev. Letters <u>19</u>,
    1056 (1967).

12. W.D. Walker et. al., Phys. Rev. Letters <u>18</u>, 630 (1967).

13. R.W. Birge et. al., Phys. Rev. <u>139</u>, B1600(1965); and
     G. Kalmus, private communication.

14. F.A. Berends, A. Donnachie, and G.C. Oades, Univ. of
     Glasgow preprint, April 1968.

15. S. Bennett et.al., Phys. Rev. Letters <u>19</u>, 997(1967).

16. J. Gezelter et. al., Nuovo Cimento <u>53A</u>, 213 (1968).

17. N. Armenise et. al., Nuovo Cimento <u>54A</u>, 999 (1968).

18. See Proc. XIII Int'l Conf. on High-Energy Physics,
     U. of Calif. Press 1967, Fig. 7-60.

19. This positive value of F-B, and of A_1, throughout this
     mass range, leads to the result that in the K mass region
     $\delta_0^{\,0}$ is positive. The argument is the following. Fig. 9
     indicates that δ_1 varies from 0° at threshold up through
     90° at the ρ mass; at the K mass δ_1 is about 10°. Below
     the ρ mass A_1 does not reverse sign, and $\left|\delta_0^{\,0}-\delta_1\right|$ there-
     fore remains (substantially) less than 90°; $\delta_0^{\,0}$ at the
     K mass is therefore positive--i.e., between 0° and $+90^\circ$.

Low Energy π π Scattering

M. Ross

University of Michigan

One of the most controversial areas of boson physics has been the 2π system. That is why a theorist is giving this talk. I will discuss extraction of $\pi\pi$ phase shifts at low $\pi\pi$ mass from $\pi N \rightarrow 2\pi N$. First let me remark that recent theoretical investigation of Pais and Trieman makes clear that we should be able to obtain in the near future theoretically clean information for the s and p scattering lengths from K_{e4} decay. Professor Pais will be happy to discuss the situation if there are questions.

For $m_{\pi\pi}$ in the ρ region, we should be able to extract the $\pi\pi$ amplitude by extrapolation from $\pi N \rightarrow 2\pi N$ as shown by Chew and Low. (Figure 1). This is largely a theoretical problem. The purpose of my talk is to stress the necessity of an empirical extrapolation, to reemphasize the difficulties of this method, and to suggest some

improved procedures for performing an extrapolation.

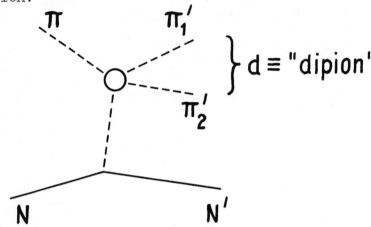

The extrapolation method has progressed recently
especially through the work of the Saclay group,
but there are newly discovered aspects of the
problem which add interest and difficulty.

The ρ was, I think, the first boson resonance found. In Figure 2 I show our present knowledge of its parameters.

RHO PARAMETERS APRIL 1968

		m_ρ	Γ_ρ
Saclay (Baton et al)	Extrapolation	755±5	110±9
Novosibirsk (Auslander et al.)	$e^+e^- \to \pi^+\pi^-$	764±11	93±15 (122±8 acc. to Roos)
Pisut and Roos analysis	Physical Region	764	147

Three different techniques are involved: (1)Extra-
polation; (2) e^+e^- colliding beam experiments (I
take the 93 MeV width more seriously than the 122);
(3) Direct examination of the dipion in $\pi N \rightarrow 2\pi N$.

By far the best statistics apply to the
latter. (Figure 3.)

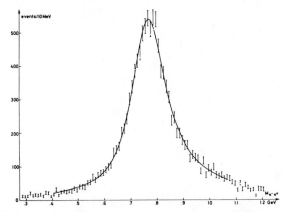

This is a compilation by Roos of a large fraction
of the world's data on ρ. This paper (Pisut and
Roos) contains a nice review of many points, by
the way. In Figure 4 we see fits to physical
region distributions compiled by Schlien and
collaborators. These fits involve momentum trans-
fer form factors$_\wedge$separating t and $m_{\pi\pi}$ distributions.
        effectively
They are very good. However, Figure 5, the extrapolation analysis of Baton et al. using some of
the same data, reveals a much smaller ρ width.
Similar large differences are observed in different
analyses of the s wave $\pi\pi$ amplitudes. The essential
point is shown in the lower curve: the variation
of the t dependence as a function of $m_{\pi\pi}$. The

Baton, Laurens, Reignier, Phys. Lett.

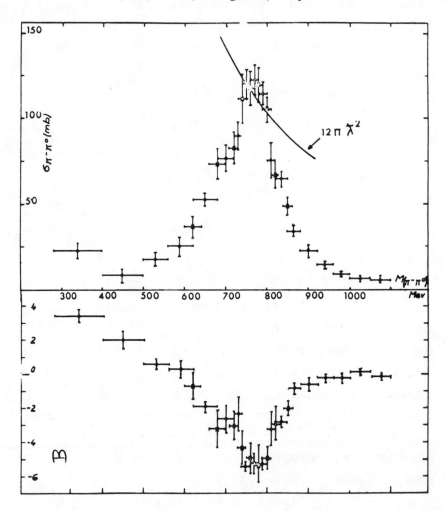

definition of B is $(t-\mu^2)^2 \frac{d\sigma}{dt} / (t-\mu^2) = A+Bt+\dots$.

There are good physical reasons for believing the narrower ρ width obtained by the extrapolation method by Baton et al. (1) Interfering backgrounds are probably present in the physical region. Their form is not yet known so it is difficult to remove them. A neglected background tends to make the resonance appear wider and less sharp in t. A probable background arises from diffraction dissociation as follows

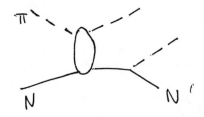

(Walker has made a preliminary study confirming this process.) The low mass $\pi\pi$ system is produced with a cross section $\propto p_L^{-2}$ just as in π exchange but it is not so steep in $t_{NN'}$ nor of course does it have the π exchange pole. (2) Final state scattering of the ρ probably stimulates its decay thus yielding a wider ρ for smaller impact parameter reactions (higher values of -t). Both of these effects are strongly reduced at very small -t.

The proper analysis will lie in detailed extrapolation of <u>moments</u>. Extraction of moments of the dipion rest frame $\pi\pi$ angular distribution has been emphasized by Schlein and collaborators.

I stress that each moment should have characteristic behavior.

Figure 6 shows Legendre moments in the
Gottfried-Jackson frame considered by Baton et al.

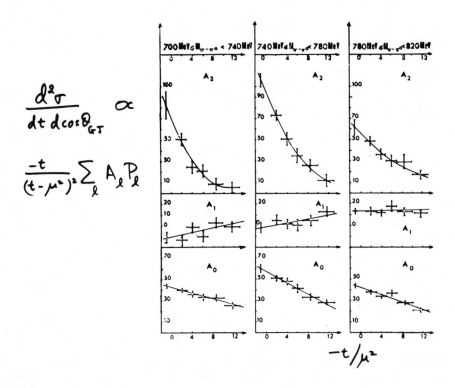

$$\frac{d^2\sigma}{dt\, d\cos\theta_{GJ}} \propto \frac{-t}{(t-\mu^2)^2} \sum_{\ell} A_{\ell} P_{\ell}$$

$$-t/\mu^2$$

This form with t in the numerator of the l.h.s.
should apply if the pion exchange model is exact.
There is clear evidence for significant deviation
of the moments from the pion exchange model.
There is the serious difficulty as we shall see
that the moments A_0 and A_2 defined this way have
a pole at t = 0. I now want to report some work
on this problem by Gordon Kane and myself.

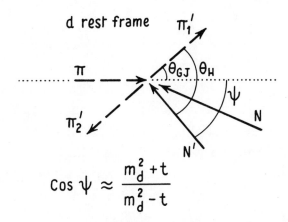

$$\cos \psi \approx \frac{m_d^2 + t}{m_d^2 - t}$$

Consider the center of mass helicity frame rather
than the G-J frame, Figure 7. This is the form
which is most convenient for absorption model
calculations and theoretical considerations
generally. The absorption model contains correct
physics for the qualitative effects I want to
discuss. The nucleon helicity flip cross section
with s and p waves is shown in Figure 8. The

S and p waves

$$\text{Amplitude} \propto \sum_{\mu} x^{n/2} \sum m_\ell^\mu Y_\ell^\mu$$

$n = 1 + \mu$

$x \equiv t_{min} - t$

$$s^2(t - \mu^2)^2 \frac{d^3\sigma}{dt \, dm_{\pi\pi}^2 \, d\Omega} \propto x|m_0|^2 + x(\text{Re } m_0^* \, m_1^0) \, 2\sqrt{3} \cos \theta$$

$$+ x|m_1^0|^2 \, 3 \cos^2 \theta + (|m_1^{-1}|^2 + x^2|m_1^1|^2) \, \tfrac{3}{2} \sin^2 \theta$$

$$+ x^{\frac{1}{2}} \Big[\text{Re } m_0^* (m_1^{-1} - x m_1^1) \Big] \, \sqrt{6} \sin \theta \cos \varphi$$

$$+ x^{\frac{1}{2}} \Big[\text{Re } m_1^{0*} (m_1^{-1} - x m_1^1) \Big] \, 3\sqrt{2} \sin \theta \cos \theta \cos \varphi$$

$$- x \Big[\text{Re } m_1^{1*} \, m_1^{-1} \Big] \, 3 \sin^2 \theta \cos 2\varphi$$

Meanwhile $\sigma_{\text{Helicity Non-Flip}} \propto 1/s^4$

powers of x which appear are due to angular
momentum conservation alone. The x, x cos θ,
x cos^2 θ terms that Baton et al. considered, arise
from simple pion exchange. The vanishing at 0°
production angle follows from the pseudoscalar
property. There are also terms with the well
known φ dependence. We also have a term which is
non-vanishing in the forward direction (the sin^2 θ
term).

    Exactly this non-vanishing term is respon-
sible for the observed sharp forward peak in
photoproduction of π$^+$ in connection with which
Reggeologists talk about conspiracies). Thus
when there is pion exchange, pi exchange plus
diffraction also occurs: both can occur at com-
pensating small angles leading to forward production. Another way of saying this is to note
that while the π is pseudoscalar, double or
higher scattering, or absorption, or Regge cuts, e.g.,

involves exchange of arbitrary spin and parity so
the vanishing at 0° no longer applies. By J_z
conservation the ρ produced at 0° is transverse.
The decay is sin^2 θ. The rate for this term is
not small but requires high resolution in t to

separate as shown in Figure 9.   The upper curve

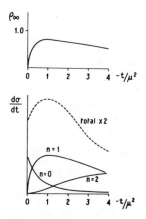

is defined in the helicity frame.   The Baton et al.
analysis, which neglects the $\sin^2 \theta$ term above,
<u>may</u> not be bad because their experiment $\pi^-p \rightarrow (\pi^-\pi^\circ)p$
doesn't include very small -t.   However I believe
it is just a pious hope that since there are complications in pion exchange at very small momentum
transfer, we will do better moving further away
from the pole.   The way to resolve this point is
to extrapolate the moments carefully from very
small momentum transfer.

Let me call the sum of simple π (trajectory)
exchange and π plus diffractions (Regge cut when
properly calculated) "generalized π exchange."
If one cannot accept dominance at small -t of
simple π exchange, the factor of t in the cross
section cannot be used as a constraint on the
extrapolation at t = 0.   In the Saclay group's
extrapolation this constraint was quite important
in keeping errors down.   The specific suggestion

we are making is that one try dominance of generalized π exchange at small -t. Then one is in
effect making the assumption of helicity flip
dominance at high energy which is a more general
assumption than π pole dominance which involves
helicity flip dominance and vanishing at 0°.

It will be most advantageous to work at 5-7
BeV/c. Theoretically we find that nucleon
helicity non flip in π exchange is very small at
0° at high energy while flip and non flip are
comparable around 2.5 BeV/c. The non flip cross
section vanishes $S^{-3/2}$ faster than the flip.(Theory).
There is evidence (Walker et al.) that π exchange
still may dominate the process at 25 BeV/c, so
that we don't have to worry about ω, A_1, A_2
exchange. 5-7 BeV/c should be ideal because flip
could be an order of magnitude larger than non
flip. If flip dominates, the t dependence of
moments is specified by J_z conservation as
indicated in the above expression. The equation
with indicated t dependence where the m's should,
according to the absorption model, be slowly
varying functions of t suggests that the coefficient
of x, x cos θ (and as a check, the φ dependent
terms), but not the coefficient of $\sin^2 θ$ should
be slowly varying functions of t and should be
suitable for extrapolation. In addition to high
statistics bubble chamber work, a very extensive
spark chamber experiment of Cork, Kerth, Wentzel
and collaborators, which will soon be completed

for $\pi^- p \rightarrow (\pi^+ \pi^-)n$ at 5 BeV/c, may make this type
of analysis possible.

I conclude that removal of the present $\approx 50\%$
uncertainties in the $\pi\pi$ amplitude requires empirical extrapolation of moments as opposed to
direct examination of the physical region or use
of formulae specifying $m_{\pi\pi}$ vs. t dependence. I
am sorry I haven't had time to discuss the
variety of nice experiments which have narrowed
the possibilities for the $\pi\pi$ amplitudes in the
recent past. I elected instead to talk about
where we should go in the immediate future.

THE SIGN OF THE S = T = 0
ππ SCATTERING PHASE SHIFT

Lawrence W. Jones
University of Michigan

We have pointed out that the analysis of our data on the reaction $\pi^- N \rightarrow \pi^+ \pi^- N^*$ (where N^* is an integral over a range of final-state nucleon systems) favors a negative value for δ_o^o the S = T = 0 ππ phase shift.[1] This is in contrast to the generally-accepted bubble chamber analyses based on $\pi^- p \rightarrow \pi^+ \pi^- n$ data which favor a positive δ_o^o. The most sensitive measure of the sign of δ_o^o in such reactions is the value of the forward-backward asymmetry, P, of the π-π scattering. The purpose of this note is to emphasize the possible bias of P from the diffraction inelastic scattering of the incident pion. This bias feeds positive values of P leading to a possibly erroneous determination of δ_o^o.

The ππ scattering in the dipion center-of-mass system is typically analyzed in terms

$$\frac{d\sigma_{\pi\pi}}{d\Omega} = A_o + A_1 \cos \theta + A_2 \cos^2 \theta \qquad (1)$$

41

integrating over the Trieman-Yang angle. Neglecting the small contribution from the isospin 2
amplitude, the value of A_1 is given by

$$A_1 = \sin \delta_o^o \, \sin \delta_1^1 \, \cos (\delta_o^o - \delta_1^1) \qquad (2)$$

which is positive either if $|\delta_o^o - \delta_1^1| < \pi/2$, δ_o^o and
δ_1^1 both positive; or if $|\delta_o^o - \delta_1^1| > \pi/2$, δ_o^o negative
and δ_1^1 positive. Near the ρ resonance, therefore,
A_1 will be positive if $\delta_1^1 \cong \pi/2$ and $\delta_o^o \cong \pm \pi/2$.
However the sign of A_1 reflects the sign of δ_o^o
when δ_1^1 is positive and the magnitudes of both are
small ($|\delta_o^o - \delta_1^1| < \pi/2$). The forward-backward
asymmetry P is given by P = (F - B)/(F + B) where
F corresponds to π^- scattering at $\theta < 90°$ in the
$\pi\pi$ c.m., etc; P is also equivalent to
$A_1/2[A_o + (1/3) A_2]$.

Now the diffraction inelastic scattering pro-
cess, $\pi^- p \rightarrow \pi^- N^* \rightarrow \pi^- (\pi^+ n)$ will contribute events
which, when interpreted as peripheral $\pi\pi$ scattering,
appear almost entirely as F events (in effect, a
small angle $\pi\pi$ scattering). Quantitatively, this
is deadly for the interpretation of $\pi\pi$ scattering
at low $\pi\pi$ masses. The contribution to the final
state $(\pi^- \pi^+ n)$ by the diffraction inelastic diagram
is comparable to the contribution by ρ^o production
in the few GeV energy range (e.g. 4 GeV/c incident
pions). The ratio of the cross sections for
$\pi^+ \pi^- \rightarrow \pi^+ \pi^-$ of s-wave to p-wave scattering is given
by $4 \sin^2 \delta_o^o / 27 \sin^2 \delta_1^1$, so that the ratio of the
s-wave scattering at energies where $|\delta_o^o| \simeq 30°$

($m_{\pi\pi} \sim$ 400 MeV) to the ρ peak is about 4%. Including other kinematic factors, the ratio of the
peripheral reaction corresponding to s-wave $\pi^+\pi^-$
scattering below 500 MeV to ρ^0 production is about
10% or less. On the other hand, the 300 - 500 MeV
range is 4% of the total range of the (π^+n) band in
the Dalitz plot of $m^2_{\pi^+n}$ vs. $m^2_{\pi^+\pi^-}$ for 4 GeV/c π^-
incident on protons. If these 4% of the diffraction-
inelastic events all contribute to values of $\theta < 90^\circ$
(F-events) when interpreted as peripheral $\pi^+\pi^-$
scattering, if the diffraction inelastic process
contains ten times the number of events contained
in peripheral $\pi^+\pi^-$ scattering with $m_{\pi^+\pi^-} < 500$ MeV,
and if this $\pi\pi$ scattering were otherwise isotropic
(P = 0), then a value of P = 0.4/1.4 = +0.28 would
be incorrectly ascribed to the $\pi\pi$ scattering. Interference effects and forward-backward peaking of the
(π^+n) states could lead to even larger apparent
values of P.

   Going to higher energies increases the range
of $m^2_{\pi^+\pi^-}$ over which the N^* isobars are spread on
the Dalitz plot and so dilutes the density of
events in the low-$m_{\pi\pi}$ band, however the cross
section for diffraction inelastic scattering is
nearly energy independent, while the cross section
for peripheral $\pi\pi$ scattering and ρ production fall
as p_{inc}^{-2}. The problem then does not disappear by
going to higher energies, although extrapolating to
$t = \mu^2$ would tend to purify the $\pi^+\pi^-$-scattering
sample at higher energies as the t-range also increases with energy.

In the data of Ref. 1 as illustrated in Fig.
1, the reaction $\pi^-N \to \pi^+\pi^-N^*$ was used for analysis.
This reaction is seen theoretically and experimentally to have a nearly constant cross section
at high energies when integrated over the kine-
matically allowed final states at the nuclear vertex
and <u>may</u> not fall prey to the confusion outlined
above to the same extent. We believe therefore
that our significant evidence for negative P at
low $m_{\pi\pi}$ is particularly strong evidence for negative δ_0^0. It should be noted that A_0 remains
positive and changes monotonically with $m_{\pi\pi}$ in our
data so that there is no evidence that δ_0^0 starts
negative from threshold and then passes through
zero at intermediate energies ($400 < m_{\pi\pi} < 600$ MeV).

Besides better data and analysis of the Ke_4
decay, very quantitative data on the reaction
$\pi^-p \to \pi^0\pi^0n$ would be particularly valuable in
settling this question, as the interference between
δ_0^0 and δ_0^2 has opposite signs in the final states
$\pi^0\pi^0$ and $\pi^+\pi^-$.

---

[1]L. W. Jones, E. Bleuler, D. O. Caldwell, B. Elsner,
D. Hartung, W. C. Middelkoop, and B. Zacharov, Phys.
Rev. <u>166</u>, 1405 (1968). See also L. W. Jones et. al.,
Physics Letters <u>21</u>, 590 (1966), and L. W. Jones et.
al., Nuovo Cimento <u>44A</u>, 915 (1966).

TABLE

Forward-backward assymmetry, P, for dipions of mass below 450 MeV. P = (F - B)/(F + B) where F is the number of events corresponding to a π^- scattering angle in the dipion c.m.s., $\theta < 90°$, and B is the number for $\theta > 90°$.

Incident Pion Momentum (GeV/c)	Upper Limit of Missing Mass M' MeV	Range of Four-Momentum Transfer t(GeV/c)^2	P (%)	Number of Events
12	2500	<0.05	-7.50 ± 4.60	467
		0.05 - 0.10	-3.96 ± 7.62	177
18	3000	<0.05	-8.46 ± 5.38	343
		0.05 - 0.10	-3.71 ± 7.26	189
12 & 18	As Above	<0.10	-6.64 ± 2.91	1176

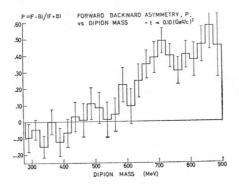

Figure 1. The forward-backward assymmetry, P, for $\pi^-\pi^+$ scattering from the reaction $\pi^-N \rightarrow \pi^-\pi^+N^*$ interpreted as peripheral $\pi\pi$ scattering.

Form Factors and Vector Mesons

R. Wilson

Harvard University

In a certain sense, form factors haven't anything to do with meson spectroscopy but there is a historical reason why they are interesting and that is because in order to understand the nucleon form factors, the vector mesons were suggested by Frazer and Fulco before any other meson resonances were found. It is interesting to see how well we can understand form factors now that vector mesons have been found in other ways. The understanding, as we shall see, is not good. I could now present slides of data accumulated about the nuclear form factors but you have seen such slides many times over the 15 years since Hofstadter first started electron proton scattering, so I will refrain from being repetitious. I will also not show slides of apparatus. I will only select a few bits of data and formulae which describe the rest of the data to show what we have to talk about and explain.

The first figure will show the form factor data of the pion. We do not yet know much about it. That is an advantage, in one sense, because   formula fits!

In our graph, q^2 is the square of the 4-momentum transfer. $q^2 > 0$, to the right hand side, is obtained in scattering experiments. $q^2 < 0$ is obtained in annihilation experiments. For colliding beams, $q^2 = -4E^2$. The previous two speakers have mentioned the colliding beam experiments and have plotted the data vs. E, where E increases <u>to the right</u>. Note the change in scale and direction. Note, also, the logarithmic scale on the y-axis (F^2 axis).

I show four experiments— In the time like region we have $|F^2|$ from Novosibirsk over the whole rho peak, and from Orsay, at the top. Note the Orsay value is 20% higher than the Novosibirsk value. The graph must also pass through $F^2 = 1$ at $q^2 = 1$. My curve is a guess; it is high for all Novosibirsk points and is too wide. It is a prediction based on the whole form factor being dominated by the vector rho meson. The mass is taken to be 760 MeV and the width, 120 MeV.

The particular form is an S-wave Breit-Wigner resonance. It has a "reasonable" analytic behavior. In principle one should use a P-wave Breit-Wigner resonance obtained by replacing the square root by a three-halves root. Bowcock, Cottingham and Lurie did this six years ago in attempting to understand the nucleon form factors. The trouble is that the form factors then fall as $(q^2)^{-3/2}$ at high q^2 and theorists (Coleman, Drell) have expressed abhorrence at this. Even more strictly, the resonance should be in the $\pi\pi$ phase and not in the form factor which gives a factor of $(q^2)^{1/2}$ to cancel part of the objectionable factor $(q^2)^{-3/2}$ but this introduces complications of analyticity at $q^2=0$. (A paper of Sakurai discusses this and adds an extra term to retain analyticity. The paper was not known to me when the figure was drawn or

the talk was given.) The effect on any part of this slide of
being more sophisticated is less than 5%, so I will make no
change. The effect of rho width increases the rho leptonic
branching ratio by 8 to 15% depending upon the exact form
chosen. We can now see graphically what the discussion of
the different rho widths means. Novosibirsk prefers 90 MeV;
my 120 MeV isn't too bad (especially if you arbitrarily re-
normalize the Novosibirsk data upwards by 20% to agree with
the Orsay data) and the 150 MeV width gives trouble. I
want now to disagree with Roos about the significance of this.
The graph of mine is drawn assuming no background; that is,
the rho is the sole contributor to the form factor. We don't
know this, and as we shall see, there is reason to expect
that F goes negative as meson energies above the rho mass
($q^2 < (-1$ BeV)). We easily see that a negative background, added
to a positive rho peak, can produce a narrower peak in F^2. So
until we have more measurements on either side of the rho peak,
the situation is not definitive. The colliding beam experiments will certainly improve and give us this data before long.

Now we pass to the right hand side of the graph ($q > 0$).
There are two sets of data shown; from Harvard, Mistretta et al
and from Cornell, Berkelman et al. They both measure electro-
production of pions from protons at energies near the first
nucleon resonance, M = 1235 MeV, J,I = 3/2, 3/2. It is a hard
experiment, but the data is better than the theory. We have
to understand the dispersion theory of the resonance in order
find the desired term, the one pion exchange. The errors come
from taking the calculation from two different competent theorists (Adler and Zagury) and making the error bars span both
answers. The problem is what to do with various small terms.
If the theory improves, the errors can improve with no extra

experimental work.

Now we note that the points fall <u>below</u> the vector dominance curve and follow more nearly the dotted curve which
is proportional to the nucleon form factor.

This is, to me, a very exciting point and I would
like to distinguish between those two curves in the space-like
region. I think that the experiments cannot yet do this.
There is already trouble in making the curve of $|F^2|$ vs. q^2
bend enough to pass through the colliding beam points at the
rho resonance and then through the point $F^2 = 1$ at $q^2 = 0$;
to bend back again to follow the nucleon form factor curve is
even harder; it could only be done by making Im F large and
positive just above threshold (below the rho mass). Although
the nucleon form factors also suggest a resonance or strong
pion-pion interaction there, as we shall see, no other field
of physics finds such effects.

The same resonances which contribute to the pion form
factor should contribute to the isovector nucleon form factor
and visa-versa. There are two isovector form factors, the
electric and the magnetic. The magnetic form factor is large
and well known because the neutron magnetic moment is comparable
with the proton magnetic moment. The neutron charge is very
much less than the proton charge and therefore its form factor
is rather harder to find than the presence of the proton form
factor. The highest momentum transfer at which the neutron
form factor has been measured is $q^2 = 7$ $(GeV/c)^2$. This is
measured by inelastic electron deuteron scattering and is actually an upper limit. We still have a number for the isovector
form factor.

There is a dispersion relation connecting the nucleon
form factor of $q^2 > 0$ with that for $q^2 < 0$. This is

$$\text{Re } G_{MV}(q^2) = \int_{-4m_\pi^2}^{\infty} \frac{\text{Im } G_{MV}(q')^2}{q^2-(q')^2} \ (d(q')^2$$

This can also be inverted. From our measurements of $G_{MV}(q^2)$ for $q^2 > 0$. We can thus derive $\text{Im } G_{MV}(q^2)$. This is a dirty way of finding out about the resonances which all occur for $q^2 < 0$. Levinger and Peirls started this work. Now Levinger always finds a peak in $\text{Im } G_{MV}(q^2)$ somewhere near the rho meson and $\text{Im } G_{MV}(q^2)$ goes <u>negative</u> above it $(q^2 < -m_\rho^2)$. Let us discuss this negative behavior before going further. We take the dispersion relation and expand in powers of $1/q^2$. Then we find

$$G_{MV}(q^2) = \frac{1}{q^2} \ \int \text{Im } G_{MV}(q')^2 \ d(q')^2$$

$$+ \frac{1}{q^4} \ \int (q')^2 \ \text{Im } G_{MV}(q')^2 \ d(q')^2 + \ \ldots \ldots$$

The most obvious feature of the form factors found at CEA and now at SLAC is that the form factors fall at least as fast as $1/q^4$. Thus

$$\int G_{MV}(q^2) \ dq^2 = 0$$

This tells us that the positive rho contribution <u>must</u> be compensated by a negative contribution.

Figure 2 shows Levinger's latest attempt to derive $\text{Im } G_{MV}(q^2)$ from the scattering data. He assumes that the rho meson contributes an amount, A, to the pion charge with its correct mass and width. He tries to fit with a minimum of

extra structure. The figure shows fits from A = 0.6 to A =
2.0 which are the limits of acceptability (rho dominance gives
A = 1). Levinger finds that he needs <u>two</u> extra adjustable
contributions to Im $G_{MV}(q^2)$; one the negative value for
$q^2 < -1(BeV/c)^2$ and the other a positive one near the threshold
$q^2 = 4m_\pi^2$. We noted the need for this before, when discussing
the pion form factor.

We have another important point; theorists have often,
in the last six years, made rash statements that the $\rho\gamma$ coupling can be derived from fitting nucleon form factors. Claims
of 25% accuracy have been made. But this just isn't so. A
factor of 2 is all that can be done. Improved data recently
has <u>not</u> improved this factor; it has only told us more about
these extra contributions.

A third point is that the resolution of the technique
is only enough to tell us the rho width to $\pm$ 50 MeV.

These other contributions to the isovector nucleon form
factor - and, hence to the pion form factor - should be studied by other means. One of them might be one of Maglic's R-
mesons (mass, 1600 MeV) which has $J^P = 1^-$ according to the
quark model. This, according to Dalitz, is a ^3D state of two
quarks and will not couple to γ rays, but that is a detail
that can presumably be dealt with by deviations from the quark
model.

Another possibility is to take the data at its face
value. The nucleon form factors fall very close to a very
simple formula

$$\frac{G_{Mp}}{\mu_p} = \frac{G_{Mn}}{\mu_n} = G_{Ep} = \left(\frac{1}{1 + q^2/0.71}\right)^2$$

This has a simple Fourier transform, $e^{-\lambda r}$. It has the form of a dipole. The rho meson certainly does not look like a dipole in the Novosibirsk pion form factor data. But dipoles are also being discussed in other connections (the A_2 meson) and we should not exclude the obvious out of hand.

Whether or not the dipole has any meaning, it is convenient, and I am glad to say, now usual, to express the data as a ratio to data calculated using the dipole formula (which fits to 25% everywhere). The form factor varies by a factor of 10^3; this method of expression shows all the data on one graph and experimenters can proudly display their small one and two percent errors without the bars being condensed into dots.

With this, the conference can proceed to the more usual methods of meson spectroscopy.[1]

---

[1]Some other topics were discussed in the talk as presented; these were not transcribed and are not included here.

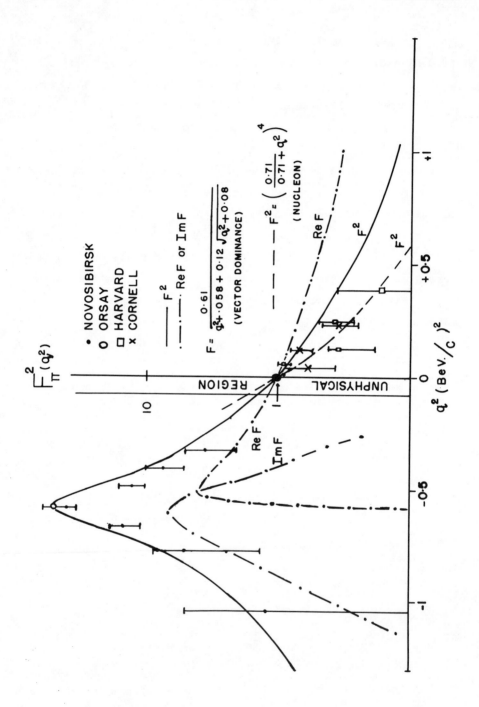

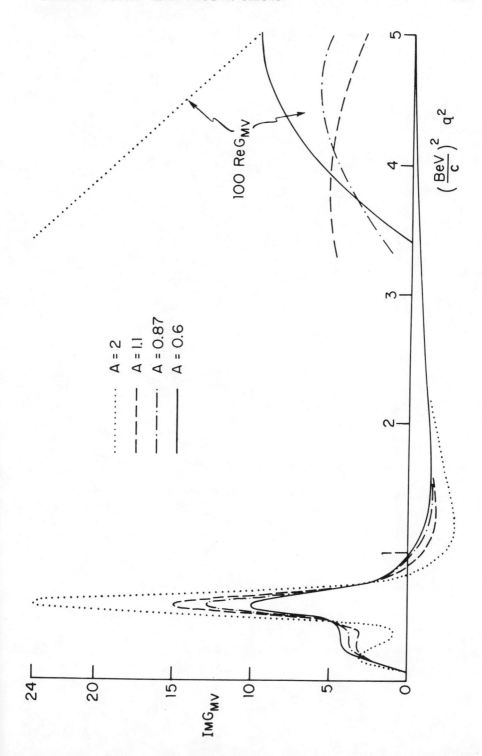

Vector Meson Coupling Constants

F. ZACHARIASEN

California Institute of Technology, Pasadena, California

Let me begin by reminding you of the peripheral model, or the OPE model, call it what you will. Look at any process where a π, say, is exchanged, as shown in the picture.

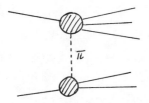

This process has a pion propagator in it, given by $1/t\text{-}m_\pi^2$. Hence at the pole at $t = m_\pi^2$, the process is completely dominated by the pion exchange, and no other diagram counts. However, the pole occurs in the unphysical region (for example, at $\cos\theta = 1 + m_\pi^2/2q^2 > 1$, where q is the CM momentum, for elastic scattering), so one never really reaches it. Nevertheless, at high energies and forward angles, the pole is close to the physical region, so one may hope it dominates there.

Two things change about this kind of argument if the pion is replaced by a vector meson. First, the vector meson (say a ρ) is unstable, so the propagator is not $1/t-m_\pi^2$, but rather $1/t-(m_\rho - i\,\Gamma_\rho/2)^2 \approx 1/(t - m_\rho^2 + i\,m_\rho\,\Gamma_\rho)$. Thus there is no true pole, only a bump. This is bad, because the "pole" is not so big. Second, because of the instability, the "pole", or bump, is no longer necessarily in the unphysical region, but can be in the physical region. This is good, because one can actually reach the "pole" experimentally.

So, vector dominance is just the same approximation as OPE, or peripheralism, or whatever you want to call it, applied to (unstable) vector mesons. As in the OPE, it is important to apply the approximation only in the vicinity of the "pole" -- it is dangerous to extrapolate far from it. For a fairly narrow width vector meson, one might try to use the vector dominance model in the region of more or less the width on each side of the peak. If we insist on using vector dominance far from the pole (as many people do, for example, in extrapolating the ρ-"pole" which occurs at m_ρ^2 all the way down to zero to analyze real photon processes) then we must not expect accurate numerical results, but may have to content ourselves with qualitative conclusions.

Keeping these cautions in mind, let us proceed to look at some experiments.

The simplest illustration of the vector dominance idea is in the pion electromagnetic form factor, and I will discuss this first. In diagrams, one measures, for timelike virtual photons, the picture shown below:

(the photons come from an $e^+ e^-$ annihilation which is not shown). The two pions have $J^P = 1^-$, and even G-parity, so the diagram can be broken into two parts connected by a ρ-meson:

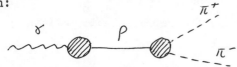

Thus, near the ρ "pole", we can write

$$F(t) \;=\; \frac{\text{const.}}{t - m_\rho^2 + i\, m_\rho \,\Gamma_\rho}$$

By looking at the picture, one sees that the constant can be written as the product of the ρ-π-π coupling constant $\gamma_{\rho\pi\pi}$ (for the right-hand vertex; the normalization we choose is such that

$$\Gamma_{\rho\pi\pi} \;=\; \frac{1}{3}\left(\frac{\gamma_{\rho\pi\pi}^2}{4\pi}\right)\left(\frac{m_\rho^2 - 4m_\pi^2}{4m_\pi^2}\right)^{3/2} m_\rho \Bigg) \quad ,$$

and a photon-ρ coupling (for the left-hand vertex). This second coupling is clearly independent of the π, and would be the same no matter what the final two particles are -- i.e., no matter which form factor we choose to study. It is conventional to write it as $- (e/2)\,(m_\rho^2/\gamma_\rho)$; this defines γ_ρ.[1]

---

[1] M. Gell-Mann and F. Zachariasen, Phys. Rev. <u>124</u>, 953 (1961).

Thus we get[2)]

$$F(t) = - \left(\frac{m_\rho^2}{t - m_\rho^2 + i\, m_\rho\, \Gamma_\rho} \right) \left(\frac{\gamma_{\rho\pi\pi}}{\gamma_\rho} \right) \quad .$$

Now this expression is, we recall, approximately valid near the ρ "pole". (It is exactly valid there in the limit of zero ρ width.) It is a drastic assumption, however, to take it to be valid far away from $t \sim m_\rho^2$ -- say near $t = 0$. If we could use the representation all the way down to $t = 0$, we would get

$$F(0) = (\gamma_{\rho\pi\pi}/\gamma_\rho) \quad ;$$

but $F(0) = 1$, so this says

$$\gamma_{\rho\pi\pi} = \gamma_\rho \quad .$$

Thus, if the ρ-pole, or vector dominance, form is valid even at $t = 0$, then the ρ-π-π coupling becomes a number independent of the pion -- and similarly the coupling of ρ to any other pair of final particles would reduce to the same γ_ρ -- that is, we would have

$$\gamma_{\rho\pi\pi} = \gamma_{\rho NN} = \ \dots \ = \gamma_\rho$$

so that we would get universality of the ρ coupling to all hadrons.

---

[2]Because of the fact that we normalize F to unity at $t = 0$, the factor $e/2$ disappears from the right-hand side of this equation. Note that ρ couples only to the isovector part of the photon; hence the factor $e/2$ rather than e in the definition of γ_ρ.

Under what circumstances would we expect the ρ-dominant expression to be valid at $t = 0$? Evidently if the ρ mass becomes very small, because then the ρ-"pole" approaches $t = 0$. In the limit $m_\rho \rightarrow 0$, in fact, the pole expression becomes <u>exact</u> at $t = 0$, so we can think of γ_ρ as the coupling that the ρ would have had to all hadrons <u>if</u> its mass had been zero. That this coupling is universal in the zero mass limit is, then, obvious, for just the same reason that the electric charge is universal for the zero mass photon.

But the ρ-mass is not in fact zero, so universality is only approximate. The measure of how approximate it is is precisely the deviation of $\gamma_{\rho\pi\pi}/\gamma_\rho$ -- or $\gamma_{\rho NN}/\gamma_\rho$, for example -- from unity.

Exactly analogous remarks, and definitions, can evidently be made for the other vector mesons which are coupled to conserved currents. We shall return to these later.

Now, what is the experimental situation? The π form factor $F(t)$ has been measured through the region of the ρ-"pole" in a clashing beam experiment at Novosibirsk,[3] and the results are as shown in Figure 1. The fit to the ρ-dominance formula, in the region of the peak, as indicated in the picture, gives

$$(\gamma_{\rho\pi\pi}/\gamma_\rho)^2 = 0.59 \pm 0.15 \qquad .$$

We also find, using the quoted ρ width of 93 ± 15, and mass of $m_\rho = 764 \pm 11$, that

---

[3]Auslander <u>et al.</u>, Physics Letters <u>25B</u>, 433 (1967).

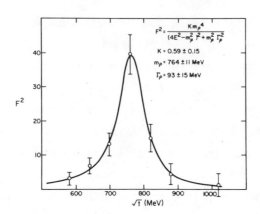

FIGURE 1

$$\gamma_{\rho\pi\pi}^2/4\pi \;=\; 0.45 \pm 0.07 \qquad .$$

Thus we find, from this experiment, that

$$\gamma_{\rho}^2/4\pi \;=\; 0.76 \pm 0.23 \qquad .$$

The peak value of $|F|^2$, at $t = m_{\rho}^2$, or, equivalently, the peak cross section for $e^+ e^- \rightarrow \pi^+ \pi^-$ measures directly the product $(\gamma_{\rho\pi\pi}^2/4\pi)(\gamma_{\rho}^2/4\pi)$.

The relation is

$$\sigma(m_{\rho}^2) \;=\; \frac{3\pi \; \alpha^2}{m_{\rho}^2} \left(\frac{4\pi}{\gamma_{\rho}^2}\right) \left(\frac{4\pi}{\gamma_{\rho\pi\pi}^2}\right) \left(\frac{m_{\rho}^2}{m_{\rho}^2 - 4m_{\pi}^2}\right)^{3/2} \quad ,$$

(neglecting terms in $(m_{\ell}/m_{\rho})^2$). It is conventional to express this peak cross section instead in terms of the branching ratio $\Gamma_{e^+ e^-}/\Gamma_{\rho}$; this branching ratio is also related to the product of the coupling constants:

$$\Gamma_{e^+e^-}/\Gamma_\rho = \frac{\alpha^2}{4}\left(\frac{4\pi}{\gamma_\rho^2}\right)\left(\frac{4\pi}{\gamma_{\rho\pi\pi}^2}\right)\left(\frac{m_\rho^2}{m_\rho^2 - 4m_\pi^2}\right)^{3/2} ,$$

so that we can write

$$\sigma(m_\rho^2) = \frac{12\pi}{m_\rho^2}\left(\frac{\Gamma_{e^+e^-}}{\Gamma_\rho}\right) .$$

The peak cross section measured at Novosibirsk is 1.2 ± 0.2 μb. The peak cross section has also been measured at Orsay,[4] in another clashing beam experiment, to give 1.53 ± 0.25 μb. Consequently,

$$\Gamma_{e^+e^-}/\Gamma_\rho = \begin{cases} 4.9 \pm 0.8 \times 10^{-5} & \text{(Novosibirsk)} \\ 6.2 \pm 1.0 \times 10^{-5} & \text{(Orsay)} \end{cases} .$$

Taking $m_\rho = 764$ MeV, this means that

$$(\gamma_\rho^2/4\pi)(\gamma_{\rho\pi\pi}^2/4\pi) = \begin{cases} 0.34 \pm 0.06 & \text{(Novosibirsk)} \\ 0.27 \pm 0.05 & \text{(Orsay)} \end{cases} .$$

(The Orsay measurement is actually at 775 MeV; they measure only at the one value of t and therefore may in fact be slightly off the peak position).

The same branching ratio can be measured in other experiments. For example, the process

$$\pi^- + p \rightarrow e^+ + e^- + n$$

should, in the neighborhood of $(p_{e^-} + p_{e^+})^2 \approx m_\rho^2$, be dominated by the ρ-"pole" diagram:

---

[4] Augustin et al., Phys. Rev. Letters 20, 126 (1968).

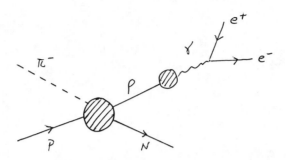

However, the disentangling of the other stuff in the diagram
is more difficult here than in the pion form factor,[5]
because the e^+e^- pairs can be produced by other vector
mesons (for example, ω) as well as by non-vector meson processes, and these will produce some sort of background to
interfere with the ρ-"pole" term we are trying to isolate.
Nevertheless, one may try.

The procedure is to compare the number of e^+e^- pairs
(or $\mu^+\mu^-$ for that matter) with the number of $\pi^+\pi^-$ pairs,
at the ρ peak, and at the same total energy. The ratio of
these numbers is just the branching ratio
$\Gamma_{e^+e^-}/\Gamma_{\pi^+\pi^-} \approx \Gamma_{e^+e^-}/\Gamma_\rho$, if all the e pairs and π pairs do
in fact come only from ρ.

The kinds of results are shown in the picture below.[6]

---

[5] See, for example, S.C.C. Ting, Proceedings of the 1967
International Symposium on Electron and Photon Interactions
at High Energies, Stanford (1967), p. 452.

[6] H. Joos, Proceedings of the Heidelberg International Conference on Elementary Particles (1967), p. 354. The
references to the experiments are given there. Joos gives
the CEA number as 5.9 ± 1.5, but it is quoted as 7.4 ± 2
at the 1967 Stanford Conference.

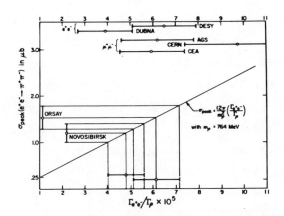

These numbers are quite consistent with the measurements of $\Gamma_{e^+e^-}/\Gamma_\rho$ from the peak cross section for $e^+ e^- \to \pi^+ \pi^-$ quoted before, and thus tend to confirm those results nicely. The average is $\Gamma_{e^+e^-}/\Gamma_\rho = (6.3 \pm 1.4) \times 10^{-5}$.

To summarize then, we can say the following:

(i) If we accept the form factor measurements, then

$$\gamma_{\rho\pi\pi}^2/4\pi = 0.45 \pm 0.07 \qquad (\Gamma_\rho = 93 \pm 15 \text{ MeV})$$

$$\gamma_\rho^2/4\pi = 0.76 \pm 0.23 \qquad \qquad \bullet$$

(ii) If we look only at the peak form factor measurements, we get

$$(\gamma_{\rho\pi\pi}^2/4\pi)(\gamma_\rho^2/4\pi) = \begin{array}{l} 0.34 \pm 0.06 \quad \text{(Novosibirsk)} \\ 0.27 \pm 0.05 \quad \text{(Orsay)} \end{array}$$

while the average of all the branching ratio measurements gives

$$(\gamma_{\rho\pi\pi}^2/4\pi)(\gamma_\rho^2/4\pi) = 0.26 \pm 0.06 \qquad \bullet$$

(Note that while the quoted error is no greater in the branching ratio measurements, the theoretical uncertainties in the analysis here are in fact much bigger than in the first two numbers.)

The conclusions stated in (i) above are in contrast to the usually quoted result that $\Gamma_\rho \sim 130$ to 150 MeV, as determined directly from strong or electromagnetic ρ production, such as in the process[7] $\pi + N \to 2\pi + N$ or the process $\gamma + N \to 2\pi + N$. I would like to emphasize that the theoretical ambiguities in the pion form factor analysis are essentially nil in comparison with those encountered in reactions like[8] $\pi + N \to 2\pi + N$. Thus, if the form factor

---

[7] See, for example, E. Malamud and P. Schlein, Phys. Rev. Letters 19, 1056 (1967). Various fits are quoted here ranging from widths of 136 MeV to 157 MeV, with errors of the order of 8 MeV. Rosenfeld et al. (Rev. Mod. Phys. 39, 1 (1967)) quote Γ_ρ as 128 MeV. The statistical errors are stated as 2-5 MeV, but of course the theoretical uncertainty is unknown.

[8] There is a CERN preprint by Roos and Pisut which argues that the ρ width determined by the Novosibirsk experiment is in error, and should really be in the vicinity of 120 MeV. Their argument is based on an attempt to extrapolate the Novosibirsk fit down to $t = 0$, in order to guarantee $F(0) = 1$. To do this, however, is to misunderstand the point of the clashing beam experiment. The whole idea is to try to fit only in the region of the ρ peak and not to attempt to extrapolate. Any extrapolation involves some dynamical model or other, and therefore drags in theoretical uncertainties, while to fit only at (or near) the ρ peak is to assume almost nothing theoretically and to isolate the ρ meson from unknown background effects.

experiments are correct, one should attach much more weight
to the ρ parameters determined there. In this connection,
it is gratifying to note, as we have above, that the inde-
pendent evaluation of the parameter $(\gamma_\rho^2/4\pi)(\gamma_{\rho\pi\pi}^2/4\pi)$
through direct measurement of the leptonic branching ratio
is entirely consistent with the form factor data (though the
leptonic production, also, of course, suffers from theoretical difficulties in its analysis).

On the other hand, one should also say that the discrepancy may still turn out not to be real. A compromise
width of, say 110 MeV, is only one standard deviation from
the Novosibirsk value, and is not out of line with strong
interaction determinations of the width. We will obviously
just have to wait and see.

Let us conclude this discussion, just for completeness, by remarking that if one does accept say 130 ± 10 MeV
as the ρ width, then one finds

$$\gamma_{\rho\pi\pi}^2/4\pi \;=\; 0.64 \pm 0.05 \qquad\qquad ,$$

and if we ignore the Novosibirsk experiment and use
6×10^{-5} as the leptonic branching ratio, we get

$$\gamma_\rho^2/4\pi \;=\; 0.43 \qquad\qquad .$$

In this case, the parameter $(\gamma_{\rho\pi\pi}/\gamma_\rho)^2$ of the Novosibirsk
experiment would have to be 1.5 instead of 0.6 as was
actually found.

Further experiments have been done to try to extract
other information on γ_ρ, using real photons. An example is
to analyze ρ photoproduction according to the diagram

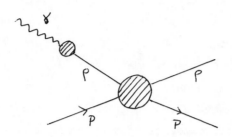

However, the use of real photons requires a large extrapolation of the ρ-dominance model, from values of t near the ρ mass all the way down to t = 0. One has to assume that the ρ-γ coupling, which we took to be $- em_\rho^2/2\gamma_\rho$ by definition when the ρ was on the mass shell, is still the same number when the γ is on the mass shell; that is to say, one has to assume that the ρ-"pole" dominates not only near the ρ mass, at $t = m_\rho^2$, but even at t = 0. This extrapolation is just as big as the one of taking the ρ-dominant expression for the pion form factor all the way from the ρ-"pole" down to t = 0, which would require $\gamma_{\rho\pi\pi} = \gamma_\rho$, for example.

Nevertheless, if one proceeds to analyze the experiment this way, one obtains $\gamma_\rho^2/4\pi = 0.49 \pm 0.12$, 0.42 ± 0.10, and 0.40 ± 0.10 in photoproduction for C, Cu, and Pb respectively,[9] with a ρ width of 130 MeV. These numbers are thus at variance with those determined from the form factor data, and are more consistent with results obtained from the strong interaction width together with a branching ratio of around 6×10^{-5}.

Finally, the ratio $\Gamma(\omega \rightarrow \pi^0\gamma)/\Gamma(\omega \rightarrow 3\pi)$ also measures the product $(\gamma_\rho^2/4\pi)(\gamma_{\rho\pi\pi}^2/4\pi)$, provided that one is willing to approximate the two decays by the diagrams

---

[9] Asbury et al., Phys. Rev. Letters 20, 227 (1968).

shown below:

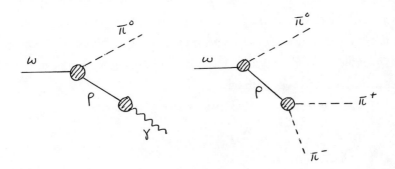

The photon in the $\omega \to \pi\gamma$ decay is real, so there is a large extrapolation away from the ρ pole here, just as in the ρ photoproduction process. The result comes out to be

$$(\gamma_\rho^{\,2}/4\pi)(\gamma_{\rho\pi\pi}^{\,2}/4\pi) \;=\; 0.41 \pm 0.4 \qquad ,$$

where we have taken for the decay rates the values quoted in Ref. 18. The fact that this number is slightly larger than those obtained from the form factor and branching ratio experiments may reflect, at least in part, the errors involved in using the vector dominance approximation for real photons. Nevertheless, the agreement is not at all bad.

Let us next turn to the ω and ϕ. We may define coupling constants γ_ω and γ_ϕ connecting the isoscalar part of the photon to ω and ϕ (on the vector meson mass shell) as in the ρ case: We write, for the diagram,

the couplings[10] $- (e/2) (m_{\omega,\phi}^2/\gamma_{\omega,\phi})$. The experimentally
observed ω and ϕ are mixtures of two vector mesons labelled
Y and B, where Y is part of the same SU(3) octet as ρ and is
coupled to the conserved hypercharge current while B is an
SU(3) singlet coupled to the conserved baryon current. Only
Y can change into a photon.

The conventional mixing theory says that

$$(\gamma_\omega^2/4\pi) = (\gamma_Y^2/4\pi) \; 1/\sin^2\theta \qquad ,$$

$$(\gamma_\phi^2/4\pi) = (\gamma_Y^2/4\pi) \; 1/\cos^2\theta \qquad ,$$

where θ is the ϕ-ω mixing angle. In exact SU(3), we would
have $(\gamma_Y^2/4\pi) = 3(\gamma_\rho^2/4\pi)$. For a mixing angle such that
$\sin\theta = \sqrt{1/3}$ and $\cos\theta = \sqrt{2/3}$ (such as predicted by
SU(6)), then, SU(3) requires

$$(\gamma_\rho^2/4\pi) : (\gamma_\omega^2/4\pi) : (\gamma_\phi^2/4\pi) = 1 : 9 : 9/2 \qquad .$$

Taking γ_ρ from the Novosibirsk experiment, we find
$\gamma_\omega^2/4\pi = 6.8$, $\gamma_\phi^2/4\pi = 3.4$.

Sakurai and Oakes[11] predict, from various relations
among the vector meson masses, that $\theta = 35°$, in a model

---

[10] The ω coupling was originally defined (Ref. 1) with a $\sqrt{3}$
included, as $- (e/2)(m_\omega^2/\sqrt{3}\,\gamma_\omega)$. This was so that if ω
was a pure octet, then SU(3) symmetry would require
$\gamma_\rho^2 = \gamma_\omega^2$. However, with the discovery of ϕ, the motivation
for this choice vanishes, so we drop it. (I make this remark
because the various normalizations used have on occasion
caused some confusion. For example, Eq. (15) in Pipkin's
article in the Proceedings of the 1967 Stanford Conference
is wrong by a factor of $3^2 = 9$, as is Ting's Eq. (6). I
have been unable to trace the origin of this wrong formula.)

[11] R.J. Oakes and J.J. Sakurai, Phys. Rev. Letters 19, 1266
(1967).

including some SU(3) symmetry breaking. They quote the
ratios

$$(\gamma_\rho^2/4\pi) : (\gamma_\omega^2/4\pi) : (\gamma_\phi^2/4\pi) = 1 : 13.8 : 6.8 \quad .$$

Using this relation, the Novosibirsk result for γ_ρ predicts
$\gamma_\omega^2/4\pi = 10.5$, $\gamma_\phi^2/4\pi = 5.2$.

So much for theoretical predictions; what is the
experimental situation?

As in the ρ case, the best determination of γ_ω would
come from a clashing beam experiment, in which one measures
the process $e^+ e^- \rightarrow \pi^+ \pi^- \pi^0$ at the ω mass. A few examples
of this process have been seen at Orsay,[4] but no numbers are
yet available.

The next best source of information about γ_ω would be
in the leptonic decays $\omega \rightarrow e^+ e^-$ or $\mu^+ \mu^-$, since this also
involves virtual photons at the ω peak. There is one quoted
result:[12] $5 \times 10^{-5} < \Gamma(\omega \rightarrow e^+ e^-)/\Gamma(\omega \rightarrow 3\pi) < 6 \times 10^{-4}$.
There is also a bit of data on $\phi \rightarrow e^+ e^-$, as a measure of
γ_ϕ. One finds $\Gamma(\phi \rightarrow e^+ e^-)/\Gamma(\phi \rightarrow \text{everything})$ to be less
than 2×10^{-3}.[13]

Next, there is a measurement of
$\Gamma(\phi \rightarrow \mu^+ \mu^-)/\Gamma(\phi \rightarrow \text{everything})$ with an upper limit of
7.4×10^{-4}.[14]   Finally, there is a measurement from

---

[12] Binnie et al., Physics Letters 18, 348 (1965).

[13] Binnie et al., Proceedings of Heidelberg Conference. The
process measured was $\pi^- p \rightarrow n\ e^+ e^-$.

[14] Chase et al., Phys. Rev. Letters 18, 710 (1967).

Dubna[15] which is stated to give
$\Gamma(\omega \to e^+ e^-)/\Gamma_\omega = (4.5 \pm 0.9) \times 10^{-5}$, and
$\Gamma(\phi \to e^+ e^-)/\Gamma_\phi = (3.5 \pm 1.1) \times 10^{-4}$.

This data can be translated into some information on γ_ω and γ_ϕ, from the formula

$$\Gamma(\omega,\phi \to e^+ e^-) = \frac{\alpha^2}{12} \left(\frac{4\pi}{\gamma_{\omega,\phi}^2} \right) m_{\omega,\phi}$$

exactly as in the case of the ρ. Thus we get, from the data of Ref. 12,

$$0.5 < \gamma_\omega^2/4\pi < 6$$

and, (taking the upper limit on $\Gamma(\phi \to \mu^+ \mu^-)/\Gamma_\phi$), from Ref. 14,

$$\gamma_\phi^2/4\pi > 1.5 \qquad .$$

Finally, from the Dubna results,[15] we get

$$\gamma_\omega^2/4\pi = 6 \pm 1.2 \qquad ,$$

and $\quad \gamma_\phi^2/4\pi = 3 \pm 1 \qquad .$

Any further information has to be obtained from experiments involving on-mass-shell photons, and as I mentioned in the discussion on the ρ, this requires a quite

---

15 Khachaturyan et al., Physics Letters 24B, 349 (1967), and A. Baldin, Proceedings of Stanford Conference (1967), p. 480. The results are obtained assuming $\omega\phi$ mixing with an angle of 38°, and as with many such experiments the analysis assumes no $\rho-\omega$ interference. It is therefore unclear what reliability is to be assigned to the quoted numbers.

large extrapolation. Thus any estimates of γ_ω or γ_ϕ from this class of experiment must be viewed with some suspicion.

The simplest experiment of this class to analyze theoretically is the π^0 decay. If we include only the diagram

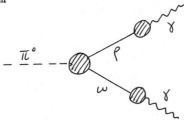

we see that the decay rate is proportional to the product $\gamma_{\pi\rho\omega}^2 / \gamma_\rho^2 \, \gamma_\omega^2$, where $\gamma_{\pi\rho\omega}$ is the coupling constant for the $\pi\rho\omega$ vertex at the left side of the picture.[16] This same constant appears in the decay $\omega \to \pi^0\gamma$, if this is analyzed through the picture

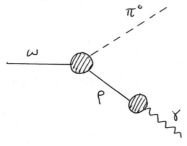

the rate here is evidently proportional to $\gamma_{\pi\rho\omega}^2 / \gamma_\rho^2$. The ratio of the two rates then measures γ_ω^2; explicitly, we have[17]

---

[16]Note we neglect ϕ here; $\gamma_{\pi\rho\phi}$ is presumably quite small.

[17]This ratio is too small by a factor of 4 in Ref. 1. See M. Gell-Mann, D. Sharp, and W. Wagner, Phys. Rev. Letters 8, 261 (1962).

$$\frac{\Gamma(\omega \to \pi^0 \gamma)}{\Gamma(\pi^0 \to 2\gamma)} \;=\; \frac{2}{3\alpha} \left(\frac{m_\omega^{\,2} - m_\pi^{\,2}}{m_\omega \, m_\pi}\right)^{3} \left(\frac{\gamma_\omega^{\,2}}{4\pi}\right) \qquad .$$

Numerically, we take $\Gamma(\omega \to \pi^0 \gamma) = 1.2$ MeV, and $\Gamma(\pi^0 \to 2\gamma) = 7.3 \times 10^{-6}$ MeV,[18] so that we get[19]

$$\gamma_\omega^{\,2}/4\pi \;=\; 11 \pm 2 \qquad .$$

That this number is outside the limits on $\gamma_\omega^{\,2}/4\pi$ obtained from the $\omega \to e^+ e^-$ decay rate is not necessarily surprising, in view of the experimental difficulties in the leptonic decay, and the large extrapolation we used in our model of the π^0 decay.

As a final approach, we may consider photoproduction of vector mesons. The diagram with which one tries to fit the data is shown below:

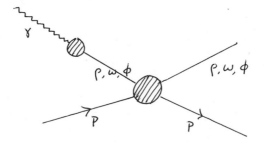

If this diagram were really all there were to it, then one could trivially relate photoproduction to elastic vector meson scattering. The photon turns into a vector meson with

---

[18] From Rosenfeld et al., Rev. Mod. Phys. 39, 1 (1967).

[19] This number is quoted incorrectly in Ref. 5 as $\gamma_\omega^{\,2}/4\pi = 1.2$. See Ref. 9.

coupling $- (e/2) (m_V^2/\gamma_V)$. There is a vector meson propagator $1/(p_\gamma^2 - m_V^2) = - 1/m_V^2$ since the photon is real.
Thus the amplitude for photoproduction is simply $e/2\gamma_V$
times the amplitude for elastic vector meson scattering --
and hence we get

$$\left(\frac{d\sigma}{d\Omega}\right)_{\gamma+p \to v+p} = \frac{\alpha}{4} \frac{4\pi}{\gamma_V^2} \left(\frac{d\sigma}{d\Omega}\right)_{v+p \to v+p} \quad .$$

In fact, of course, there are many other diagrams contributing to the photoproduction, and it is by no means clear
that they are all dominated by the one we have drawn,
particularly since for real photons we are so far from the
vector meson "pole".

Qualitative features such as, for example, that
$\gamma_\omega^2/4\pi$ should be much bigger than $\gamma_\rho^2/4\pi$, seem to be consistent with such photoproduction data as exist, but I think
that further pursuit of this approximation is not really
worthwhile now.

Summary of Photoproduction

and

Leptonic Decays of Vector Mesons

Samuel C. C. Ting
Massachusetts Institute of Technology
and
Deutsches Elektronen-Synchrotron DESY

I am grateful for the help received from members of the DESY-MIT groups; Drs. U Becker, M. Binkley, C. L. Jordan, T. M. Knasel, R. Marshall, D. Quinn, M. Rohde, Miss A. H. Grantz and Miss I. Schultz.

I wish to thank also Dr. E. Lohrmann for many helpful discussions on the DESY Bubble Chamber data.

SUMMARY OF PHOTOPRODUCTION

Reaction (E_γ)	Methods and Groups (Ref)	Dominant Production Mechanism and Cross Sections Note: $\frac{d\sigma}{d\Omega} = \frac{d\sigma}{d\Omega}_{0^{\circ}lab}$ (mb/st) $\frac{d\sigma}{dt} = a\,e^{-bt}$; $a(\mu b\ GeV^{-2})$, $b(GeV^{-2})$ $\sigma_v = \sigma(\gamma+p\rightarrow p+v)$ (μb) All other units are in GeV; $\hbar=c=1$	Mass and Width; in MeV BW(m) = Simple Breit-Wigner distribution function BWJ(m) = Jackson relativistic distribution function BWJRS = $\left(\frac{m_\rho}{m}\right)^4$ BWJ(m); with Ross-Stodolsky factor
$\gamma+p\rightarrow p+\rho^0$ 2 -5.8	DESY-HBC. (1968) To be published in P.L.	Diffraction; $\sigma\rho = (18.2\pm1.7)\ E_\gamma^{-.08\,\pm.07}$. And the data fits the form $\frac{d\sigma}{dt} = a\,e^{-bt}$ for .05<t<0.5. For values of σ, a, b, see Table I and Fig. 1. $\frac{d\sigma}{d\Omega}_{0^{\circ}} = (0.88\pm0.09)$ at $E_\gamma = 4.4$	A good fit was obtained by BWJRS(m) with $\Gamma_0=143$, the mass was consistent with $m_\rho = 770$.
$\gamma+p\rightarrow p+\rho^0$ 1.8-6.0	CEA-HBC P.R. 146, 994 (1966)	Agrees with the DESY-HBC DATA above. And $\frac{d\sigma}{d\Omega}_{0^{\circ}}$ (3.5-6.0 GeV) = (0.60±0.15)	$m_\rho = 728\pm8$, $\Gamma_\rho = 175$, fitted with BW(m)
$\gamma+p\rightarrow p+\rho^0$ 3.2-4.4	DESY-Spark Chamber DESY F32/4 (1968)	Diffraction; $a = 125\pm15$, $b = 8.1\pm1.5$, $\sigma_\rho = 14.6\pm1.8$	$m_\rho = 764\pm12$, $\Gamma_\rho = 124\pm15$ BWJRS (m)
$\gamma+p\rightarrow p+\rho^0$ 2.5-4.8	CEA-Counter P.R. 166, 1365, (1968)	Diffraction; $a = 250$ $b = 9.6$ $E_\gamma = 4.4, 4.8$ $a = 300$ $b = 9.6$ $E_\gamma = 2.5, 2.6$ see remarks in summary of this paper	$m_\rho = 740\pm10$. $\Gamma_\rho = 160\pm10$. BW(m). From carbon data only
$\gamma+A\rightarrow A+\rho^0$ A=(Be,C, Al,Cu,Ag, Pb) 2.7-4.5	DESY-MIT Counter P.R.L. 19, 865, (1967) and erratum	a) Diffraction, $\frac{d\sigma}{d\Omega dm} = C(A)\ f'(p)\ 2mR(m)\ p^2 \times f_T(t,\sigma_{\rho N},R)$; $C(A)$: Normalization. $f'(p) = (1 + \frac{0.91}{p})^2 \beta_\rho$; Energy variation of $\sigma_{\pi\rho}^2(p)\beta_\rho$, f_T describes effects of nuclear size and reabsorption of ρ by nuclear matter. $2mR(m)$ = BWJRS(m). Experimentally $C(C) = 2.37\pm0.32$, $C(Cu) = 46.0\pm6.4$, $C(Pb) = 287.5\pm48.8$ in units of mb sr^{-1} GeV^{-2} $Atom^{-1}$. b) Using $R=\gamma_0 A^{1/3}$, the relative A-dependence at forward angles yield $\sigma_{\rho N}=30.7\pm5.3$ mb, at 4.5 GeV and $\gamma_0 = 1.35\pm0.04f$. (Fig. 2) c) Using $\sigma_{\rho N} = 30$mb, fitting $Z = \frac{1}{f'(p)}\frac{d\sigma}{dt}$ $= x\ f_T(t,30,R) + y\ e^{10t}$ to the data on C, Cu, Pb at 2.7 GeV yields $\gamma_0=1.30\pm0.05f$. (Fig.3). Note that the errors are statistical only. To obtain absolute differential cross section a non-resonant background has to be subtracted; and one then has $Z=\pi C(A) f_\rho + y\ e^{10t}$ In the region 700<m<800: $\{J_1(R\sqrt{t_0}) = 0\}$ 1.For $t \le t_0$, with $Z=x\ e^{bt}$; b(C)=47±5, b(Cu)=139±7, b(Pb)=290±12. 2.For $t \le \frac{t_0}{2}$, with $Z=x\ e^{bt}$; b(C)=53±5. 3.For $t \le \frac{t_0}{2}$, with $Z=x\ e^{bt}+1.6A^{1.3}\ 0.15e^{10t}$; b(C)=60.0±6.0 4.For $t\le\frac{t_0}{2}$, using $b = \frac{\gamma_0^2 A^{2/3}}{4}$ and γ_0 average = 1.30±0.10f, b(C)=56.±10.0, b(Cu)=170.±20. , b(Pb)=370.±50.	The values of Γ_ρ varies from 100±15 to 180±20, and that of m_ρ varies from 730 to 770 depending on;(1) the assumption of the nature of non-resonant background. (2) The assumption of production mechanism and thus the weighting of each event. (3) The form $2mR(m)$ used and (4) the mass range used in the fit. With the mass spectrum $U(m) = C(A)\ BWJRS(m) + B_1(m)$ ($B_1(m)$ = phenomenological background; a power series in m), the "Best fits" on Cu, and Pb spectra at 4.5 GeV yields $\Gamma_\rho = 130\pm5$, $m_\rho = 765\pm5$. (Fig. 4) In general, without the $\left(\frac{m_\rho}{m}\right)^4$ factor the fitted value of $m_\rho=740$ and $\Gamma_\rho \le 130$. Using $\Gamma_\rho = 130$, $m_\rho = 765$, and $2mR(m)=$BWJRS(m). One obtains a resonable good fit to the $\pi^+\pi^-$ spectra in 930<m<1130. (Fig. 5b)

OF VECTOR MESONS

Continued

Reaction	Methods and Groups	Dominant Production Mechanism and Cross Sections	Mass and Width; in MeV
		d) Comparison of nuclear radius with that deduced from proton-nucleus scattering (Nuclear Physics 79 (1966) 609-624):	

Targets   C   Cu   Pb
$R(\gamma A \cdot A_C)$ 3.0±0.3f   5.2±0.5f   7.7±0.8f
2.7-4.5
γ_0=1.30±0.10
$R(pA \cdot pA)$ 3.24±0.10f 5.60±0.10f 7.5±0.25f
20 GeV

e) The value of b(C) determined from fitting

$$\frac{1}{f'(p)} \frac{d\sigma}{dt} = x \, e^{bt}$$ in the region 930<m<1130,

$t \leq \frac{t_0}{2}$ agrees reasonably well with that deduced from (C) in the region 700<m<800.
(For absolute cross section see note in C).

f) Earlier work by the CEA Counter Group and the DESY Spark Chamber Group are in qualitative agreement with this data.

$\gamma + p \rightarrow p + \omega$ 2.1-5.8	DESY – HBC To be published in P.L. (1968)	The cross section decreases significantly with increasing E_γ, which suggests that a diffraction model alone can not give a good description of the experimental cross section below 6 GeV: $\sigma_\omega = (18.4 \pm 5.8) E_\gamma^{-1.6} + (1.9 \pm 0.9) E_\gamma^{-.08}$ (See Fig.1 and Table I). Note: $E_\gamma^{-1.6}$: the behavior of one meson exchange; $E_\gamma^{-.08}$: diffraction. The cross section agrees with earlier work at CEA on ω production. (P.R. 155. 1468) The CEA experiment yields m_ω=785±5.	Not quoted
$\gamma + p \rightarrow p + \phi$ 2 – 5.	DESY – HBC To be published in P.L. (1968)	With the statistics and the range of energy available, the energy behavior of cross section for $\gamma p \rightarrow p \phi$ shows no significant dependence on E_γ. See Fig. 1 and Table I.	Not quoted
$\gamma + A \rightarrow A + \phi$ A=(Be,C, Al,Cu,Ag, Ta,Pb). 5.2	DESY – M.I.T. Preliminary Data.	a) Diffraction, the data agrees well with $\frac{d\sigma}{d\Omega} = C(A) p^2 f_T(t, \sigma_{\phi N}, R)$. b) With $R=\gamma_0 A^{1/3}$, using Drell-Trefil model, the relative A dependence yields $\sigma_{\phi N}=15.0 \pm {}^{5.0}_{4.0}$ mb. Fig. 6, 7. c) For $t \ll t_0$ $\frac{d\sigma}{dt} \rightarrow x \, e^{bt}$. d) The decay angular distribution in the ϕ rest system is consistent with $W_{\phi \rightarrow KK}(\theta^*) = \frac{3}{8\pi} \sin^2\theta^*$; θ^* angle measured with respect to recoil nucleus direction Fig. 8.	Consistent with published values.

Table 1

Cross Sections for the Production of Vector Mesons

(Corrected for unobserved decay modes)

Reaction	Primary Photon Energy (GeV)		
	2.5 - 3.5	3.5 - 4.5	4.5 - 5.8
$\sigma(\gamma p \rightarrow p\rho^0)$ *) $\quad d\sigma/d\Delta^2 = a\,\exp(-B\Delta^2)$	$(17.8 \pm 2.0)\,\mu b$	$(16.4 \pm 2.0)\,\mu b$	$(16.0 \pm 2.0)\,\mu b$
$a =$	$(147 \pm 13)\,\mu b/GeV^2$	$(149 \pm 18)\,\mu b/GeV^2$	$(130 \pm 16)\,\mu b/GeV^2$
$B =$	$(6.9 \pm 0.4)GeV^{-2}$	$(8.1 \pm 0.7)GeV^{-2}$	$(7.9 \pm 0.7)GeV^{-2}$
$\sigma(\gamma p \rightarrow p\rho^0\pi^+\pi^-)$	---	$(2.9 \pm 0.8)\,\mu b$	$(3.2 \pm 1.5)\,\mu b$
$\sigma(\gamma p \rightarrow p\omega)$ *)	$(4.8 \pm 0.8)\,\mu b$	$(3.6 \pm 0.6)\,\mu b$	$(3.1 \pm 0.7)\,\mu b$
$d\sigma/\Delta^2 = a\,\exp(-B\Delta^2)$	$a = (28.4 \pm 5.2)\,\mu b/GeV^2$ $\quad B = (7.6 \pm 1.2)\,GeV^{-2}$		
$\sigma(\gamma p \rightarrow p\omega\pi^+\pi^-)$	$(1.8 \pm 0.5)\,\mu b$	$(3.8 \pm 0.8)\,\mu b$	$(2.7 \pm 1.0)\,\mu b$
$\sigma(\gamma p \rightarrow p\phi)$	$(0.41 \pm 0.14)\,\mu b$	$(0.45 \pm 0.13)\,\mu b$	
$d\sigma/d\Delta^2 = a\,\exp(-B\Delta^2)$	$a = (1.6 \pm 0.6)\,\mu b/GeV^2$ $\quad B = (3.5 \pm 0.9)\,GeV^{-2}$		
$\sigma(\gamma p \rightarrow p\phi\pi^+\pi^-)$	---	$(0.2 \pm 0.1)\,\mu b$	$(0.6 \pm 0.2)\,\mu b$

*) The errors for these cross sections include estimated systematic
uncertainties from the fitting procedure.

TABLE II   SUMMARY OF DATA ON $\rho \to \ell^- + \ell^+$ EXPERIMENTS

Experiments	B.R. × 10⁵	Mass Resolution	Production Mechanism and Density Matrix and Normalization	Estimated [43] Contribution
$\pi^- + Fe^C \to \mu^+ + \mu^-$ (PRL 18,929)	5.8 ± 1.2	124 Mev/c²	Via O.P.E., $\rho^{00} \approx 1.0$ for t < 0.3, normalized to bubble chamber data	(11 ± 6) %
$\pi^- + LiH \to \mu^+ + \mu^- + \pi^+ + \pi^-$ (PL 24B,634)	$9.7 \,^{+2.0}_{-2.3}$	± 20 Mev/c²	Observed $\rho^{00} = \pm 0.07 \,^{+0.24}_{-0.07}$ on $\mu^+\mu^-$ samples. Normalized to $\pi\pi$ yields in same apparatus.	Additional 25 % uncertainty due to ρ,ω interference.
$\gamma + C \to C + \mu^- + \mu^+$ (PRL 16,35 ; PRL 18,710)	5.9 ± 1.5	35 Mev/c²	Production not measured but used published values	Small
$\gamma + C \to C + e^+ + e^-$ (PRL 18,65)	6.5 ± 1.4	± 15 Mev/c²	Measured to be diffraction ρ^0 yields measured in same apparatus.	Small (see Fig.9)
$e^+ + e^- \to \pi^+ + \pi^-$ (PRL 20,126)	6.2 ± 1.0		Obtained $m_\rho = 764 \pm 11$, $\Gamma_\rho = 93 \pm 15$ (see Fig.10)	
$e^+ + e^- \to \pi^+ + \pi^-$ (PL 25B,433)	$\sigma_{ee \to \pi\pi} = 1.2 \pm 0.2 \,\mu b$			

$\pi^- + p \to e^- + e^+ + \cdots$ (PL 24B,349)

$BR_\rho G_\rho + BR_\omega G_\omega = (0.41 \pm 0.08) \times 10^{-4}$ mb

$BR \phi G_\phi = (0.12 \pm 0.06) \times 10^{-4}$ mb

≈ 30 events with spark chambers and shower counters

if θ mixing = 38° $B_\rho = (0.35 \pm 0.09) \times 10^{-4}$

if $G_\omega = 0$ $B_\rho = (0.55 \pm 0.14) \times 10^{-4}$

TABLE III   SUMMARY OF COUPLING CONSTANTS

	Values	References	Remarks
$\dfrac{\gamma_v^2}{4\pi}$			
$\dfrac{\gamma_\rho^2}{4\pi}$	$0.44 \begin{smallmatrix}+0.16\\-0.09\end{smallmatrix}$	(PRL 16,35; PRL 18,710)	
	$0.45 \begin{smallmatrix}+0.11\\-0.08\end{smallmatrix}$	(PRL 18,929)	Determined from $\rho \rightarrow \mu^- \mu^+$
	$0.27 \begin{smallmatrix}+0.08\\-0.05\end{smallmatrix}$	(PL 24B,634)	
	$0.40 \begin{smallmatrix}+0.11\\-0.07\end{smallmatrix}$	(PRL 18,65)	Determined from $\rho \rightarrow e^- e^+$
	$0.42 \begin{smallmatrix}+0.08\\-0.06\end{smallmatrix}$	(PRL 20,126)	Determined from $e^+ + e^- \rightarrow \pi^+ + \pi^-$
	0.49 ± 0.12	(PRL 20,227)	Determined from $\gamma + A \rightarrow A + \rho^0$ using VDM
	0.62		Determined from $F_\pi(0) = 1$. Thus $g_{\rho\pi\pi} = 2\gamma_\rho$ with $g_{\rho\pi\pi}$ obtained from $\Gamma_{\rho\rightarrow\pi\pi} = 130$ Mev, $M_\rho = 765$ Mev
$\dfrac{\gamma_\omega^2}{4\pi}$	10 ± 2	(PRL 19,1266)	From ratio of $\Gamma(\omega^0 \rightarrow \pi^0 + \gamma)\,/\,\Gamma^0(\pi^0 \rightarrow 2\gamma)$; calculated by Sakurai and Oakes
	$0.5 < \dfrac{\gamma_\omega^2}{4\pi} < 5.8$	(PRL 14,721)	From experiment on $\omega \rightarrow e^- e^+$. Based on SU3 mixing angle
$\dfrac{\gamma_\varphi^2}{4\pi}$	$3.8 \begin{smallmatrix}+3.8\\-1.9\end{smallmatrix}$	(PRL 20,748)	(with $\Gamma = 3.4$ Mev)

Precise measurements will be available soon from DESY

Figure Captions

Fig. 1   Cross sections for $\gamma p \to p\rho$, $\gamma p \to p\omega$, $\gamma p \to p\phi$ as a
            function of photon energy E_γ . Corrections for unobserved
            decay modes are included. Results for the rho meson are
            shown for different fitting methods.

Fig. 2   Dependence of $A^{-1} \frac{d\sigma}{d\Omega}$ upon A, the atomic number of the target
            nucleus. Results are shown for average ρ^0 momentum p = 2.700,
            3.500 and 4.500 GeV/c. The curves are best fits to the model of
            Drell and Trefil as discussed in the text. The data are normal-
            ized to 1 for Beryllium.

Fig. 3a),   The quantity $f'(p)^{-1} \frac{d\sigma}{d|t|}$ is shown as a function of t, the
    b),c)   square of the momentum transfer to the nucleus, for carbon,
            copper, and lead targets. The curves are best fits to the model
            of Drell and Trefil with an additional incoherent contribution
            from individual nucleons; but without removal of non-resonant
            background. For absolute cross section see Section C.

    d)   Comparison of $\frac{d\sigma}{d\Omega} (\gamma + A \to A + \rho^0)$ with $\frac{d\sigma(\pi N \to \pi N)}{d\Omega}$ as a
            function of p. Only events having mass $m = m_\rho \pm 2\%$ are in-
            cluded. The constancy of the ratio $(p^2 \, f'(p) \, f_T)^{-1} \frac{d\sigma}{d\Omega}$ shows
            that the two cross sections have the same momentum dependence in
            the forward direction.

Fig. 4   Pion pair invariant mass spectra $(p^2 \, f'(p) \, f_T)^{-1} \frac{d\sigma}{d\Omega dm}$ in units
            of nb $(GeV/C)^{-2}$ $(MeV/c^2)^{-1}$ sr^{-1}, for: a) carbon, p = 3.158 GeV/c,
            k_{max} = 4.35 GeV/c; b) carbon, p = 4.500 GeV/c, k_{max} = 6.00 GeV/c;
            c) copper, p = 4.500 GeV/c, k_{max} = 6.00 GeV/c; and d) lead,
            p = 4.500 GeV/c, k_{max} = 6.00 GeV/c. The solid curve is the best
            fit of the data to the function U(m) as described in the text.
            The dashed curve is the estimate of the non-resonant background
            contribution $B_l(m)$. As this background is small the best-fit
            values of m_ρ, the central mass of the ρ^0 meson, and Γ_0, its
            width, are insensitive to the explicit form of the background.
            The transverse polarization of the ρ^0 mesons was taken into account
            to obtain the absolute values shown.

Fig. 5   Pion-pair invariant mass spectrum $(p^2 \, f'(p) \, f_T)^{-1} \frac{d^2\sigma}{d\Omega dm}$
in units of nb $(GeV/c)^{-2}$ $(MeV/c^2)^{-1}$ sr^{-1} $(atom)^{-1}$ for
carbon target. In the mass region 400<m<930 MeV/c^2 the
data were fitted to U_1 (m) (solid line) and U_2 (m) (dotted
line) to determine the parameters m_ρ, Γ_0. With the spectrum functions 2m R(m) and 2m BW(m) so determined their
behaviours over the region 1130>m>930 MeV/c^2 were then
plotted (x10) and compared with the experimental data.

Fig. 6   Kaon pair invariant mass spectra as function of $K^+ K^-$
invariant mass. The acceptance of each mass bin was calculated
by Monte Carlo method, without any weighting of the production
mechanism. The existence of ϕ^0 meson is clearly seen and no
other enhancement were found.

Fig. 7   Dependence of $A^{-1} \frac{d\sigma}{d\Omega}$ upon A, the atomic number of the target
nucleus. The curve are best fits to the model of Drell and
Trefil, Ross and Stodolsky as discussed in the text. The data
are normalized to 1 for Beryllium.

Fig. 8   The decay angular distribution of the K^+, K^- pairs in the ϕ^0
rest frame, Θ^* is the angle in the ϕ^0 rest system between the
K^+, K^- and the incident γ-ray direction. The solid line is
the distribution function $W(\Theta^*) = \frac{3}{8\pi} \sin^2\Theta^*$. The agreement of
the data with $W(\Theta^*)$ implies that the ϕ^0 produced are completely
transversely polarized.

Fig. 9 a)   Pair yield from $\rho^0 \rightarrow e^+ e^-$ as a function of invariant mass.
Bethe-Heitler background has been subtracted, and the magnitude
of the yield includes the effect of the complete polarization
of the ρ^0 mesons. The peak bremsstrahlung energy k_{max} = 6.0
GeV. The smoothness and approximate symmetry of the distribution indicates that the $\omega \rightarrow e^- e^+$ contribution is small.

     b)   Pair yield from $\rho^0 \rightarrow \pi^- \pi^+$ as function of invariant mass. Again
the effect of polarization of ρ^0 mesons is included in the
calculation of the yield. The momentum P_ρ is 2.8 GeV/c and
k_{max} = 6.0 GeV.

Fig. 10 $\pi^- \pi^+$ spectra obtained from the Novosibirsk Colliding Beam
Experiment.

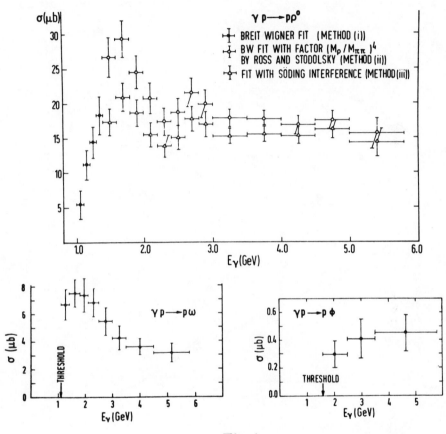

Fig. 1

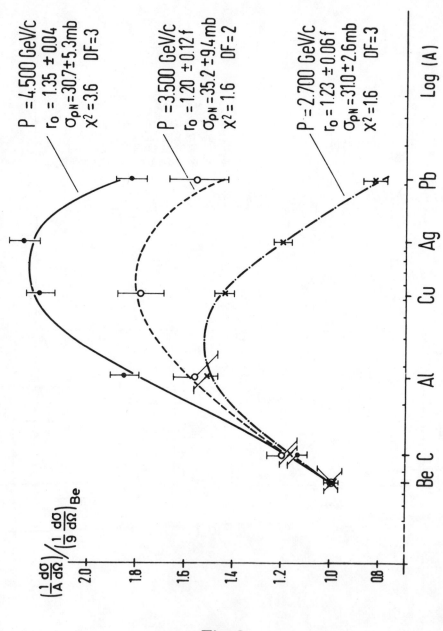

Fig. 2

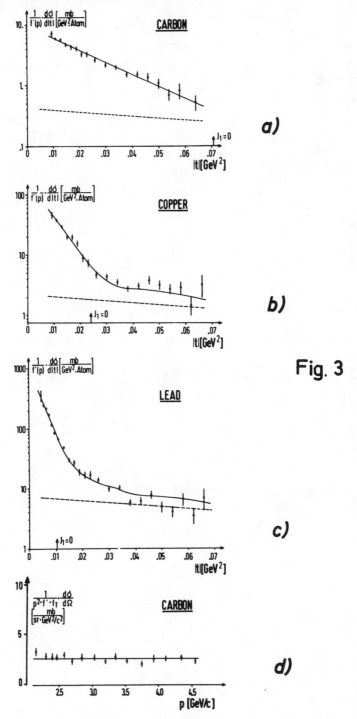

Fig. 3

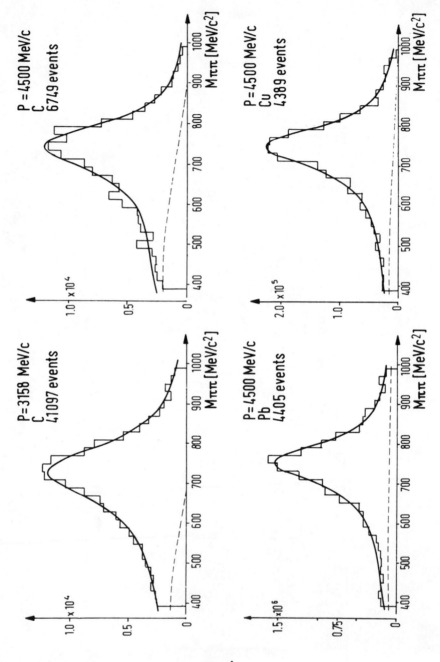

Fig.4

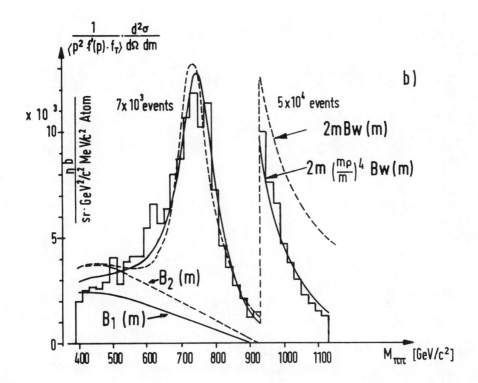

Fig. 5

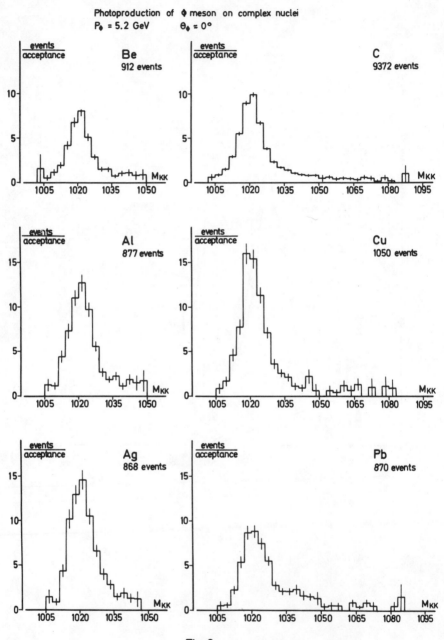

Fig. 6

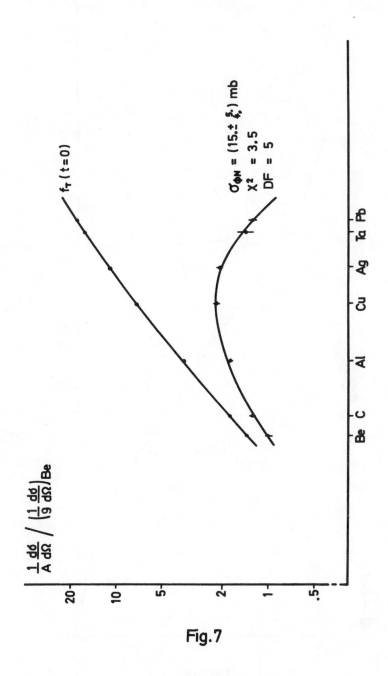

Fig.7

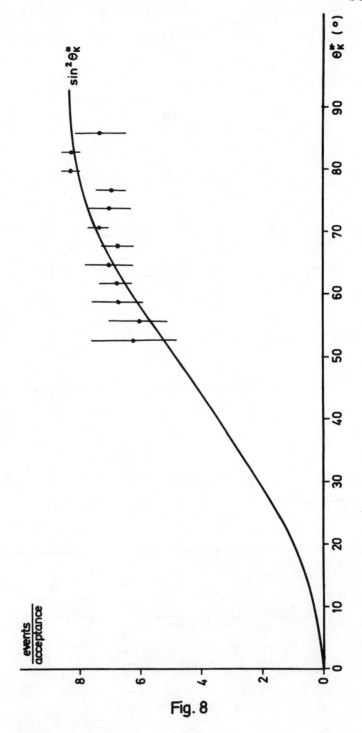

Fig. 8

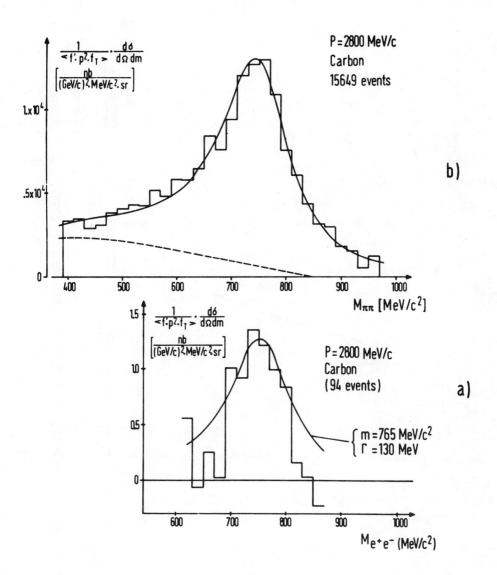

Fig. 9

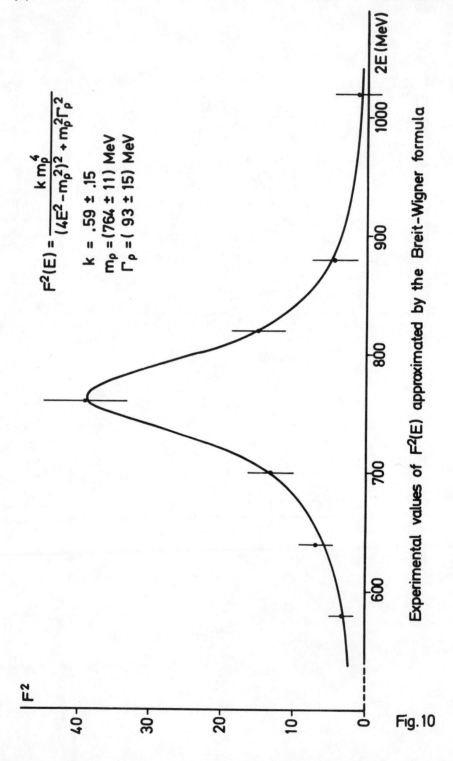

$$F^2(E) = \frac{k\,m_\rho^4}{(4E^2 - m_\rho^2)^2 + m_\rho^2\Gamma_\rho^2}$$

$k = .59 \pm .15$
$m_\rho = (764 \pm 11)$ MeV
$\Gamma_\rho = (\ 93 \pm 15)$ MeV

Experimental values of F^2(E) approximated by the Breit–Wigner formula

Fig. 10

ETA MESON DECAY

C. Baltay

Columbia University

Supported in part by the Atomic Energy Commission.

The eta meson, with a mass of approximately 549 MeV, was discovered through its decay into three pions by Pevsner and co-workers[1] in 1961. Soon thereafter a variety of other decay modes were found and the spin, parity, isotopic spin and G-parity quantum numbers of this meson were established to be $J^P I^G = 0^- 0^+$. In recent years, much experimental and theoretical work has been devoted to the study of the decay modes of the eta meson. The probable reason for the large amount of interest in the decay modes of this particular meson is that the electromagnetic interactions are responsible for eta decay; thus a study of these decays can yield information about the nature of the electromagnetic interactions. The purpose of this review is to summarize the presently available experimental information about the decay of the eta meson.

I. LIFETIME OF THE ETA MESON

An experimental measurement of the η° lifetime has been performed at the DESY electron accelerator by Bemporad et al[2] using the Primakoff effect. The η° were produced by the interaction of
an incident photon with a virtual photon associated
with the field of a target nucleus, and the η° were
detected by their decay into two photons. The η°
lifetime thus measured depends on the branching
fraction of the η° into two photons. The quantity
directly measured in the experiment was the pro-
duct of B, the branching ratio $\eta \rightarrow \gamma\gamma/\eta \rightarrow$ all modes,
and $\Gamma_{\gamma\gamma}$, the partial width for η° decay into $\gamma\gamma$:

$$B \times \Gamma_{\gamma\gamma} = 0.38 \pm 0.08 \text{ keV} .$$

Using a value of B = 0.403 ± 0.016 (see the following section for the justification of this branching ratio), the above number leads to the following
partial and total widths[*]:

$$\Gamma_{\gamma\gamma} = 0.94 \pm 0.20 \text{ keV} \quad \text{and}$$

$$\Gamma_{total} = 2.3 \pm 0.5 \text{ keV.}$$

This total width corresponds to an η° lifetime of
the order of 3×10^{-19} seconds.

---

[*]The authors of reference 2 actually quote $\Gamma_{\gamma\gamma}$ =
1.21 ± 0.26 keV, based on a value of
B = 0.314, which was the $\gamma\gamma$ branching ratio favored at the time of their publication.

II. BRANCHING RATIOS FOR THE DOMINANT DECAY MODES

The dominant decay modes of the η^o observed to date are the decays into $\gamma\gamma$, $\pi^o\gamma\gamma$, $3\pi^o$, $\pi^+\pi^-\pi^o$, and $\pi^+\pi^-\gamma$. There has been much controversy recently about the branching fractions for these decay modes. Significant inconsistencies exist between various individual experiments. If a single fit is attempted to obtain the branching fractions for the five dominant modes, using all of the available experimental data, a very poor fit results, with an overall probability[3] of the order of 10^{-4}. In order to get a clearer view of the nature and extent of these discrepancies, an alternate procedure will be followed in this review. The various experimental results can be expressed in terms of four ratios:

$$R_1 = \frac{\eta \to \pi^o\gamma\gamma}{\eta \to \gamma\gamma}$$

$$R_2 = \frac{\eta \to 3\pi^o}{\eta \to \gamma\gamma}$$

$$R_3 = \frac{\eta \to \pi^+\pi^-\gamma}{\eta \to \pi^+\pi^-\pi^o}$$

$$R_4 = \frac{\eta \to \text{all neutral modes}}{\eta \to \text{charged modes}}$$

The best value for each ratio is taken to be the weighted average of the individual experiments. From these four ratios, together with the assumption that no other dominant modes exist, the branching fractions can be calculated.

In this procedure some problems arise in the
calculation of the errors. For some of the experiments, correlations exist between these ratios,
but the correlation errors are usually not available and can therefore not be taken into account.
Furthermore, the error on the ratio of two numbers
with gaussian errors is not necessarily gaussian;
but the errors on the ratios above are treated as
gaussian in taking weighted averages and calculating χ^2 values. However these effects are small
for the present case and they do not significantly
change the final results. The four ratios defined
above were chosen such that correlations between
them are minimized; for most of the experiments,
R_3 and R_4 are independent of each other and independent of the measurements of R_1 and R_2.

The available experimental measurements of
the ratios R_1 to R_4 are listed in Tables I to IV,
respectively. An examination of these tables shows
that:

a)   The measurements of the $\pi^o \gamma\gamma/\gamma\gamma$ ratio,
R_1, are in very poor agreement with each other.
The χ^2 for the nine experiments listed is 33.3,
which has a very low probability.

b)   The measurements of all of the other ratios, R_2, R_3, and R_4, are in very good agreement
with each other. The χ^2 values are as follows:
for the ten experiments on R_2, $\chi^2 = 5.7$:   for the
seven experiments on R_3, $\chi^2 = 8.3$: and for the
eight experiments on R_4, $\chi^2 = 6.0$.   All of these
are quite acceptable fits.

It should be pointed out that the χ^2 values quoted above do not necessarily have their usual meaning since, as mentioned above, the errors on the experimental ratios are not strictly gaussian. However, they do provide a rough guide, from which it can be concluded that the problem is in the $\pi^\circ\gamma\gamma/\gamma\gamma$ ratio. If the disagreement there can be resolved, the rest of the measurements are in reasonably good agreement.

Table I

Measurements of the Ratio

$$R_1 = \eta \rightarrow \pi^\circ\gamma\gamma/\eta \rightarrow \gamma\gamma$$

Group	Ref.	Method	R_1
Di Giugno et al	4	Counters	0.90 ± 0.20
Feldman et al	5	Spark Ch.	0.42 ± 0.10
Grunhaus	6	Spark Ch.	0.61 ± 0.40
Strugalski et al	7	Xenon B.C.	0.86 ± 0.47
Wahlig et al	8	Spark Ch.	0 ± 0.30
Baltay et al	9	Deut. B.C.	0 ± 0.14
Bonamy et al	10	Spark Ch.	0.05 ± 0.04
Buniatov et al	11	Spark Ch.	0.06 ± 0.09
Jacquet et al	12	Spark Ch.	0 ± 0.15

Table II

Measurements of the Ratio

$$R_2 = \eta \to 3\pi^{\circ}/\eta \to \gamma\gamma$$

Group	Ref.	Method	R_2
Chretien et al	13	Propane B.C.	0.90 or more
Bacci et al	14	Spark Ch.	1.25 ± 0.30
Crawford et al	15	Hydrogen B.C.	0.67 ± 0.42
Muller et al	16	Deut. B.C.	0.91 ± 0.50
Foster et al	17	Hydrogen B.C.	0.56 ± 0.20
Grunhaus	6	Spark Ch.	0.66 ± 0.25
Fortney et al	18	Hydrogen B.C.	0.77 ± 0.27
Baltay et al	9	Deut. B.C.	0.88 ± 0.16
Buniatov et al	11	Spark Ch.	0.70 ± 0.06
Michael et al	19	Heavy Liq.	0.60 ± 0.16
Baglin et al	20	Heavy Liq.	0.75 ± 0.24

Table III

Measurements of the Ratio

$$R_3 = \eta \rightarrow \pi^+\pi^-\gamma / \eta \rightarrow \pi^+\pi^-\pi^o$$

Group	Ref.	Method	R_3
Foelsche et al	21	Hydrogen B.C.	0.14 ± 0.08
Kraemer et al	22	Deuterium B.C.	0.10 ± 0.10
Foster et al	17	Hydrogen B.C.	0.20 ± 0.04
Crawford et al	43	Hydrogen B.C.	0.30 ± 0.06
Baltay et al	23	Deuterium B.C.	0.28 ± 0.04
Litchfield et al	24	Deuterium B.C.	0.25 ± 0.035
Fortney et al	18	Hydrogen B.C.	0.17 ± 0.05

Table IV

Measurements of the Ratio

$$R_4 = \eta \rightarrow neutrals / \eta \rightarrow charged$$

Group	Ref.	Method	R_4
Buschbeck et al	25	Hydrogen B.C.	2.6 ± 0.9
Kraemer et al	22	Deuterium B.C.	3.3 ± 0.8
Crawford et al	15	Hydrogen B.C.	1.65 ± 0.53
Foster et al	17	Hydrogen B.C.	2.1 ± 0.4
Alff-Steinberger	26	Hydrogen B.C.	2.35 ± 0.46
Baltay et al	23	Deuterium B.C.	2.64 ± 0.23
Buniatov et al	11	Spark Ch.	3.7 ± 1.3
Fortney et al	18	Hydrogen B.C.	2.6 ± 0.4

The weighted average of all of the experiments is $R_1 = 0.11 \pm 0.03$. The first two experiments listed in Table I are both more than three standard deviations from this average, and they are somewhat inconsistent with each other. If one assumes that the best procedure is to average the seven self-consistent experiments without including the two which are more than three standard deviations from the average, the ratio becomes $R_1 = 0.05 \pm 0.03$. The χ^2 value is 5.2 for the seven remaining experiments, which is quite acceptable.

For some of the experiments listed in Table II a correlation exists between the $3\pi^{\circ}/\gamma\gamma$ ratio and the $\pi^{\circ}\gamma\gamma/\gamma\gamma$ ratio. The ratios in Table II are based on the conclusion that the $\pi^{\circ}\gamma\gamma/\gamma\gamma$ ratio is small.

The weighted averages of the four ratios are:

$$R_1 = 0.05 \pm 0.03$$
$$R_2 = 0.72 \pm 0.05$$
$$R_3 = 0.23 \pm 0.02$$
$$R_4 = 2.48 \pm 0.15$$

Assuming that no other decay modes contribute significantly, the following branching fractions, expressed as percentage of all η decays, are obtained:

$$\eta \rightarrow \pi^+ \pi^- \gamma \qquad 5.4 \pm 0.6$$

$$\pi^+ \pi^- \pi^o \quad 23.3 \pm 1.2 \qquad \Big\} \quad 28.7 \pm 1.3\%$$

$$3\pi^o \qquad 29.0 \pm 2.5$$

$$\gamma\gamma \qquad 40.3 \pm 1.6 \quad \Big\} \quad 71.3 \pm 1.3\%$$

$$\pi^o \gamma\gamma \qquad 2.0 \pm 1.2$$

It may be interesting to note that these numbers lead to a three-pion branching ratio of

$$\frac{\eta \rightarrow 3\pi^o}{\eta \rightarrow \pi^+ \pi^- \pi^o} = 1.25 \pm 0.13 \ .$$

This branching ratio can be predicted[52], assuming that three pions are in an isotopic spin 1 state and that the linear matrix element sufficiently describes the decay, to be

$$\frac{\eta \rightarrow 3\pi^o}{\eta \rightarrow \pi^+ \pi^- \pi^o} = 1.5 \times 1.13 \times \frac{1}{1 + 1/4 \ \alpha^2} = 1.58$$

where $\alpha = -0.54 \pm 0.017$ is the slope of the $\pi^+ \pi^- \pi^o$ Dalitz plot (see section IV for the justification of this value of α).

The three-pion branching ratio of 1.25 ± 0.13 given above is much closer to this prediction than it had been believed to be on the basis of the early experiments on η decay.

III.   SEARCH FOR RARE DECAY MODES

A. $\eta \rightarrow \pi^{o}e^{+}e^{-}$.   The search for this decay mode has
been very active since its existence would be an
indication of C nonconservation in the electromagnetic interactions.[27]   No evidence has been found
so far for the existence of this decay mode.   Sev-
en independent experiments have been performed in
liquid hydrogen, deuterium, or heavy liquid bubble
chambers, looking for the decay into $\pi^{o}e^{+}e^{-}$ in a
combined effective sample of 14,000 η decays.
Some features of these experiments are summarized
in Table V.[35]   These results lead to the following
90% confidence level upper limit:

$$\frac{\eta \rightarrow \pi^{o}e^{+}e^{-}}{\eta \rightarrow \text{all decays}} \leq 2 \times 10^{-4}$$

Table V

Search for the Decay $\eta \rightarrow \pi^{o}e^{+}e^{-}$

Group	Ref.	Method	Effective η Sample
Foster et al	28	Hydrogen B.C.	611
Price et al	29	Hydrogen B.C.	406
Rittenberg et al	30	Hydrogen B.C.	330
Berley et al	31	Hydrogen B.C.	226
Baglin et al	32	Heavy Liq.	2,460
Billing et al	33	Heavy Liq.	6,300
Bazin et al	34	Deut. B.C.	3,910
TOTAL			14,243

B. $\eta \to \mu^+\mu^-$ and $\eta \to \pi^0\mu^+\mu^-$. Wehman et al have carried out an experiment at the Brookhaven AGS looking for $\mu^+\mu^-$ pairs produced by K^- and π^- mesons on carbon and iron.[36] They report the following 95% confidence level upper limits:

$$\frac{\eta \to \mu^+\mu^-}{\eta \to \text{all modes}} \leq 2 \times 10^{-5}$$

$$\frac{\eta \to \pi^0\mu^+\mu^-}{\eta \to \text{all modes}} \leq 5 \times 10^{-4}$$

C. $\eta \to \pi^+\pi^- e^+ e^-$. Two experiments have searched for this decay mode. Rittenberg and Kalbfleisch[30] found no such decays in a sample of eighty-nine charged η decays. Grossman et al[37] found one e-vent that they unambiguously identified as this decay in a sample of thirty-eight $\eta \to \pi^+\pi^-\gamma$ events. Combining the two experiments gives one $\pi^+\pi^- e^+ e^-$ decay in an effective sample of 1,010 total η de-cays, or a branching ratio of

$$\frac{\eta \to \pi^+\pi^- e^+ e^-}{\eta \to \text{all modes}} \approx 1 \times 10^{-3}$$

D. $\eta \to \pi^+\pi^-\pi^0\gamma$ and $\eta \to \pi^+\pi^-\gamma\gamma$. These decay modes have been searched for in three bubble chamber ex-periments.[38,39,23] The experimental problem is to separate these decays from the dominant decays in-to $\pi^+\pi^-\gamma$ and $\pi^+\pi^-\pi^0$. The three experiments pro-ceeded in essentially the same way; events which were $\eta \to \pi^+\pi^- X^0$ were separated out, where X^0 is

either a γ, a π^0, or a $\gamma\gamma$ or $\pi^0\gamma$ combination.
Events were classified as possible $\pi^+\pi^-\pi^0\gamma$ or
$\pi^+\pi^-\gamma\gamma$ decays if m_x^2 was larger than approximately
$2\ m_\pi^2$. The number of events found together with the
number of $\eta \rightarrow \pi^+\pi^-\pi^0$ events in each of the three
experiments is summarized in Table VI:

Table VI

Search for the Decay Modes $\eta \rightarrow \pi^+\pi^-\pi^0\gamma$
And $\eta \rightarrow \pi^+\pi^-\gamma\gamma$. m_x is the Effective
Mass of the $\pi^0\gamma$ or $\gamma\gamma$ Combination.

Group	Ref.	Events with $m_x^2 \geq 2\ m_\pi^2$	$\eta \rightarrow \pi^+\pi^-\pi^0$ Sample
Flatte	38	6	246
Price et al	39	0	255
Baltay et al	23	4	1,520

To correct for the number of $\pi^+\pi^-\pi^0\gamma$ and
$\pi^+\pi^-\gamma\gamma$ decays lost due to the cut in m_x^2, the $\pi^0\gamma$
and $\gamma\gamma$ effective mass distributions were calculated
using a matrix element for the $\pi^+\pi^-\pi^0\gamma$ mode given
by Singer[40], and the simplest gauge invariant ma-
trix element[23] for the $\pi^+\pi^-\gamma\gamma$ mode. The result is
that for both modes, approximately 40% of the
events have $m_x^2 \geq 2\ m_\pi^2$. This number will be assumed
for calculating the upper limits for these modes;

if some other matrix element turns out to be more
correct, however, the numbers can be adjusted
accordingly. The best upper limits are obtained
if the last two experiments listed in Table VI
are combined; this is fair since the six events
found in the first experiment listed could be due
to some other, non-η source, as pointed out in
Ref. 38. There are then four possible (but not
definite) events due to these decay modes in a
sample of 1,775 $\eta \rightarrow \pi^+\pi^-\pi^o$ decays. This leads to
the 90% confidence level upper limits of

$$\frac{\eta \rightarrow \pi^+\pi^-\pi^o\gamma}{\eta \rightarrow \text{all modes}} \leq 2.6 \times 10^{-3}$$

$$\frac{\eta \rightarrow \pi^+\pi^-\gamma\gamma}{\eta \rightarrow \text{all modes}} \leq 2.6 \times 10^{-3}$$

IV. DALITZ PLOT DISTRIBUTIONS FOR THE CHARGED DECAY MODES

A.   The Decay $\eta \rightarrow \pi^+\pi^-\pi^o$. The Dalitz plot distribution for this decay deviates from the uniform
distribution that might be expected for the decay
of a $J^P = 0^-$ meson into three pions. The deviation
seems to be mainly a function of T_o, the kinetic
energy of the π^o. This decay is well described,
within the limits of currently available statistics,
by the linear matrix element

$$|f|^2 = |1 + \alpha y|^2$$

where $y = 3T_o/Q - 1$, Q is the η mass minus the mass
of the three pions, and α is a complex parameter,
often referred to as the "slope" of the Dalitz
plot.

A fit to the above matrix element has been
carried out by a number of groups; the results of
these fits are summarized in Table VII. Some of
the early fits performed by various bubble chamber
groups are not listed separately since their data
is included in the Bubble Chamber Compilation, the
first entry in the table.

Table VII

Fits of the $\eta \rightarrow \pi^+\pi^-\pi^o$ Decay Dalitz

Plot to the Linear Matrix Element

$f = 1 + \alpha(3T_o/Q - 1)$

Group	Ref.	η Sample Used in Fit	Re α	Im α
B. C. Collab.	41	1300	-0.48 ± 0.04	0.05 ± 0.39
Columbia-SUNY	42	1215	-0.54 ± 0.04	0 ± 0.22
CERN	51	7170	-0.55 ± 0.02	0 ± 0.11

The agreement among the three fits listed is
very good. All of the fits prefer α to be real.
The weighted average of the three fits is

$$\alpha = -0.54 \pm 0.017$$

where α is a real number.

All three fits listed were characterized by good χ^2 probabilities, implying that the linear matrix element is sufficient to describe the decay, and higher powers of the Dalitz plot variables are not required. However, in the CERN experiment, which has the best statistics, slightly better fits were obtained by a quadratic matrix element.[51]

B. __The Decay $\eta \to \pi^+\pi^-\gamma$.__ Angular momentum conservation and 0 spin for the η require that the two pions have angular momentum 1 or larger. Furthermore, since the charge conjugation quantum number is +1 for the η and -1 for the γ, C conserving decay processes lead to odd angular momenta for the two pions. Thus J = 1 seems likely for the two pions. Experimentally, it has been demonstrated that the two pions are predominantly in a J = 1 state by studying the distribution in the cosine of the angle between the π^+ and the γ in the dipion rest frame.[24,43,44]

The simplest gauge invariant matrix element for this decay with a J = 1 dipion is

$$|M|^2 = |\bar{p} \times \bar{q}|^2$$

where p is the momentum of the γ, and q is the momentum of either π in the dipion rest frame.

Four experimental groups[24,42,43,44] have compared their samples of $\eta \to \pi^+\pi^-\gamma$ decays with this

matrix element. They[42,43,44] find that the fit is
poor; the group with the largest sample[44] (1,088
$\eta \to \pi^+\pi^-\gamma$ decays) can exclude the fit quite strongly
(χ^2 = 48 for 8 bins). The distributions are
shifted toward lower γ momenta, and therefore higher dipion effective masses, than is predicted by
the matrix element. It is clear that the p wave
$\pi\pi$ interaction in the final state must be taken
into account. When the simple matrix element given
above is multiplied by a resonance factor for the
ρ meson, good agreement is found with the experimental data in all four experiments. The details
of these fits are shown in Fig. 1.

V.   CHARGE ASYMMETRY IN ETA DECAY

         A statistically significant difference in the
energy spectra of the π^+ and π^- in the decays
$\eta \to \pi^+\pi^-\pi^0$ or $\eta \to \pi^+\pi^-\gamma$ would be an indication of
charge conjugation non-invariance in these pro-
cesses.[27] A simple way of parametrizing such a
difference in the energies of the pions is by defining the asymmetry A as

$$A = \frac{N_+ - N_-}{N_+ + N_-}$$

where N_+ is the number of decays in which the π^+
is more energetic than the π^- and N_- is the number
of decays where the opposite is true.

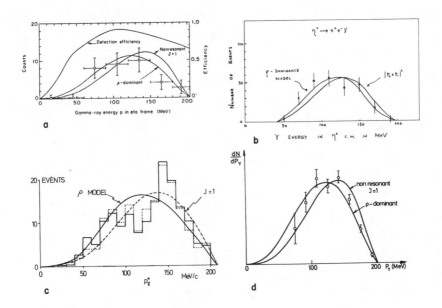

Figure 1   Fits to the momentum spectrum of the γ
            in the η center of mass in the decay
            $\eta \rightarrow \pi^+\pi^-\gamma$.

            a)   33 events from Berkeley (Ref. 43).
            b)   252 events from Columbia-SUNY
                         (Ref. 42).
            c)   160 events from Rutherford-Saclay
                         (Ref. 24).
            d)   1,088 events from CERN (Ref. 44).

        A large amount of experimental effort has
been devoted to the measurement of A.   Table VIII
contains a summary of the results for the $\eta \rightarrow \pi^+\pi^-\pi^0$
decay.   The weighted average is A = 1.45 ± 0.44%
with a χ^2 of 10.7 for the six experiments.   The
agreement between the various measurements is not
as good as might be expected.   However, the errors
on A listed in the table are only the statistical

errors. An inclusion of systematic errors (which
are very hard to evaluate for some of these experiments) would tend to decrease the χ^2 and thus tend
to alleviate the disagreement between the experiments; also the 0.44% error on the average would
be increased somewhat.

Table VIII

Summary of the Charge Asymmetry

Measurements in the Decay $\eta \to \pi^+\pi^-\pi^0$

Group	Ref.	$\eta \to \pi^+\pi^-\pi^0$ Sample	Asymmetry in %
B.C. Compilation	41	1,300	5.8 ± 3.4
Duke	45	565	4.1 ± 4.1
Columbia-SUNY	47	1,351	7.2 ± 2.8
Rutherford-Saclay	46	705	-6.1 ± 4.0
CERN	48	10,665	0.3 ± 1.1
Columbia	50	36,800	1.5 ± 0.5

The results on the asymmetry measurement in
the $\eta \to \pi^+\pi^-\gamma$ decay are summarized in Table IX.
The weighted average of these four experiments is
A = 2.0 ± 1.2%

Thus the possibility of C violation in η decay is still an open question. More experimental

work is in progress.

Table IX

Summary of the Charge Asymmetry

Measurements in the Decay $\eta \rightarrow \pi^+\pi^-\gamma$

Group	Ref.	$\eta \rightarrow \pi^+\pi^-\gamma$ Sample	Asymmetry in %
Berkeley	43	33	-2 ± 17
Rutherford-Saclay	24	160	-4 ± 8
CERN	49	1,620	1.5 ± 2.5
Columbia	50	6,710	2.4 ± 1.4

REFERENCES

1 A. Pevsner, M. Nussbaum, C. Richardson, R. Strand, T. Toohig, R. Kraemer, P. Schlein, M. Block, A. Engler, R. Gessaroli, and C. Meltzer, Phys. Rev. Letters $\underline{1}$, 421 (1961).

2 C. Bemporad, P. L. Braccini, L. Foa, K. Lubelsmeyer, and D. Schmitz, Phys. Letters $\underline{25B}$, 380 (1967).

3 See for example the discussion on the η meson in the compilation by Rosenfeld et al, Rev. Mod. Phys. $\underline{40}$, 77 (1968).

4 G. Di Giugno, R. Querzoli, G. Troise, F. Vanoli, M. Giorgi, P. Schiavon, and V. Silvestrini, Phys. Rev. Letters $\underline{16}$, 767 (1966).

5 M. Feldman, W. Frati, R. Gleeson, J. Halpern, M. Nussbaum, and S. Richtert, Phys. Rev. Letters $\underline{18}$, 868 (1967).

6 J. Grunhaus, Thesis, Columbia University (1966).

7 Z. S. Strugalski, I. V. Chuvilo, I. A. Ivanovska, L. S. Okhrimenko, B. Niczyporuk, T. Kanarek, B. Stowiuski, and Z. Jablonski, JINR-EI-3100 (1967).

8 M. A. Wahlig, E. Shibita, and E. Mannelli, Phys. Rev. Letters $\underline{17}$, 221 (1966); and E. Shibita, Private Communication (April, 1968).

9 C. Baltay, P. Franzini, J. Kim, R. Newman, N. Yeh, and L. Kirsch, Phys. Rev. Letters $\underline{19}$, 1495 (1967).

10 P. Bonamy and P. Sonderegger, Preprint submitted
    to the Heidelberg International Conference on
    Elementary Particles, Sept., 1967.

11 S. Buniatov, E. Zavatini, W. Deinet, H. Muller,
    D. Schmitt, and H. Staudenmaier, Phys. Letters
    25B, 560 (1967).

12 F. Jacquet, U. Nguyen-Khac, C. Baglin, A. Beza-
    guet, B. Degrange, R. J. Kurz, P. Musset, A.
    Haatuft, A. Halsteinslid, and J. M. Olsen,
    Phys. Letters 25B, 574 (1967).

13 M. Chretien et al, Phys. Rev. Letters 9, 127
    (1962).

14 C. Bacci, G. Penso, G. Salvini, A. Wattenberg,
    C. Mencuccini, R. Querzoli, and V. Silvestrini,
    Phys. Rev. Letters 11, 37 (1963).

15 F. S. Crawford, L. J. Lloyd, and E. C. Fowler,
    Phys. Rev. Letters 10, 546 (1963).

16 A. Muller, E. Pauli, R. Barloutand, L. Cardin,
    J. Meyer, M. Beneventano, G. Gialanella, and
    J. Paoluzi, Proceedings of the Sienna Inter-
    national Conference on Elementary Particles,
    p. 99 (1963).

17 M. Foster, M. Peters, R. Hartung, R. Matsen,
    D. Reeder, M. Good, M. Meer, F. Loeffler, and
    R. McIlwain, Phys. Rev. 138, B652 (1965); and
    M. Foster, Thesis, University of Wisconsin
    (1965).

18 L. R. Fortney and E. C. Fowler, Private Communi-

cation (April, 1968).

[19] W. B. Michael, Thesis; the ratio quoted in this paper is,

$$\frac{\eta \to 3\pi^{0}}{\eta \to \pi^{+}\pi^{-}\pi^{0}} = 1.05 \pm 0.25.$$

The value of R_2 used in Table II was calculated from this ratio by multiplying it by the $\eta \to \pi^{+}\pi^{-}\pi^{0}/\eta \to \gamma\gamma$ ratio.

[20] C. Baglin, U. Nguyen-Khac, A. Bezaguet, B. De-grange, F. Jacquet, P. Musset, G. Nihoul-Boutang, H. H. Bingham, G. M. Irwin, and W. Michael, Bull. Am. Phys. Soc. 12, 567 (1967). These authors presented the ratio

$$\frac{\eta \to 3\pi^{0}}{\eta \to \pi^{+}\pi^{-}\pi^{0}} = 1.3 \pm 0.4.$$

The value of R_2 used in Table II was calculated from this ratio by multiplying it by the $\eta \to \pi^{+}\pi^{-}\pi^{0}/\eta \to \gamma\gamma$ ratio.

[21] H. W. Foelsche and H. L. Kraybill, Phys. Rev. 134, B1138 (1964).

[22] R. Kraemer, L. Madansky, M. Meer, M. Nussbaum, A. Pevsner, C. Richardson, R. Strand, R. Zdanis, T. Fields, S. Orenstein, and T. Toohig, Phys. Rev. 136, B496 (1964).

[23] C. Baltay, P. Franzini, J. Kim, L. Kirsch, R. Newman, N. Yeh, J. Cole, J. Lee-Franzini, and H. Yarger, Phys. Rev. Letters 19, 1498 (1967).

24 P. J. Litchfield, L. K. Rangan, A. M. Segar, J. R. Smith, A. Laribbe, A. Leveque, A. Muller, E. Pauli, D. Revel, and B. Tallini, Phys. Letters 24B, 486 (1967).

25 B. Buschbeck-Czapp, I. Wacek, W. A. Cooper, A. Fridman, E. Malamud, G. Otter, E. Gelsema, and A. Tenner, Proceedings of the Sienna International Conference on Elementary Particles, p. 166 (1963).

26 C. Alff-Steinberger, D. Berley, D. Colley, N. Gelfand, D. Miller, U. Nauenberg, J. Schultz, T. H. Tan, H. Brugger, P. Kramer, and R. Plano, Phys. Rev. 145, 1072 (1966). The authors quote the ratio

$$\frac{\eta \to \text{neutrals}}{\eta \to \pi^+\pi^-\pi^o} = 2.89 \pm 0.56 \ .$$

This ratio has been multiplied by 23.3/28.7 to obtain the $\eta \to$ neutral/$\eta \to$ charged ratio used in Table IV.

27 J. Bernstein, G. Feinberg, and T. D. Lee, Phys. Rev. 139, B1650 (1965).

28 M. Foster, M. Good, M. Meer, in the Second Athens Topical Conference on Resonant Particles, June, 1965 (Ohio University Press; Athens, Ohio, 1965).

29 L. R. Price and F. S. Crawford, Phys. Rev. Letters 15, 123 (1965).

30 A. Rittenberg and G. R. Kalbfleisch, Phys. Rev.

Letters $\underline{15}$, 556 (1965).

31 D. Berley, E. L. Hart, D. C. Rahm, D. L. Stone-
hill, B. Thevenet, W. J. Willis, and S. S. Yama-
moto, Phys. Rev. $\underline{124}$, 893 (1966).

32 C. Baglin, A. Bezaguet, B. Degrange, F. Jacquet,
P. Musset, U. Nguyen-Khac, G. Nihoul-Boutang,
H. H. Bingham, and W. Michael, Phys. Letters
$\underline{22}$, 219 (1966) and $\underline{24B}$, 637 (1967).

33 K. D. Billing, F. W. Bullock, M. J. Esten,
M. Govan, C. Henderson, W. L. Knight, D. J.
Miller, A. A. Owen, F. R. Stannard, E. Tompa,
S. Tovey, and O. C. Waldron, Phys. Letters $\underline{25B}$,
435 (1967).

34 M. Bazin, A. T. Goshaw, R. Zacher, H. Blumenfeld,
T. Kitagaki, and C. R. Sun, Phys. Rev. Letters
$\underline{19}$, 1157 (1967).

35 The entries in this table are based on a summary
made by M. J. Bazin, A. T. Goshaw, A. R. Zacher,
and C. R. Sun, Phys. Rev. Letters $\underline{20}$, 895 (1968).

36 A. W. Wehman, E. Engels, C. M. Hoffman, P. G.
Innocenti, R. Wilson, W. A. Blanpied, D. J.
Drickey, L. N. Hand, and D. G. Stairs, Phys.
Rev. Letters $\underline{20}$, 748 (1968).

37 R. A. Grossman, L. R. Price, and F. S. Crawford,
Phys. Rev. $\underline{146}$, 993 (1966).

38 S. M. Flatte, Phys. Rev. Letters $\underline{18}$, 976 (1967).

39 L. R. Price and F. S. Crawford, Phys. Rev. Letters $\underline{18}$, 1207 (1967).

40 P. Singer, Phys. Rev. 154, 1592 (1967).

41 Columbia-Berkeley-Purdue-Wisconsin-Yale Collab-
    oration, Phys. Rev. 149, 1044 (1966).

42 J. Kim, C. Baltay, P. Franzini, L. Kirsch, R.
    Newman, N. Yeh, J. Cole, J. Lee-Franzini, and
    H. Yarger, Bull. Am. Phys. Soc. 13, 16 (1968).

43 F. S. Crawford and L. R. Price, Phys. Rev.
    Letters 16, 333 (1966).

44 A. M. Cnops, G. Finocchiaro, P. Mittner, P.
    Zanella, J. P. Dufey, B. Gobbi, M. A. Pouchon,
    and A. Muller, Phys. Letters 26B, 398 (1968).

45 L. R. Fortney, J. W. Chapman, S. Dagan, and
    E. C. Fowler, Paper submitted to the X 111th
    International Conference on High Energy Physics
    at Berkeley, 1966.

46 A. Larribe, A. Leveque, A. Muller, E. Pauli,
    D. Revel, B. Tallini, P. J. Litchfield, L. K.
    Rangan, A. M. Segar, J. R. Smith, P. J. Finney,
    C. M. Fisher, and E. Pickup, Phys. Letters 23,
    600 (1966).

47 C. Baltay, P. Franzini, L. Kirsch, D. Zanello,
    J. Lee-Franzini, R. Loveless, J. McFadyen, and
    H. Yarger, Phys. Rev. Letters 16, 1224 (1966).

48 A. M. Cnops, G. Finocchiaro, J. C. Lasalle,
    P. Mittner, P. Zanella, J. P. Dufey, B. Gobbi,
    M. A. Pouchon, and A. Muller, Phys. Letters 22,
    546 (1966).

49 R. A. Bowen, A. M. Cnops, G. Finocchiaro,

P. Mittner, J. P. Dufey, B. Gobbi, M. A. Pouchon, and A. Muller, Phys. Letters 26B, 206 (1967).

50 M. Gormley, E. Hyman, W. Lee, T. Nash, J. Peoples, C. Schultz, and S. Stein, two papers to be published in Phys. Rev. Letters.

51 A. M. Cnops, G. Finnochiaro, P. Mittner, J. P. Dufey, B. Gobbi, M. A. Pouchon, and A. Muller, Phys. Letters 27B, 113 (1968).

52 K. C. Wali, Phys. Rev. Letters 9, 120 (1962).

Status of η' and δ Bosons [*]

N. P. Samios

Brookhaven National Laboratory

Upton, New York

The two topics I would like to discuss are the status of the η' (or X^o) and δ bosons. These reported particles have approximately the same mass and width. The question then arises as to whether a) the δ exists and b) if it exists, is it the same or different than the η'.

The situation concerning the η' is now rather clear. All experiments agree with spin parity $J^P = 0^-$, isotopic spin $I = 0$, and G parity $G = +1$. The source of information is summarized in Table I.

[*] Work performed under the auspices of the U. S. AEC.

Table I

Source	Information
$\eta' \to \pi\pi\eta$	Decay Angular Distribution Allows
Ratio $\dfrac{K^- n}{K^- p} \to \dfrac{\Lambda\eta'^-}{\Lambda\eta'^{\,o}}$	$\neq 2$ therefore $I = 0$
$\eta' \to 3\pi$	Not observed therefore $G = +1$
$\eta' \to \pi\pi\gamma$	Decay Angular Distribution $C = +1$ $J^P = 0^-$

For the first row, the allowed values:

	$C = +1$	$C = -1$
J^P	0^- 2^-	1^+

The more recent experiments have been concerned with measurements of the relative cross section for η'^{o} and η'^{-} at the same energies. These groups[1] all agree that this ratio is much less than two, thereby demonstrating that $I = 0$ for the η'. It is also noted that $C = +1$, $G = +1$, and $I = 0$, which are independently determined, are in agreement with each other (i.e. $G = C(-1)^{I}$). Therefore the η' is distinct from the δ which must have $I \neq 0$.

The question of the δ is unfortunately not as settled. I remind you of the original experiment by Kienzle et al.[2] in which the δ^- was observed as a narrow resonance in a missing-mass experiment. The data is shown in Figure 1a and 1b.

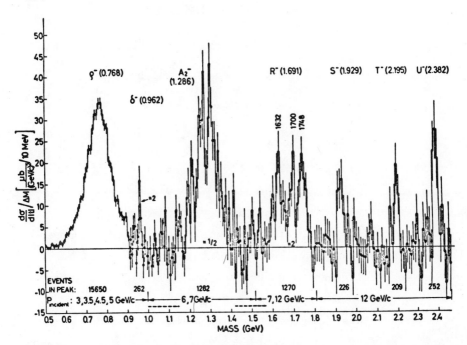

Figure 1a. Compiled spectrum of bosons X^- of isospin $I = 1$ or 2, produced in the reaction $\pi^- + p \rightarrow p + X^-$, observed by the CERN missing-mass spectrometer.

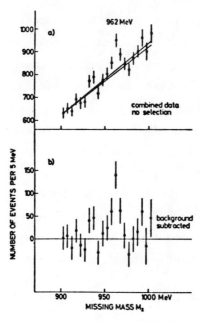

Figure 1b. a) Missing-mass spectrum of the combined data
(p_1 = 3.0, 3.5, 4.5, and 5.0 GeV/c) measured in
$\pi^-p \rightarrow pX^-$ in the mass interval between M_x = 0.9
and 1.0 GeV. No selection on decay multiplicity
of X^- has been applied. The straight lines are
least square fits to all points (upper line) and
to background (lower line, three points in the
peak left out).

b) Same data, background (lower straight line)
subtracted.

The δ excess is a multistandard deviation effect. As has
been emphasized by Magliĉ, the ρ is also very prominent in
the missing-mass distribution and this latter signal may be
used as a guideline as to whether the δ should be expected
to be produced in any given experiment.

Since this time there have been three separate experiments claiming to have verified the existence of the δ, each
followed by another experiment claiming not to see the δ.
The first of these was the reaction[3]

$$p + p \rightarrow d + X^+$$

at a proton kinetic energy of 3 BeV where the deuteron is
produced at 0° in the lab and the mass of the recoiling particle is determined by the deuteron momentum. The exact experiment was repeated by Banner et al.[4] in two ways, first
by keeping the incoming proton energy fixed and measuring
the deuteron momentum (same as Oostens et al.) and second by
varying the incoming proton energy and keeping the deuteron
momentum fixed. The results of both experiments are shown
in Figure 2.

Oostens et al.

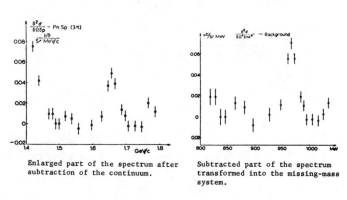

Enlarged part of the spectrum after
subtraction of the continuum.

Subtracted part of the spectrum
transformed into the missing-mass
system.

Banner et al.

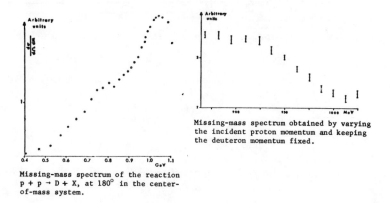

Missing-mass spectrum of the reaction
p + p → D + X, at 180° in the center-
of-mass system.

Missing-mass spectrum obtained by varying
the incident proton momentum and keeping
the deuteron momentum fixed.

Figure 2

They are in direct contradiction. (The question of resolution arose in the later discussion and Figure 3, supplied by
Banner, shows dσ/dΩdp for the indicated three separate experiments. The peaking at p = 1.1 BeV/c is due to the recoiling π^{+} which is indeed sharper in the experiment by
Banner et al. compared with that of Oostens et al.).

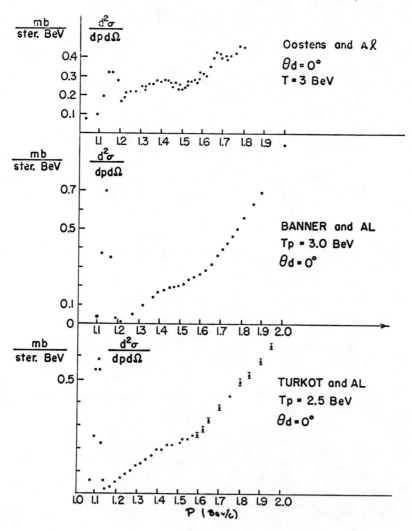

Figure 3

The second experiment is that of Allen et al.[5] which involves
the reaction

$$\pi^- p \rightarrow p\pi^- \pi^o$$

at a pion momentum 1.7 BeV/c. The $\pi^- \pi^o$ mass distribution
for this experiment is shown in Figure 4 as well as the data
from a similar experiment by Banner et al.[6] performed at an
incoming π momentum of 1.8 BeV/c. Allen et al. claim to see
the δ^- while the data of Banner et al. show no deviation at
the expected mass of 960 MeV.

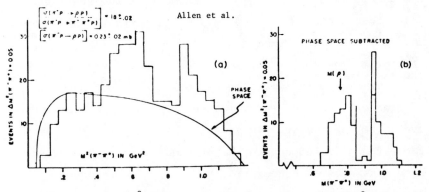

a) Distribution versus $M^2(\pi^- \pi^o)$ for 391 events of 1.7 GeV/c $\pi^- p \rightarrow \pi^- p\pi^o$. The
solid curve labeled "phase space" has been evaluated from the distribution
of the same events in a scatter plot of $M^2(\pi^- \pi^o)$ versus $\Delta_4^2(p_{in}, p_{out})$ from
the regions outside the rho peak.

b) Distribution of $M(\pi^- \pi^o)$ with phase space subtracted.

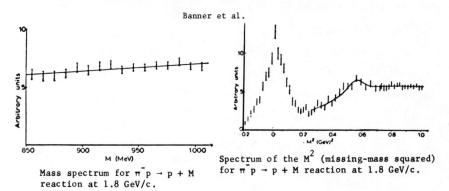

Banner et al.

Mass spectrum for $\pi^- p \rightarrow p + M$
reaction at 1.8 GeV/c.

Spectrum of the M^2 (missing-mass squared)
for $\pi^- p \rightarrow p + M$ reaction at 1.8 GeV/c.

Figure 4

The third experiment is that of Allison et al.[7] which
involves the study of five body $\Sigma^{\pm}$ production, specifically

$$K^-p \rightarrow \Sigma^+ \pi^+ \pi^- \pi^+ \pi^- \pi^o \qquad \text{(a)}$$

$$K^-p \rightarrow \Sigma^- \pi^+ \pi^+ \pi^- \pi^+ \pi^o \qquad \text{(b)}$$

at 6 BeV/c. This involves 316 events from (a) and 493
events from (b). The identical reactions were studied by
a BNL-Syracuse collaboration at 4.6 BeV/c with roughly
double the data and an Illinois group[8] at 5.5 BeV/c with
comparable data. It should be stated that the statistical
significance of the claimed bump in the data of Allison et
al. is minuscule. The combined three pion mass spectra for
all three experiments for reactions (a) and (b) are shown
in Figure 5. Only unweighted events with the length of the
$\Sigma^{\pm}$ greater than 1 cm were plotted. There is no excess of
events at the δ mass. In general these final states are
rather complicated due to the presence of five bodies and
many possible resonances (Y^*, ρ, etc.). Therefore one
should be cautious in the treatment of such states. To
summarize the results of Figures 3, 4, and 5, there is no
positive evidence for the δ and furthermore, since the ρ
is not produced prominently, it may not be unexpected that
the δ is not produced.

    I would like to conclude my discussion with a presenta-
tion of some preliminary results of the BNL-Syracuse collaboration in the further study of K^-p interactions at 4.6
BeV/c. The particular channel of interest is

$$K^-p \rightarrow \Lambda \pi^+ \pi^- MM \quad \text{where} \quad MM > 1\pi^o \quad .$$

A sample of 2800 such events has been accumulated. There is
a small $Y^{*\pm}(1385)$ and η' ($\pi^- \pi^+ \eta^o$) signal observed and these
events are removed in the further analysis. In Figure 6 are

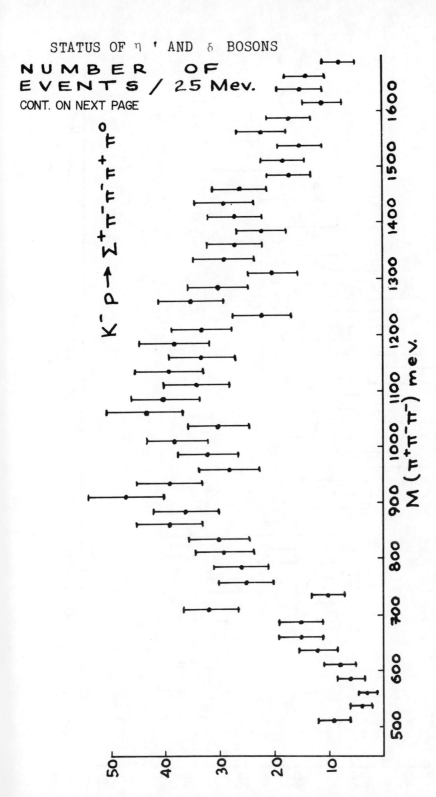

NUMBER OF
EVENTS / 25 Mev.

CONT. ON NEXT PAGE

$K^- p \rightarrow \Sigma^+ \pi^- \pi^+ \pi^- \pi^0$

$M (\pi^+ \pi^- \pi^-)$ mev.

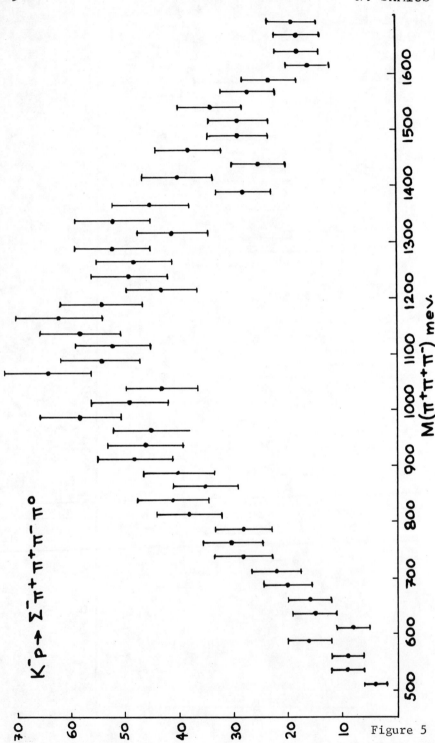

Figure 5

plotted the $(\pi^+ MM)$ and $(\pi^- MM)$ effective masses (i.e. mass recoiling against the $\Lambda\pi^-$ and $\Lambda\pi^+$ respectively). The two distributions are similar except for the deviation of ≈ 3.5 standard deviations at a mass of 975 MeV in the $(\pi^- MM)$ distribution. An examination of the (MM) of the events in this peak shows some evidence for the presence of an $\eta(550)$, thereby suggesting an $\eta\pi^-$ decay mode. However this cannot explain the whole peak, so that there appears to be alternate decay modes. With the limited data, little can be said concerning the width of this peak although it is certainly consistent with experimental resolution and therefore can be quite narrow. An examination of the production angular distribution indicates that it is not produced peripherally. This peaking at $M \approx 975$ can therefore certainly be associated with the δ. The data will shortly be doubled and therefore will allow stronger statements to be made.

In the free wheeling spirit of this Conference, I would not like to turn to some speculations concerning the possible properties of the δ. Since the δ is charged and produced in $K^- p$ interactions with Λ^o, it's isotopic spin must be $I = 1$. The experimental evidence indicates $\delta^- \rightarrow \pi^- \eta$ and $\delta^- \not\rightarrow \pi\pi$ or $\delta^- \not\rightarrow 3\pi$. This indicates $J^P = 0^+$, for such a spin parity forbids both 2π and 3π decay modes. If the δ decay is via the strong interaction, then $G = -1$, $C = +1$, and the mode $\delta \rightarrow 5\pi$ is allowed. However explaining the narrow width may be a problem. On the other hand if the decay is electromagnetic then $G = +1$ and $C = -1$ with the possibility $\delta \rightarrow 4\pi$. It should be noted that the determination of G (or equivalently C) for the δ has an important bearing on the quark model. Specifically, the $J^P = 0^+$ octet arises from a p state of the quark antiquark system with

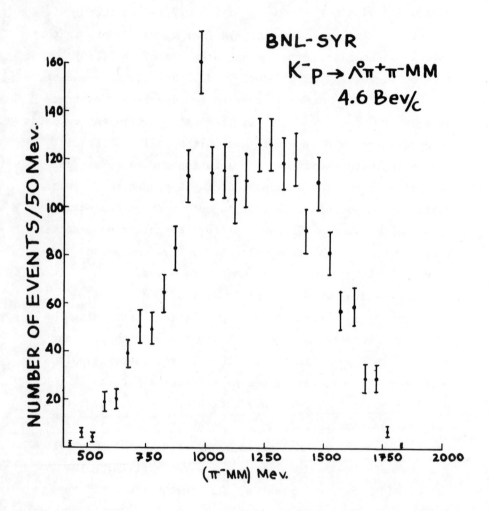

Figure 6

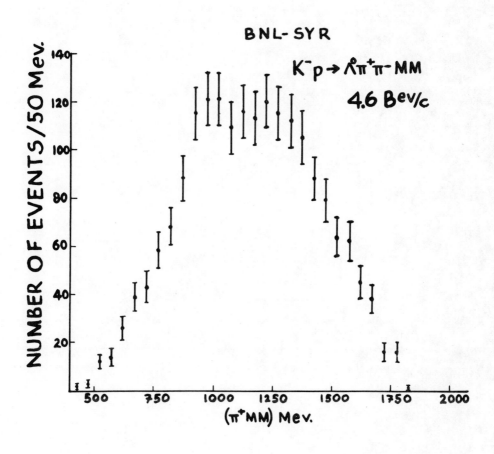

$C = +1$ $(G = -1)$ and does not allow for a state with $J^P = 0^+$ and $C = -1$. It is therefore of extreme interest to determine the quantum numbers of the δ, if it exists as present data seems to indicate.

References

1. H.J. Martin et al., Physics Letters <u>22</u>, 352 (1966);
    Amsterdam-Bologna-Paris-Rehoveth-Saclay Collaboration,
    <u>Proceedings of the International Conference on Elementary
    Particles</u>, Heidelberg, Germany, Abstract #131; A. Barbaro-
    Galtieri et al., Physical Review Letters <u>20</u>, 349 (1968).

2. W. Kienzle et al., Physics Letters <u>19</u>, 438 (1965).

3. J. Oostens et al., Physics Letters <u>22</u>, 708 (1966).

4. M. Banner et al., Physics Letters <u>25B</u>, 569 (1967).

5. D.D. Allen et al., Physics Letters <u>22</u>, 543 (1966).

6. M. Banner et al., Physics Letters <u>25B</u>, 300 (1967).

7. W.W.M. Allison et al., Physics Letters <u>25B</u>, 619 (1967).

8. U. Kruse and J. Loos (University of Illinois), Private
    Communication.

IS THERE EVIDENCE FOR AN H MESON?
(IS IT JUST THE η' ?)[*]

A. Barbaro-Galtieri and P. Söding

Lawrence Radiation Laboratory
Berkeley, California

Analysis of $\pi^+ p$ and $\pi^+ n$ data, in the 3- to 4-GeV/c incident π^+ momentum range, shows that at present there is no convincing evidence for existence of the so-called H meson (M $\approx$ 990 MeV, suggested quantum numbers $I^G J^P = 0^- 1^+$). The enhancement observed in the neutral three-pion invariant mass distribution near 990 MeV can be attributed to the $\pi\pi\gamma$ decay mode of the η'.

This paper contains a discussion of the following points:

(A) Reported evidence in favor of and against the H meson. (See page 3.)

(B) Effects of the ρ cut. In studying an enhancement in the three-pion mass plot it is useful to analyze the $\rho\pi$ decay mode of the enhancement, since it might improve the signal-to-noise ratio and conclusions on the I-spin could easily be obtained. In the 1-GeV region of 3π mass, however, one has to be careful because the kinematics of the $\rho\pi$ system can produce a bump. (See page 4.)

(C) Possibility of appearance of the $\pi\pi\gamma$ decay mode of the η' at higher mass if a supposed π^0 is substituted for the real γ. Experiments in deuterium can produce additional mass shifts. The mass resolution in D_2 experiments is also essential in determining the size of an enhancement. (See page 7.)

(D) Reanalysis of all the data from which evidence for the H meson has been reported. To get a proper estimate of the background under the 990-MeV enhancement, a

[*]Work done under the auspices of the U. S. Atomic Energy Commission.

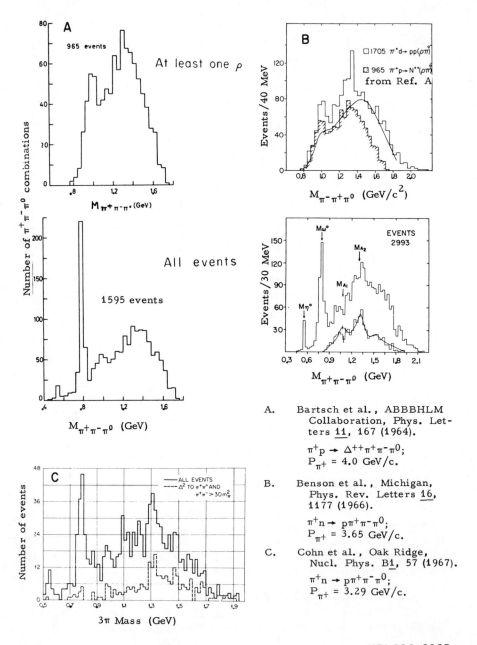

XBL686-2985

Fig. 1. Summary of the evidence reported in favor of the H meson.

model including production of all the resonances observed in these reactions was fitted to the data. A compilation of 13 000 events of the type $\pi^+ p \to \Delta^{++} \pi^+ \pi^- \pi^0$ has also been fitted in order to establish the cross section for the H enhancement. In none of the cases was the cross section for production of the H enhancement found to exceed by more than two standard deviations the value expected for η' production with subsequent decay $\eta' \to \pi^+ \pi^- \gamma$. (See page 9.)

A. EVIDENCE FOR THE H MESON

The first report of an enhancement in the neutral three-pion invariant mass at $M \approx 980$ MeV was given in 1964 by a British-German collaboration,[1] two months after the discovery of the η' at $M = 960$ MeV.[2] The reaction studied was

$$\pi^+ p \to \Delta(1236)^{++} \pi^+ \pi^- \pi^0 \tag{1}$$

at 4.0 GeV/c incident π^+ momentum. Although the mass of the enhancement (975 ± 15 MeV) was very close to the mass of the η', the observed 120-MeV width was believed to be in disagreement with $\Gamma_{\eta'} < 12$ MeV. The cross section for the enhancement was 150 µb, or 90 events in a total sample of 1595 examples of reaction (1). Figure 1A shows these data. The $\rho\pi$ mass distribution is also shown. The authors estimated that both plots contain about 90 events in the H enhancement. At that time the authors had no evidence[3] that η' was produced in the reaction $\pi^+ p \to \Delta^{++} \eta'$.

Benson et al.[4] reported evidence for the H meson in the reaction

$$\pi^+ d \to (p_s) p \pi^+ \pi^- \pi^0 \quad (p_s = \underline{\text{visible}} \text{ spectator proton}) \tag{2}$$

at 3.65 GeV/c incident π^+ momentum. Their data are shown in Figure 1B. The mass and width quoted were 998 ± 10 MeV and 45 ± 30 MeV respectively. The cross section for the H enhancement was 75 ± 15 µb, and the cross section for $\eta' \to \pi^+ \pi^- \gamma$ is estimated to be 16 ± 7 µb.[5,6] The number of events above background in the H region was 58 for both the $\pi^+ \pi^- \pi^0$ and the $(\rho\pi)^0$ effective-mass plots.

In a study of reaction (2) at 3.29 GeV/c, Cohn et al.[7] also observed an enhancement in the H region. Their data are shown in Figure 1C. They estimated that the cross

section for this enhancement could be as large as 50 μb
(corresponding to 46 events); on the other hand, a cross
section as low as 15 μb also appears compatible with these
data. Therefore, the enhancement may well be due to the
$\pi\pi\gamma$ decay of the η' (since π^0 and γ can hardly be distin-
guished in this type of experiment), for which a cross sec-
tion of 11^{+6}_{-4} μb is expected. [8]

In two other experiments on reaction (1) at 3.65 and
3.2 to 3.5 GeV/c, [9,10] small enhancements were also observed in the $(\rho\pi)^0$ mass distributions near 1000 MeV. The
situation as of November 1966 is summarized in Ref. 11.

More recently in a large statistics experiment,
Fung et al. [12] studied reaction (1) for π^+ incident momentum
in the 3- to 4-GeV/c region and did not observe an enhancement in the H region. A study of reaction (2) at 5.1 GeV/c
by Armenise et al. [13] also failed to show any enhancement,
although the statistics was better than in Ref. 4. At lower
energies (1.8 to 2.5 GeV/c), Abolins et al. [14] do not find any
evidence for the H enhancement, and quote an upper limit of
100 μb (averaged over their momentum range).

B. THE $\rho\pi$ MASS PLOT

The two upper plots of Figure 1 show the three-pion
invariant-mass distributions for the data of the British-
German collaboration[1] and of Benson et al. [4] when the condition that at least one dipion combination falls in the ρ
band is applied to the data. In this case the H enhancement
appears to be sharper; however, the shape of the background is also changed by the ρ cut applied to the data.
Benson et al. first pointed out that even a smooth phase-
space-distributed three-pion mass spectrum can show an
enhancement at ≈ 1000 MeV if a ρ cut is applied.

Fung et al. [12] have made an interesting study of the
effect of the ρ cut in the three-pion mass distribution. They
have analyzed 3159 events of reaction (1) between 2.95 and
4.1 GeV/c, which do not indicate any enhancement in the H
region for the uncut data. Figure 2 shows some of their
plots. The Dalitz plots in the upper corner, taken from
Rosenfeld et al., [11] illustrate the situation. The ρ bands
cover almost the whole Dalitz plot at the H mass, whereas
at the A_2 mass they leave part of the area uncovered.
Figure 2A (taken from Fung et al.) shows this nicely. As
a function of $M_{3\pi}$ it plots the fraction of the Dalitz plot

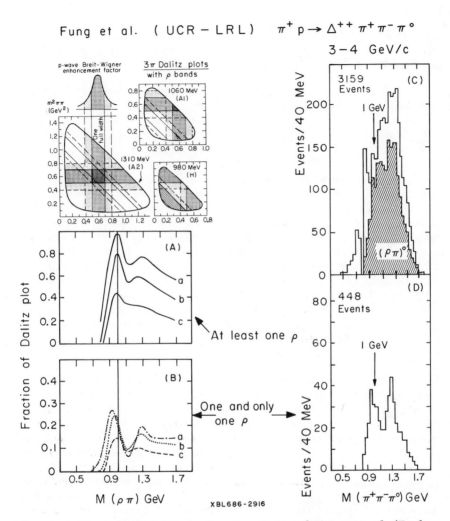

Fig. 2. The effect of the ρπ cut. Data of Fung et al. (Ref.
12). (A) shows the fraction of the three-pion Dalitz plot
covered by the three ρ bands. This has been calculated using
three different widths: (a) ΔM = ± 120 MeV, (b) ΔM = ± 80
MeV, (c) ΔM = ± 40 MeV (while current $\Gamma_\rho/2 \approx 50$ MeV); the
bands were centered at M = 740 MeV. (B) shows the corresponding fractions of the Dalitz plot covered by only one ρ
band, excluding the overlap regions of this band with the
other two bands. (C) is the experimental $M(\pi^+\pi^-\pi^0)$ distribution (note that the ω band has been eliminated); the shaded
area corresponds to events in the ρ bands. (D) shows the
same data with the restriction that one and only one $M_{\pi\pi}$
falls into a ρ band (ΔM = ± 80 MeV).

covered by ρ bands of three different widths (labeled a, b, c). The striking feature of these curves is the peak at 1 GeV and the dip at 1.15 GeV.

Figure 2B differs from 2A in that only one band is taken, and band-overlap areas are excluded. (Figure 1A corresponds to the selection of events with at least one ρ; 1B with one and only one ρ.) Here the valley between the peaks is even deeper, and consequently the peaks are moved farther apart.

One can study the effects of ρ cuts by multiplying the curves of Figure 2A with the uncut $M_{3\pi}$ distribution. In particular, if the uncut $M_{3\pi}$ is assumed to be the three-pion phase space (which corresponds to selecting events with at least one ρ from a phase-space-distributed sample), the cut distribution will have a shoulder at $M \approx 1000$ MeV. This is illustrated by the curve in the upper part of Figure 1B, taken from Benson et al. [4] If instead of phase space one used a distribution peaking at lower $M_{3\pi}$ than phase space [e.g., due either to low momentum transfers (however, see Figure 8), or to reflections of other resonant processes], this shoulder would be enhanced (see, for example, Figures 5 and 8).

If the curves of Figure 2B were used instead (corresponding to selecting on one ρ only), a bump would appear at $M_{3\pi} \approx 1000$ MeV as shown by Benson et al. [4] and Fung et al. [12] Figure 2C shows the uncut data from the experiment of Fung et al., which do not show any enhancement at the H mass (note that the ω band has been eliminated in the plot). The shaded histogram shows the experimental distribution when the mass of at least one of the three possible $\pi\pi$ combinations falls into the ρ band. Figure 2D shows the experimental plot for those events which have one (and only one) $\pi\pi$ mass combination falling in the ρ region. This plot shows a very nice peak at the H mass, quite similar to what one gets just from multiplying the original histogram (2C) (without ρ cuts) with the weight functions of Fig. 2B! This, of course, shows nothing more than that the H Dalitz plot is nearly uniformly populated.

The conclusion from this is that under certain conditions, bumps near threshold in a $\rho\pi$ mass spectrum might occur as a consequence of the particular criteria used for selecting "ρ events." It is obviously very important to take this effect into account when one tries to establish the significance of $\rho\pi$ (or similar) enhancements.

C. MASS SHIFTS AND RESOLUTION

A 2.5-standard-deviation effect at the H mass was presented by one of us at the Heidelberg Conference, in the reaction $K^- n \to \Sigma^- \pi^+ \pi^- \pi^0$ at 2.1 GeV/c incident K^- momentum. [14] The experiment was performed in deuterium, and this fact produces various problems resulting in bad resolution and mass shifts. These problems have been carefully investigated in this experiment, and about 35% more events have been added, with the result that the whole H enhancement is now accounted for by the $\pi\pi\gamma$ decay mode of the η'. [15] At this incident energy it is not possible to distinguish a π^0 from a γ ray in the bubble chamber, and this problem is common to all the experiments which reported an H meson enhancement.

Figure 3A shows the three-pion invariant-mass distribution from this experiment. Figure 3B shows the plot of $M^2(\pi^+ \pi^- MM)$ versus the missing mass squared (MM^2) against the $\Sigma^- \pi^+ \pi^-$ system. The decay mode $\eta' \to \pi^+ \pi^- \eta_n$ (by η_n or η_c we indicate η decaying into only neutral particles, or into $\pi^+ + \pi^- +$ neutral, respectively) can be detected here and, by use of the known branching ratios, [6] the expected number of events for $\eta' \to \pi^+ \pi^- \gamma$ can be calculated. As can easily be seen in Figures 3A and 3B, the mass resolution for $\pi^+ \pi^- \pi^0$ or $\pi^+ \pi^- \eta_n$ is very bad, therefore the number of events of the type $\eta' \to \pi^+ \pi^- \eta_n$ has to be counted by using the actual resolution. When this is done the H enhancement is all explained as being η'.

The curve of Figure 3A is a maximum-likelihood fit to the data. [16] The model used in the fit takes into account nonresonant background as well as production of various resonances in the final state (neglecting interferences between the various resonances). The mass required to fit the H enhancement is $M \approx 1000$ MeV (whereas $M_{\eta'} = 958$ MeV); the width is consistent with the resolution. This 40-MeV mass shift can be understood in terms of two different effects: (a) the events have been fitted with the π^0 mass instead of the γ mass (this accounts for ≈ 15 MeV); (b) in about 70% of the events the unmeasurable momentum of the spectator proton has been assumed to be $0 \pm \Delta p_i$, with Δp_i an error in the three-momentum components. This turns out to be an inadequate approximation to the Hulthén distribution, and accounts for the remaining mass shift. More details can be found in Ref. 15.

A. BARBARO-GALTIERI and P. SODING

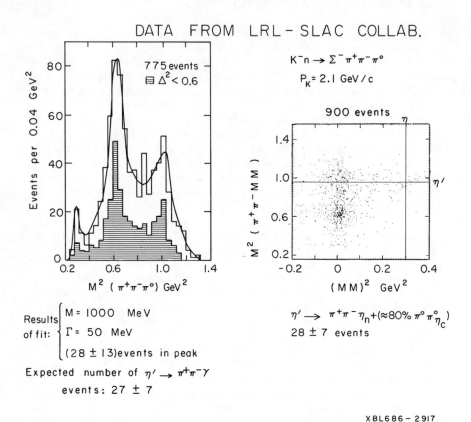

Fig. 3. Data of Barbaro-Galtieri et al. [15] on $K^-n \to \Sigma^- \pi^+ \pi^- \pi^0$ at 2.1 GeV/c. The enhancement around 1000 MeV is entirely explained by $\eta \to \pi^+ \pi^- \gamma$ decay.

The Argonne-Northwestern collaboration[17] has also investigated this point. In studying the reaction $K^-p \rightarrow \Lambda\pi^+\pi^-\pi^0$ at 4.1 and 5.5 GeV/c incident K^- momentum they observe the effect shown in Figure 4. The lower graphs show the three-pion invariant-mass distribution (unshaded) and the $\rho^0\pi^0$ mass plot (shaded). The same events have been also fitted with the γ mass instead of the π^0 mass, and are plotted in the upper part of Figure 4. The η' signal appears now at the correct mass, and sharper.

D. FITS TO THE H DATA

Our final task is to examine in detail the reactions in which the H has been reported, in order to see if the data still show a significant non-η' signal in the 980-MeV mass region. We do this by fitting to the data on reactions (1) and (2) a model similar to that mentioned in Section C. Data summary tapes have been made available to us by the authors of Refs. 3, 4, 9, 10, and 12. We have been able, therefore, to perform maximum-likelihood fits[16] of this model to the complete data on these experiments. In the fits, the masses, widths, and magnitudes of the various resonance contributions were varied. In order to test and display the goodness of fit, the mass distributions of all the two- and three-particle combinations in the final state, as calculated from the model, were compared with the experimental distributions. In each case, satisfactory agreement has been reached. Also inserted into the model were factors depending on various four-momentum transfers, in order to closely simulate the observed distributions of the four-momentum transfer between the incident pion and the various final-state two- and three-pion combinations. The effects of these factors on the three-pion mass distributions, however, turn out to be small. (As an example, in the insert in Figure 8 we show how this "peripheralization" modifies the phase-space distribution.)

After such a model has been fitted, one can most easily assess the kinematical effects of making ρ cuts on the 3π mass spectrum, by simply subjecting the distributions, calculated from the model, to the same cuts. Some of the results of these fits are shown and discussed below. It is hardly necessary to emphasize that a model such as the one we have used, although containing many different terms, over-simplifies grossly the actual behavior of these complicated reactions. We therefore do not attach deep physical significance to the detailed results of these fits, as

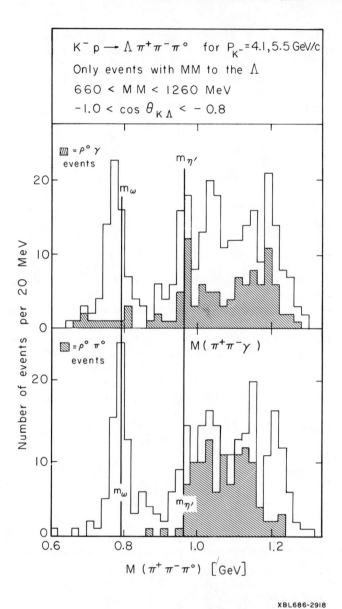

XBL686-2918

Fig. 4.   Data of the Argonne-Northwestern Collaboration,[17] showing the effect of fitting the reaction $K^- p \rightarrow \Lambda \pi^+ \pi^- \pi^0$ with a γ (upper histogram) vs. π^0 (lower histogram).   Only events with $600 < MM < 1260$ MeV were used, where we write $K^- + p \rightarrow \Lambda + MM$. Note in particular the effect in the $\rho^0 \gamma^0$ spectrum ($\eta' \rightarrow \pi^+ \pi^- \gamma$ is mainly $\eta' \rightarrow \rho^0 \gamma$).

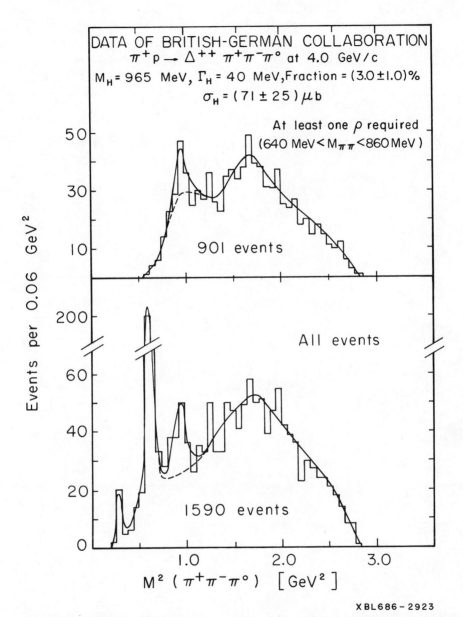

Fig. 5. Our fit (full curve) to the data of the British-German Collaboration. [1] The dashed curves have been drawn to show the background under the H enhancement according to our fit. For the upper plot and curve, a ρ cut has been imposed (at least one dipion mass in the region $M_{\pi\pi}$ = 750 ±110 MeV, as used by the authors of ref. 1).

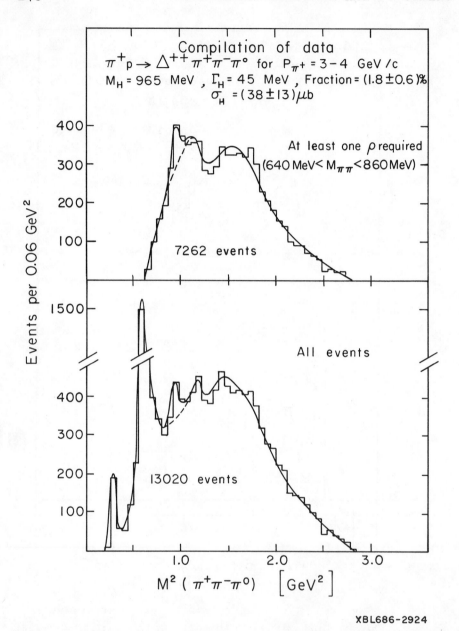

XBL686-2924

Fig. 6. Our fit (full curve) to the combined data from ref. 3, 9, 10, and 12. Dashed curves: same fit with H contribution subtracted. The histogram and curve for the cut data (at least one dipion mass in the ρ band $M_{\pi\pi} = 750 \pm 110$ MeV) is shown in the upper part of the figure.

far as production of the various resonances is concerned.
All we need is a plausible model that fits the data, and
thereby furnishes us with a smooth "background distribution" against which to compare an enhancement that has not
otherwise been accounted for.

In Figure 5 we show the three-pion mass spectra
from the data of the British-German collaboration,[1] with
(upper) and without (lower histogram) a ρ cut (i. e. , at
least one dipion mass in the ρ resonance band). The full
curves are results of our fit.[18] The fitted model includes
production of η, ρ, ω, and A_2, as well as nonresonant (peripheralized phase space) background and an H enhance-
ment. The dashed curves have been drawn to show the contribution of the H enhancement to the fit. Processes like
$N^{**} \rightarrow \Delta^{++} \pi^0$ for higher nucleon isobars have also been allowed for, but were not found significantly present in the
data. The mass and width of the H enhancement (including
experimental resolution) were found to be M = 965 MeV and
Γ = 40 MeV. If the effects discussed in Section C are taken
into account, these values are consistent with mass and
width of the η'. The cross section obtained for production
of the H enhancement is 70 ± 25 μb, to be compared with an
expected cross section for η' production, with $\eta' \rightarrow \pi^+ \pi^- \gamma$
decay, of 25 ± 12 μb (as derived from the cross section for
$\eta' \rightarrow \pi^+ \pi^- \eta_c$, measured recently also by the British-German
collaboration--Ref. 19). These two values agree to within
1.6 standard deviations (corresponding to a confidence level
of 10%).

The same procedure was applied to a compilation of
13 000 events of the type of reaction (1) (including those of
Figure 5) for π^+ incident momenta between 3 and 4 GeV/c.
These data are from Refs. 1, 9, 10, and 12, and are shown
in Figure 6. The distribution of the c. m. energies was
taken into account in the fit. The best fit[18] to the data was
similar to the one obtained for the subset of events of the
British-German collaboration. The H bump, however, is
reduced to 38 ± 13μb, or 1.8 ± 0.6% of the data (to be compared with 3 ± 1% for the British-German collaboration
data). Assuming that this signal is due to η', we can calculate the total cross section $\sigma(\eta')$ for η' production from
the known branching ratios[6] in order to be able to compare
it with $\sigma(\eta')$ as derived from the $\pi\pi\eta$ decay mode. This
comparison is shown in Figure 7, where all the measured
cross sections above 2 GeV/c for $\pi^+ p \rightarrow \Delta^{++} \eta'$ production
are shown along with those for $\pi^+ p \rightarrow \Delta^{++} \eta$ and $\pi^+ p \rightarrow \Delta^{++} \omega$.[20]

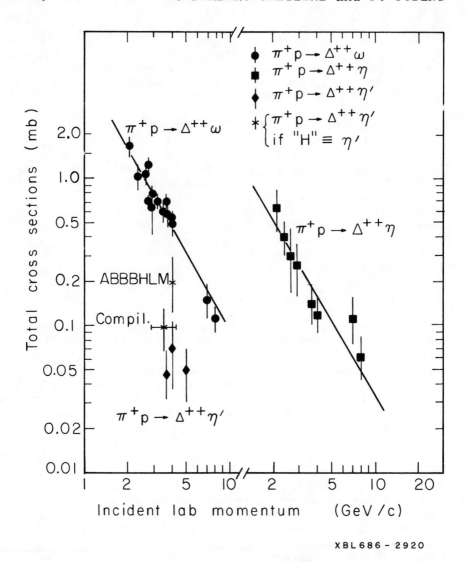

XBL 686 - 2920

Fig. 7.   Total cross sections for the reactions
$\pi^+ p \rightarrow \Delta^{++}(1236)$+meson as a function of incident π^+ momentum.[20]   The straight lines are hand drawn through the points.
Crosses indicate total cross sections for η' production if
the "H" signal were $\eta' \rightarrow \pi^+ \pi^- \gamma$.   The η' cross sections (◆)
were obtained through the measurement of the partial cross
section for $\eta' \rightarrow \pi \pi \eta$.

(Unfortunately the $\pi\pi\eta$ decay mode for the η' has not been measured in all the experiments used in our compilation, so that a direct comparison cannot be made for this sample.) Both the η and ω production cross sections seem to obey a linear law in this log-log plot, and it is reasonable to expect that the η' cross section follows a similar behavior. The η' cross section obtained from the compiled data is then seen to be in perfect agreement with the other three measured cross sections for η' production.

In Figure 8, the 3π and $\rho\pi$ mass plots of Benson et al. [4] from reaction (2) at 3.65 GeV/c are shown, together with the distributions obtained from our fit. [18] The spread in the incident c.m. momentum in the π^+n rest system, due to the Fermi motion in the deuteron, has been taken into account. We allowed for the presence of various higher nucleon resonances in the data, and we also found it necessary to add an $A_{1.5}$ (M = 1160 MeV, Γ = 120 MeV including resolution) production term [21] in order to fit the shoulder in the three-pion mass spectrum that is apparent in the data at 1160 MeV. For the H enhancement, values of M = 998 MeV and Γ = 40 MeV (resolution not subtracted) were obtained. We were not able to study in detail the possible mass shift and resolution effects (cf. Section C) for this experiment, since these depend on many experimental details. Realizing the difficulties peculiar to analyzing reactions on deuterium, we believe that the possibility cannot be excluded that the above values for mass and width of the observed H enhancement are consistent with mass and width of the η'.

The production cross section for the H enhancement that we obtain on the basis of this fit is 41 ± 18 µb. Under the assumption that all the observed H signal is due to $\eta' \rightarrow \pi^+\pi^-\gamma$, we obtain [6] from this a $\pi^+n \rightarrow p\eta'$ cross section of 117 ± 53 µb. This value is compared in Figure 9 with the other known values for the η' production cross section; [22] we conclude that there is reasonable agreement between them. In particular, the value of 46 ± 20 µb obtained in the same 3.65-GeV/c π^+d experiment [4,5] from the observation of the $\eta' \rightarrow \pi\pi\eta$ mode agrees with the value of 117 ± 53 µb from the H enhancement to within better than 1.5 standard deviations (confidence level > 15%).

From studies of the Dalitz plot [1,4] and of the decay angular distributions [4] of the events in the H region, it has been suggested that J^P of the three-pion states in the enhancement is most likely to be 1^+, 2^-, $\cdots$. In particular,

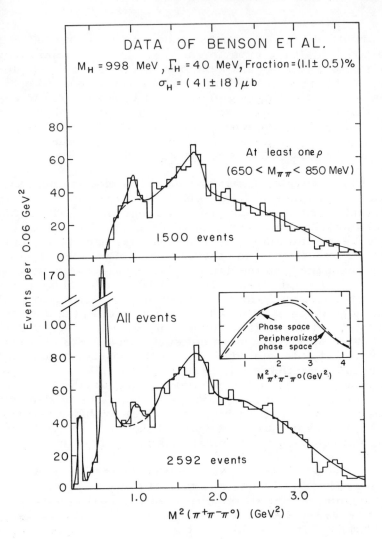

XBL686-2919

Fig. 8.   Our fit (full curve) to the data of Benson et al. [4]
The dashed curves show the background under the H enhancement according to our fit.   The upper plot and curves refer
to events which contain at least one dipion mass in the ρ
band $M_{\pi\pi} = 750 \pm 100$ MeV (as used by Benson et al.).
The insert shows the three-pion mass distribution according to phase space (dashed curve), and to peripheralized
phase space (full curve) that includes momentum-transfer-
dependent factors, as explained in the text.

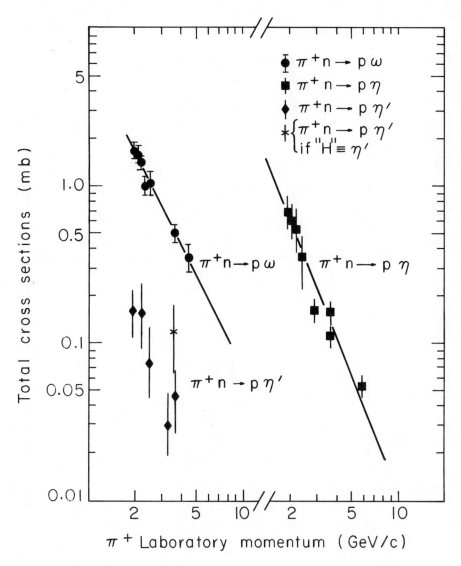

XBL686-2921

Fig. 9. Total cross sections for the reactions $\pi^+ n \to p +$
+ meson as a function of incident π^+ momentum.[22] The
straight lines are hand drawn through the points. $\ast$ indicates the total cross section for η' production if the "H" enhancement seen by Benson et al.[4] were due to $\eta' \to \pi^+ \pi^- \gamma$.
The η' cross sections (◆) were obtained through measurement of the partial cross section for $\eta' \to \pi\pi\eta$.

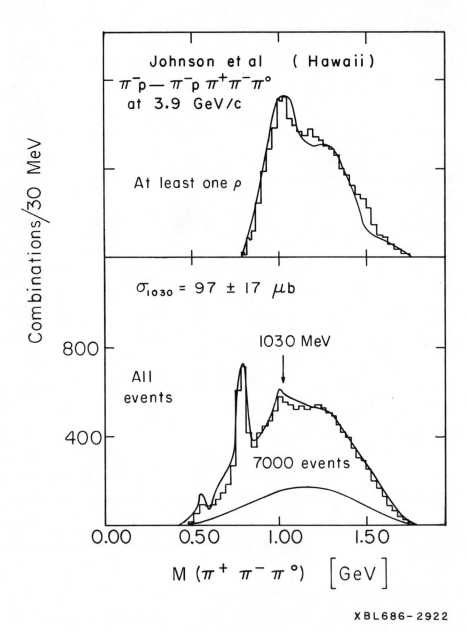

Fig. 10. Data and fit of Johnson et al.[23] for the reaction $\pi^- p \to \pi^- p \pi^+ \pi^- \pi^0$ at 3.9 GeV/c. The enhancement centered at ≈ 1030 MeV is being investigated to ascertain its possible connection with the "H" enhancement.

$J^P = 0^-$ appeared unlikely because the density distribution did not seem to vanish along all three medians of the Dalitz plot (i.e., along the lines $M^2_{\pi^+\pi^-} = M^2_{\pi^-\pi^0}$, $M^2_{\pi^-\pi^0} = M^2_{\pi^0\pi^+}$ and $M^2_{\pi^0\pi^+} = M^2_{\pi^+\pi^-}$ as required for an I = 0, $J^P = 0^-$ three-pion state), and also because the events in the H region showed a nonisotropic decay angular distribution with respect to the beam direction and to the normal of the production plane. For a $\pi^+\pi^-\gamma$ Dalitz plot, however, the first argument against $J^P = 0^-$ is no longer valid. From examination of the Dalitz plots of the experiments discussed here, we conclude that the distribution expected for $\eta' \to \pi^+\pi^-\gamma$ decay, with the $\pi^+\pi^-$ system being ρ^0, is compatible with the data in view of the large background that our fits predict under the H peak. Because of this large background we also believe $J^P = 0^-$ is perfectly compatible with the observed (weak) anisotropies in the decay angular distributions.

We know of no other published evidence for the H enhancement, although Johnson et al. [23] report an enhancement in the same general region in the reaction $\pi^-p \to \pi^-p\,\pi^+\pi^-\pi^0$ at 3.9 GeV/c. Their data are shown in Figure 10. The enhancement in question is about 60 MeV wide, centered at ≈ 1030 MeV, the quoted cross section being $\sigma = 97 \pm 17$ μb; however, a cross section as low as 50 μb seems to be compatible with the data. The η' cross section for this same experiment has not been measured yet, although there is an indication that it is considerably smaller than the signal seen here. These authors are now looking into the problem of the mass shift and investigating the possibility that this signal is due to neutral A_1 production, since its location seems to be closer to the A_1 mass than to the η'.

In conclusion, it appears that the original evidence for the H meson of the British-German collaboration, which according to our analysis and with our present knowledge on η' branching ratios seems to be only a 1.6 standard deviation effect, has not been supported by the additional data available now at similar energies. In deuterium experiments, the H has shown up in only one experiment and has failed to appear in others; furthermore, the statistical significance is not large. In our opinion this does not, at present, constitute sufficient evidence for an H resonance.

The discrepancy between our evaluation of the cross sections for production of the H enhancement, and those in the literature, is due to our different treatment of the background. In our fits to the data we included, apart from the resonances in the three-pion system, various other possible resonance production processes, in order to get a good fit to the overall reaction, and thereby a more reliable (though probably conservative) background estimation. This was[16] possible because we used a complicated computer program and a larger computer capacity than was available to the authors of the original papers on the H meson at the time of their analysis.

ACKNOWLEDGMENTS

We are indebted to the authors of Refs. 3, 4, 9, 10, 12, and 17, in particular to Dr. H. Butenschön, Dr. D. Sinclair, Dr. B. Shen, Dr. P. M. Yager, Dr. G. Gidal and Dr. S. Dagan for making their data available to us on magnetic tape. We also would like to thank William J. Podolsky for his help in handling the data, Maxine J. Matison for programming efforts, and Dr. J. Friedman for advice on the maximum-likelihood fits. Finally, we thank Dr. E. Marquit, Dr. R. T. Pu, and Dr. J. Vander Velde for useful discussions.

REFERENCES

1. J. Bartsch et al., Aachen-Berlin-Birmingham-Bonn-Hamburg-London-München Collaboration, Phys. Letters 11, 167 (1964).
2. G. R. Kalbfleisch et al., Phys. Rev. Letters 12, 527 (1964); M. Goldberg et al., Phys. Rev. Letters 12, 546 (1964).
3. Aachen-Berlin-Birmingham-Bonn-Hamburg-London-München Collaboration, Phys. Rev. 138, B897 (1965).
4. G. Benson, E. Marquit, B. Roe, D. Sinclair, and J. Vander Velde, Phys. Rev. Letters 17, 1234 (1966); Phys. Rev. Letters 16, 1177 (1966). See also G. Benson, Thesis, University of Michigan Technical Report COO-1112-4, 1966.
5. The authors observed 13 ± 5 events, or $17 \pm 7 \mu b$ [using their normalization $(1.3 \pm 0.2) \mu b/$event, see Ref. 4], for η' production with subsequent decay $\eta' \to \pi^+\pi^- X^0$, where mass $(X^0) > 2 M_\pi$. Since publication of their data, the most probable value of the branching ratio $\Gamma(\eta' \to \pi^+\pi^-\gamma)/[\Gamma(\eta' \to \pi^+\pi^-\eta_n) + \Gamma(\eta' \to \pi^0\pi^0\eta_c)]$ has become 0.94 ± 0.13 (see Ref. 6). Using this, we arrive at $\sigma(\eta' \to \pi^+\pi^-\gamma) = 16 \pm 7 \mu b$. For the total η' production cross section in this experiment, we

get $\sigma(\eta') = 46 \pm 20\,\mu b$. (By η_n or η_c we indicate η
decaying into only neutral particles, or into
$\pi^+ + \pi^- +$ neutral, respectively.)

6. The present best estimate of the η' branching ratios is
$\Gamma(\eta' \to \pi\pi\eta)/\Gamma_{total} = 0.65 \pm 0.04$, $\Gamma(\eta' \to \pi^+\pi^-\gamma)/\Gamma_{total}$
$= 0.35 \mp 0.04$. All η' decay seems to be accounted
for by these two modes.. Alan Rittenberg (Lawrence
Radiation Laboratory), private communication. We
also use $\Gamma(\eta \to \pi^+\pi^-$ neutral$/\eta \to$ total$) = 0.29$.

7. H. O. Cohn, R. D. McCulloch, W. M. Bugg, and G. T.
Condo, Nuclear Phys. B1, 57 (1967).

8. These authors measured an η' total cross section of
$30^{+18}_{-11}\,\mu b$ in the same experiment, by measuring the
partial decay $\eta' \to \pi^+\pi^-\eta_n$. Using the current value
(Ref. 6) of $\Gamma(\eta' \to \pi^+\pi^-\gamma)/\Gamma_{total} = 0.35 \pm 0.04$, we
arrive at $11^{+6}_{-4}\,\mu b$ for $\eta' \to \pi^+\pi^-\gamma$.

9. G. Goldhaber, in Proceedings of the 1965 Coral Gables
Conference on Symmetry Principles at High Energies
(University of Miami, Florida, 1965) page 34.

10. M. Abolins, R. Lander, N. Xuong, and P. Yager
(University of California—San Diego, at La Jolla),
private communication.

11. A. H. Rosenfeld, N. Barash-Schmidt, A. Barbaro-
Galtieri, W. J. Podolsky, L. R. Price, P. Söding,
C. G. Wohl, M. Roos, and W. J. Willis, Rev. Mod.
Phys. 39, 1 (1967) (Appendix A2 on the H meson,
p. 50), and 40, 77 (1968).

12. S. Y. Fung, W. Jackson, R. T. Pu, D. Brown, and G.
Gidal, "Phys. Rev. Letters, 21, 47 (1968).

13. N. Armenise et al., Bari-Bologna-Firenze-Orsay Collaboration, Phys. Letters 26B, 336 (1968).

14. See I. Butterworth, Rapporteur's Talk on Meson Resonances, in Proceedings of the Heidelberg International Conference on Elementary Particles (North-
Holland Publishing Company, Amsterdam, 1968),
page 24.

15. A. Barbaro-Galtieri, M. J. Matison, A. Rittenberg,
G. B. Chadwick, Z. G. T. Guiragossián, and E.
Pickup, Search for I = 2 Hyperons and Study of
Resonances in K⁻d Interactions, Lawrence Radia-
tion Laboratory Report UCRL-18237, June 1968.

16. J. Friedman, MURTLEBERT, Alvarez Programming
Group Note P-156, 1966 (Lawrence Radiation Laboratory).

17. Argonne-Northwestern Collaboration; R. G. Ammar

and R. Davis (Northwestern University), S. Dagan
(ANL) private communication, 1968.

18.   Results of the fits:

(a)   For the $\pi^+p \rightarrow \Delta^{++}\pi^+\pi^-\pi^0$ data (Ref. 1) at 4 GeV/c
(Figure 5): $\Delta^{++}\eta$ (1.4%), $\Delta^{++}\omega$ (21%), $\Delta^{++}H$[M
= 965 MeV, Γ = 40 MeV, (3.0 ± 1.0)%], $\Delta^{++}A_2$ (7%),
$\Delta^{++}\rho^+\pi^-$ (11%), $\Delta^{++}\rho^0\pi^0$ (9%), peripheralized phase
space (48%).   The Δ^{++} events were selected in the
band 1.13 to 1.33 GeV; events in which both $p\pi^+$ combinations were in the band were included.

(b)   For the $\pi^+p \rightarrow \Delta^{++}\pi^+\pi^-\pi^0$ data, compilation in the
3- to 4-GeV/c region (Figure 6): $\Delta^{++}\eta$ (1.5%), $\Delta^{++}\omega$
(25%), $\Delta^{++}H$[M = 965 MeV, Γ = 45 MeV, (1.8 ± 0.6)%],
$\Delta^{++}A_1^0$ (0.5%), $\Delta^{++}A_2$ (1%), $\Delta^{++}\rho^+\pi^-$ (14%), $\Delta^{++}\rho^0\pi^0$(9%),
$N^{*+}(1690)\pi^+\pi^0$(2%), four-body phase space (45%).
For the Δ^{++} selection, see under (a), above.

(c)   For the $\pi^+n \rightarrow p\pi^+\pi^-\pi^0$ data near 3.65 GeV/c
(Ref. 4) (Figure 8): $p\eta$(1.5%), $p\omega$(16%), p A_2(6.6%),
pH[M = 998 MeV, Γ = 40 MeV, (1.1 ± 0.5)%],
$pA_{1.5}$(3.8%), Δ^+(1236) ρ^0 (1.8%), Δ^{++}(1236)$\pi^-\pi^0$(8.8%),
Δ^0(1236)$\pi^+\pi^0$ (1.5%), $p\pi^-\rho^+$(9.9%), $p\pi^+\rho^-$(4.2%),
$p\pi^-\rho^0$(10%), $N^{*0}(1690)\pi^+$ (8.3%), $N^{*+}(1690)\pi^0$(6.0%),
$N^{*0}(1520)\pi^+$(6.0%), $N^{*+}(1520)\pi^0$ (4.0%), $N^{*+}(2190)\pi^0$
(2.7%), $\Delta^0(1920)\pi^+$(7.8%), phase space (0%).   For the
ω contribution, we used a Breit-Wigner resonance
curve, folded with a resolution function similar to
the one we had observed in an experiment using a
deuterium bubble chamber at 2.1 GeV/c (Ref. 15).
The resulting function had a full width at half maximum of 44 MeV.

For the H enhancement a S-wave Breit-Wigner
form was used.   This is usually a reasonable approximation to the resolution functions in bubble chamber
experiments.   The quoted errors in the amount of
H present in these three fits include all the uncertainties of the multiparameter fits, therefore are
larger than the statistical errors in the one-dimen-
sional histograms.   We give these results in order
to allow the reader to check our calculations, and
not because we believe that they necessarily have
much physical significance.   Although preference for
small momentum transfers in the production of the
various resonances has been taken into account (see
text), all interferences between the different contributions, as well as anisotropies of the decay angular
distributions of the resonances with respect to the incoming beam direction, have been neglected.

19. The cross section for the H enhancement has been cal-
    culated by using as normalization the total cross
    section for $\pi^+ p \to p \pi^+ \pi^+ \pi^- \pi^0$ of 3.43 mb for 2363
    events (Ref. 3). The cross section for $\eta' \to \pi^+ \pi^- \eta_c$
    was measured and found to be 8.6 ± 3.5 μb. Using
    the known branching ratios (Ref. 6), we derive the
    total cross section $\sigma(\eta') = 71 \pm 32$ μb, and
    $\sigma(\eta' \to \pi^+ \pi^- \gamma) = 25 \pm 12$ μb. Aachen-Berlin-Bonn-
    Hamburg-München Collaboration, Nuovo Cimento
    44A, 530 (1966); and G. Wolf (SLAC), private com-
    munication.

20. The cross sections were taken from the following
    papers: 2.08 GeV/c (η and ω) from James and
    Kraybill, Phys. Rev. 142, 896 (1966); 2.35, 2.62,
    and 2.90 GeV/c (ω) from Yamamoto et al., Phys.
    Rev. 140, B730 (1965); 2.75 GeV/c (ω) from Saclay-
    Orsay-Bari-Bologna Collaboration, Nuovo Cimento
    40, 273 (1965); 2.95, 3.20, 3.50, 3.75, 4.08 GeV/c
    (ω) from Brown et al., Phys. Rev. Letters 19, 664
    (1967); 3.65 GeV/c (ω, η, and $\eta' \to \pi^+ \pi^- \eta_n$ converted
    to total) from Trilling et al., Phys. Letters 19, 427
    (1965); 4.0 GeV/c (ω, η) from ABBBHLM Collabora-
    tion, Phys. Rev. 138, B879 (1965) and from G. Wolf
    (SLAC), private communication 1968; 4.0 GeV/c (η'),
    see Ref. 19; 5.0 GeV/c (η') Bonn-Durham-Nijmegen-
    Turin Collaboration, Phys. Rev. 161, 1356 (1967);
    7.0 GeV/c (ω, η) from Ferbel et al., University of
    Rochester Report UR875-153, 1966; 8.0 GeV/c (ω, η)
    from Aachen-Berlin-CERN Collaboration, Nucl.
    Phys. B4, 501 (1968).

21. G. Ascoli, H. B. Crawley, U. Kruse, D. W. Mortara,
    E. Schafer, A. Shapiro and B. Terreault, Mass
    Spectrum for $\pi^+ \pi^- \pi^-$ Produced in $\pi^- p$ at 5 GeV/c,
    University of Illinois preprint COO-1195-121,
    March 1968. This paper also gives the references
    on $A_{1.5}$.

22. The cross sections for $\pi^+ n \to p +$ meson were taken
    from the following papers: 1.98 to 2.46 GeV/c
    (η, ω, η') from Abolins et al. in "Production of I = 0
    Mesons Near Threshold in $\pi^+ d$ Interactions",
    Lawrence Radiation Laboratory preprint; 2.91, 3.7,
    5.9 GeV/c (η) from Guisan et al., Phys. Letters 18,
    200 (1965); 3.29 GeV/c (η') from Cohn et al., Phys.
    Letters 15, 344 (1965); 3.65 GeV/c (ω, η, η') from
    Benson's thesis, see Ref. 4.

23. D. Johnson, Meson and Baryon Resonance Production
    in the Interaction $\pi^- p \to p \pi^- \pi^- \pi^+ \pi^0$ at 3.9 GeV,

University of Hawaii Report UH-511-18, 1968, and
D. Johnson and V. Stenger (University of Hawaii),
private communication.

Kπ SCATTERING AND NORMAL PARITY K*'S

Invited Talk at the Informal Conference on Meson Spectroscopy,
University of Pennsylvania, March 26, 27, 1968

Kπ Scattering and Normal Parity K*'s

Peter E. Schlein[*]
University of California, Los Angeles

1. INTRODUCTION

In the study of elementary particle interactions,
bump hunting in mass spectra is an extremely fashionable and
obviously very important activity. However, there are clearly other phenomena in the field that are more subtle and
experimentally more elusive. The study of meson-meson interactions is one such area which is of great interest. Pending
the perhaps not too distant time when real meson-meson scattering experiments may be done with the use of storage rings,
we are compelled to study these interactions in somewhat less
direct ways. One such way is to try to convince oneself that
peripherally produced meson systems can, under certain circumstances, realistically be thought of as resulting from a
scattering of the beam particle on a virtual π in the cloud
around a target nucleon. It is this approach that I will
review today with particular emphasis on our state of knowledge of the Kπ interaction and various problems associated
with this type of analysis.

161

Motivated by the extent of the agreement between on-
and off-mass-shell pπ elastic scattering angular distributions,[1,2] Malamud and I[3,4] performed a comprehensive angular
correlation analysis of the reaction $\pi^- p \to \pi^- \pi^+ n$ using a
large sample of $\sim$ 20,000 events with beam momenta 2.1 - 3.1
GeV/c (compiled from groups at LRL, Purdue, Penn-Saclay, and
Argonne-Toronto-Wisconsin). In a desire neither to ignore
the well-known effects of absorption, nor to have to depend
on detailed theoretical calculations of these effects, we
showed that it was possible to extract the interesting T = 0
s-wave $\pi\pi$ phase shift (δ_s^o) in the neighborhood of the
ρ-meson without complete prior knowledge of the helicity amplitudes. The essential point of that work was that utiliza-
tion of the complete set of spherical harmonic moments in the
$\pi\pi$ system leads with minimal assumptions to a highly over-
constrained analysis in which both δ_s^o and the helicity amplitudes are the unknown parameters. Thus, in the fits, the
validity of the assumptions was subjected to test on a χ^2
basis. The acceptable χ^2's which resulted from the analysis
imply the necessary compatibility between the data and the
model. Although the magic words "pole extrapolation" were
not invoked in the analysis, it was shown that the model allowed for the effects of multiplicative off-mass-shell modi-
fications to the on-shell amplitudes $e^{i\delta}\sin\delta$. Because of the
relevance of this work to future Kπ phase shift analysis work,
the two papers are appended to this report. Although the
related analysis of $K^- p \to K^- \pi^+ n$ involving the Kπ interaction
has not yet been done, as discussed below the prospects for
success are very good indeed.

In this talk I will concentrate most of the discussion
of the Kπ interaction on the reaction $K^+ p \to K^+ \pi^- \pi^+ p$. The

reasons for this are mainly historical.

2. $K^+p \rightarrow K^+\pi^-\pi^+p$

Many of the dominant features of this reaction are
displayed in Figure 1. This is the data at 5 GeV/c of the
Brussels-CERN-Birmingham collaboration.[5] The features seen
on this plot are representative of the situation for the entire range of available beam momenta. One sees the well-
known spots corresponding to simultaneous production of
$K^*(890)\Delta^{++}$ and of $K^*(1400)\Delta^{++}$. In addition, several interesting effects other than these two spots exist in the distribu-
tion.

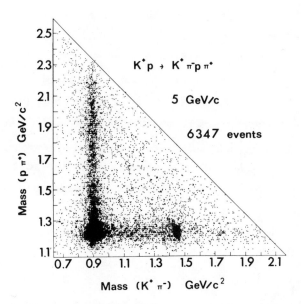

Fig.1. CERN-Brussels-Birmingham collaboration results[5].

One of these is the large amount of K*(890) out of
the Δ^{++} region, the so-called K*(890)-non Δ^{++} production.
These events are generally interpreted as arising from the
Deck production of the K*(1300) effect (the threshold $K^{*o}\pi^{+}$
or Q enhancement) and will be discussed by Professor Goldhaber in his talk. Thus, we do not consider them further
here.

Another striking effect is the evident enhancement
corresponding to Δ^{++} production in the region between the two
K*'s as compared with the apparent lack of enhancement above
the K*(1400). I will summarize in this talk the evidence
that most of the enhancement in $K^{+}p \rightarrow K^{+}\pi^{-}\Delta^{++}$ for Kπ effective mass in the neighborhood of 1.1 - 1.2 GeV is due to a
very large T = 1/2 s-wave Kπ phase shift $\delta_{s}^{1/2}$. $\delta_{s}^{1/2}$ appears to increase slowly from threshold, apparently reaching
$\sim 90°$ in this region. Thus, there is evidence for the existence for a very broad scalar Kπ resonant system, looking very
similar to the broad scalar T = 0 $\pi\pi$ system around 730 MeV.

The results of the UCLA group[6] to be discussed below
also show that the drop-off in the enhancement above K*(1400)
can be understood in terms of the Kπ interaction becoming
extremely inelastic in this region.

Thus, for the present, we will confine most of our
discussion of the Kπ interaction to the reaction

$$K^{+}p \rightarrow K^{+}\pi^{-}\Delta^{++} \tag{1a}$$

$$K^{+}p \rightarrow K^{o}\pi^{o}\Delta^{++} \tag{1b}$$

which is dominated by low momentum transfer to the Δ^{++}.
Figure 2 is from the UCLA work of Trippe et al.[6] at 7.3 GeV/c
beam momentum. The events are selected with momentum trans-

fer to the π^+p system $t < 0.5$ GeV^2. In Fig. 2b are shown
the spherical harmonic moments of the angular distribution
in the π^+p rest frame $<Y_1^0>$, $<Y_2^0>$, $<Y_3^0>$. The black (white)
points are for reaction 1a (1b). Reaction (1a) corresponds
to elastic $(K^+\pi^- \rightarrow K^+\pi^-)$ scattering at the upper vertex in
Fig. 2a and reaction (1b) corresponds to charge exchange
scattering $(K^+\pi^- \rightarrow K^0\pi^0)$. Since the black and white points
are compatible, the π^+p spin state seems to be independent
of whether elastic or charge-exchange scattering occurs at
the Kπ vertex.

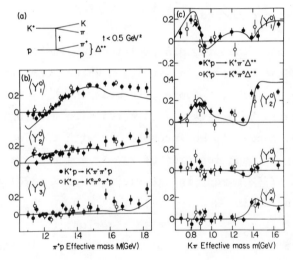

Fig. 2. Kπ and π^+p moments at 7.3 Gev/c from Trippe et al.[6].

The curves drawn in Fig. 2b summarize the energy dependence of these moments for real particle π^+p elastic scattering experiments. The behavior is similar to that observed
earlier by Gellert et al.[1] in pp → $p\pi^+p\pi^-$ at 6.6 GeV/c. The
disagreement at low π^+p mass is tentatively interpreted as

being due to off-mass-shell effects and at the high end of
the spectrum as being due to the onset of K*(1300) effects.
For large π^+p mass, you have diffraction scattering and one
may think of a picture with final-state K*π interaction which
distorts the π^+p angular distribution although, as discussed
below, this situation is far from clear.

In Fig. 2c are shown the $<Y_\ell^0>$ moments of the angular
distribution in the Kπ rest frame for reactions (1a) and (1b).
The amplitudes for Kπ scattering are

$$A_{elastic} = \frac{2}{3} A^{T=1/2} + \frac{1}{3} A^{T=3/2}$$

$$A_{charge\ exchange} = \frac{\sqrt{2}}{3} (-A^{T=1/2} + A^{T=3/2})$$

so that if one isotopic spin amplitude dominates, $K^+\pi^-$ and
$K^0\pi^0$ should be the same, a situation which seems to be the
case for $M_{K\pi} \lesssim 1$ GeV. Above this mass the $K^0\pi^0$ statistics
are too sparse to draw any such conclusion although the UCLA
data do not appear to be incompatible with this assumption.
Several significant features of the Kπ moments are: (a) the
pronounced $<Y_1^0>$ moment in the vicinity of K*(890) indicating
a slowly increasing s-wave; (b) $<Y_1^0> \simeq 0$ at $M_{K\pi} \sim .95$ GeV
indicates that $\delta_s^{1/2} \sim 60°$ in this region; (c) the onset of
d-wave interaction evident in $<Y_2^0>$ and $<Y_4^0>$ in the K*(1400)
region. Although a detailed angular correlation phase shift
analysis was not performed by the UCLA group, the solid
curves in Fig. 2c which show a rough compatibility with the
data are calculated with no off-shell or absorption corrections and assume, in addition to the p-wave K*(890) and d-
wave K*(1400) Breit Wigners (the latter with an x = 0.5
inelasticity), an s-wave Breit Wigner amplitude with E_o =
1.1 GeV and $\Gamma = 0.4$ GeV. The curves clearly are not in

perfect agreement with the data. Among other things, it is
unrealistic to use a Breit-Wigner form for such a large Γ.
Thus these curves should probably be taken as a rough indication that $\delta_s^{1/2}$ increases smoothly from threshold and seems
to reach $90°$ somewhere in the vicinity of 1.1 - 1.2 GeV.
Additional evidence for this behavior, discussed below, is
obtained by Trippe et al.[6] from a detailed analysis of the
distribution in the Chew-Low plane involving an extrapolation
to the pion-exchange pole.

3.   DECK EFFECT IN $K\pi\Delta^{++}$ VS. OPE

Before going on to discuss the general question of
Chew-Low extrapolation, there is another important facet to
this field which should be discussed. In Fig. 3 the $<Y_1^0>$
Kπ moments are shown for the data of the International K^+
Collaboration. The groups whose data are represented here
are:

LRL, Berkeley (Goldhaber- Trilling)	(4.6 and 9.0 GeV/c)
UCLA	(7.3 GeV/c)
Brussels-CERN collaboration)	(3, 3.5, 5.0 GeV/c)
British collaboration (Oxford, Birmingham, Glasgow)	(10.0 GeV/c)
Johns Hopkins U. (Pevsner)	(5.5 GeV/c).

With nearly an order of magnitude increase in the statistics
for reaction (1b), a striking difference between the elastic
and charge exchange moments is seen for m $\gtrsim$ 950 MeV. At
first glance one may conclude that this is evidence for T =
3/2 Kπ interaction. However Fu et al.,[7] in a paper to this
conference, have pointed out a related effect and emphasized

that a problem may exist in such a superficial interpretation
of the difference between reactions (1a) and (1b).

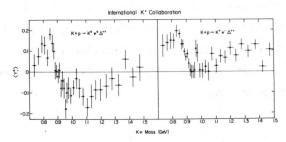

Fig. 3. International K^+ Collaboration $\langle Y_1^0 \rangle$ moments for
$K^0\pi^0$ and $K^+\pi^-$ in $K^+p \rightarrow K^0\pi^0\bar{\Delta}^{++}$.

In Fig. 4 are shown the $K^+\pi^-\Delta^{++}$ Dalitz plots of Fu et
al.[7] at 4.6 and 9.0 GeV/c. A striking $\Delta^{++}\pi^-$ enhancement is
seen near threshold (the N*(1400) effect) and is clearly related to a pronounced $K^+\pi^-$ fore-aft asymmetry, in the now
well-known manner characteristic of the Deck-type phenomenon.
In Fig. 5 we see the same Dalitz plots but now with the same
momentum transfer cut used in the UCLA analysis. The strong
asymmetry in the K*(890) band remains, although between
$K^*(890)$ and $K^*(1400)$ it seems to have diminished.

In the $p\pi^+\pi^0$ mass spectrum of the K^0 events shown in
Fig. 6, no such threshold effect is apparent. As a Deck effect this may be understood as due to the fact that $p\pi^+\pi^0$
is a pure isotopic spin 3/2 state in this reaction (1b) while
$p\pi^+\pi^-$ in reaction (1a) has a T = 1/2 component. If the Deck
effect in this process were due to a T = 1/2 $\Delta^{++}\pi$ interaction
it would be seen in reaction (1a) but not in (1b), as seems
to be the case.

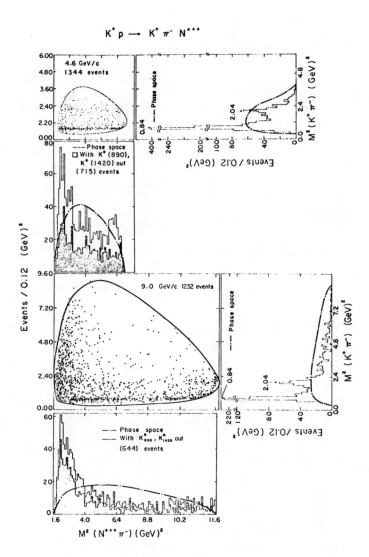

Fig. 4. $K^+\pi^-\Delta^{++}$ Dalitz Plots at 4.6,9.0 Gev/c from Fu et al.[7].

$$K + P \rightarrow K^+ \pi^- \Delta^{++}, \Delta^2(\Delta^{++}) < .5 \; (\text{GeV}/c)^2$$

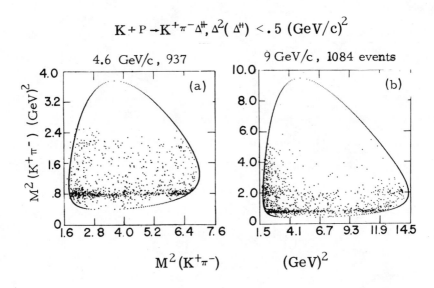

Fig. 5. $K^+\pi^-\Delta^{++}$ Dalitz plots with low t to Δ^{++} from Fu et al.[7].

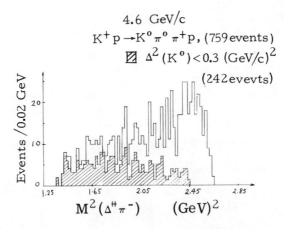

Fig. 6. Mass($p\pi^+\pi^0$) in $K^+p \rightarrow K^0\pi^0\pi^+p$ from Fu et al.[7].

It is important to note, however, that $<Y_1^0>$ for $K^+\pi^-$ and $K^0\pi^0$ does seem to have the same behavior for $m_{K\pi} \lesssim 900$ MeV, thus suggesting that the scattering interpretation is safe at least in this region. An additional argument in favor of this interpretation, at least up to the K*(1400), is that $<Y_3^0>$ and $<Y_4^0>$ in the UCLA data[6] of Fig. 2b are generally compatible with zero until $\sim$ 1400 MeV. If the Kπ scattering distribution were distorted by a $\Delta^{++}\pi^-$ interaction, it seems surprising that its effect would stop at $\ell = 1$ (or 2). Nevertheless, the interpretation ambiguity between Deck effect and Kπ scattering is a serious problem and is not to be dismissed lightly. Fu et al.[7] pose the problem in these words: "We are thus faced with a dilemma: which effect causes the asymmetry" (in scattering), "or even whether the two represent alternative descriptions of the same physical phenomenon."

There seem to be two ways in which some understanding may be brought to the problem. (a) Reactions may be studied in which there occurs a Deck effect but where the on-mass-shell vertex scattering is known, e.g., pp $\rightarrow$ $(p\pi^+)(p\pi^-)$, pp $\rightarrow$ $(p\pi^+)$n. Colton et al.[8] have presented some results to this conference which bear on this question and which will be discussed below. (b) Kπ scattering from several different reactions, and at different beam momenta, may be compared, e.g., $K^+p \rightarrow (K^0\pi^0)\Delta^{++}$, $K^-p \rightarrow (K^-\pi^+)$n, $K^+n \rightarrow K^0\pi^0$p. It is important to determine whether or not the Kπ moments are reaction dependent.

4.   CHEW-LOW DISTRIBUTIONS IN OPE

I would now like to digress for a while from the question of angular correlation work and turn to detailed considerations of another aspect of one-pion-exchange processes, that of the intensity distributions in the Chew-Low plane. With the intention of reaffirming the essential one-pion exchange character of a large number of reactions, I would like to discuss a particular large body of data resulting from many experiments where it seems possible to form a consistent picture to describe the differential cross sections $d^2\sigma/dtdm$ of a large number of reactions over a large range of beam momenta. The interpretation of the $K\pi$ data in the UCLA work of Trippe et al.[6] is made within the context of this picture.

The reactions in question are of two classes, namely,

$$\textbf{I} \quad xp \to x\pi^{+}n \qquad \left(\text{or in deuterium:} \quad xn \to x\pi^{-}p \right.$$

$$\textbf{II} \quad xp \to x\pi^{-}\Delta^{++} \qquad \qquad\qquad\qquad \left. xn \to x\pi^{+}\Delta^{-} \right)$$

where we are interested only in low-momentum transfer to the final state baryon system (i.e., $t \lesssim 0.3$ GeV^2). We interpret these in terms of π-exchange according to the processes

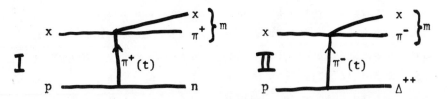

where x may be in general either $\pi^{\pm}$, $K^{\pm}$, p or $\bar{\text{p}}$. m is the effective mass at the upper vertex, and t is the momentum transfer to the baryon. The reason for selecting only these two classes of reactions is an empirical one. Namely, for various reasons, we know that the ω-meson couples strongly to the nucleon and that it is a frequent exchange contributor.

Thus, to avoid it for the present, we consider only charge exchange processes. Because of the relatively weak T = 2 ππ and T = 3/2 Kπ interactions (compared with the T = 0, 1 and T = 1/2 interactions, respectively), we will also initially not consider those reactions in which the upper vertex would be $\pi^{\pm}\pi^{\pm}$ or $\pi^{\pm}K^{\pm}$.

5.   FITS USING DÜRR-PILKUHN OPE

I would now like to present the collected evidence that a charged pion exchange model accounts for a large set of reactions of classes I and II. I will do this within the context of the pole equations modified by the off-shell vertex correction factors of Dürr and Pilkuhn.[9] The pole equations for processes I and II are, respectively,[10,11]

$$\frac{d^2\sigma}{dtdm} \xrightarrow{t \to -\mu^2} \frac{1}{4\pi m_p^2 P_{Lab}^2} \frac{G^2}{4\pi} \frac{t}{(t + \mu^2)^2} qm^2\sigma(m)$$

$$\frac{d^3\sigma}{dtdmdM} \xrightarrow{t \to -\mu^2} \frac{1}{4\pi^3 m_p^2 P_{Lab}^2} \frac{1}{(t + \mu^2)^2} qm^2\sigma(m) \; QM^2\sigma(M)$$

where M is the mass at the Δ^{++} vertex, m_p is the proton mass, P_{Lab} is the lab momentum of the beam particle X, $(G^2/4\pi) \simeq$ 29.2, q and Q are the on-shell momenta at the n and Δ^{++} vertices, respectively, and $\sigma(m)$ and $\sigma(M)$ are the on-shell vertex scattering cross sections.

Dürr and Pilkuhn[9] (DP) have suggested that these equations be off-shell corrected through the use of vertex factors which are relativistic generalizations of potential theory results on angular momentum barrier penetration factors, etc.

While, as you will see, the resulting factors work exceedingly well in the sense of fitting a large amount of data with only a very small number of free parameters, it is my opinion that this must be considered, to some extent, fortuitous. Their arguments do not cover the entire story in the sense, for example, that absorption effects are not explicitly mentioned. The fits, of course, speak for themselves. However, I think it appropriate to suggest that the Dürr-Pilkuhn modified OPE (DP-OPE) functional forms be taken as a convenient representation of the empirical Chew-Low distributions for the class of reactions considered.

Before showing the results of these fits, I list as examples, the DP factors for the $P_{3/2}\Delta^{++}$ and p-wave ρ vertices respectively:

Δ^{++} vertex

$$\{Q\sigma(M)\}_{\text{off-shell}} = \left(\frac{(M + m_p)^2 + t}{(M + m_p)^2 - \mu^2}\right) \times \left(\frac{Q_t}{Q}\right)^2$$

$$\times \left(\frac{1 + R_{N*}^2 Q^2}{1 + R_{N*}^2 Q_t^2}\right) \{Q\sigma(M)\}_{\text{on-shell}}$$

where

$$Q_t^2 = [(M - m_p)^2 + t][(M + m_p)^2 + t]/4M^2 \quad .$$

ρ vertex

$$\{q\sigma(m)\}_{\text{off-shell}} = \left(\frac{q_t}{q}\right)^2 \left(\frac{1 + R_\rho^2 q^2}{1 + R_\rho^2 q_t^2}\right) \{q\sigma(m)\}_{\text{on-shell}} \quad .$$

TABLE I.   REACTIONS FIT WITH DP-OPE

Reaction Quasi-Two-Body	Beam Momenta	Ref.	Figures in This Paper	R_ρ	R_{N*} GeV^{-1}	R_n GeV^{-1}	R_{K*}	c GeV^2
$\pi^- p \to \rho^0 n$	1.59,2.75,8.0		-					
$\pi^+ p \to \rho^0 \Delta^{++}$	2.35,3-4,6.95	12	7	8.3 ±2.0	4.0 ±0.2	2.7 ±0.1	-	2.3 ±0.3
$pp \to \Delta^{++} n$	4,10		-					
$\bar{p}p \to \Delta^{++}\bar{\Delta}^{++}$	3.6,5.7		7					
$K^+ p \to K^{*0}\Delta^{++}$	3,3.5,5,7.3,13	6	8,18	-	(4.0)[a]	-	1.3 ±0.2	(2.3)
$K^- p \to K^{*0} n$	3,4.1,5.5		9	-	-	(2.7)	(1.3)	(2.3)
Extended Mass Range at One Vertex (Maximum Likelihood)								
$pp \to (\pi^- p)\Delta^{++}$	6.6,28.5[20]	8	10-13	-	3.5 ±0.7	-	-	1.2 ±0.5
$K^+ p \to (K^+\pi^-)\Delta^{++}$	7.3	6	2,18	-	(4.0)	-	1.0 ±0.5	(2.3)
High Statistics Maximum Likelihood (Pole Extrapolation)								
$pp \to (p\pi^+)n$	6.6	21	14,15	-	5.2 ±0.8	2.8 ±0.2	-	(2.3)
$\pi^- p \to (\pi^-\pi^+)n$	2.1-3.1	22	16,17	8.3	-	2.9	-	(2.3)

[a] A bracketed parameter means that parameter was held fixed in the calculation.

Corresponding correction factors exist for other partial
waves. For those reactions of class I, the pnπ vertex is
corrected by introducing into the pole equation the factor

$$\frac{1 + R_n^2 q^2}{1 + R_n^2 q_t^2}$$

where

$$q_t^2 = [(m_n - m_p)^2 + t][(m_n + m_p)^2 + t]/4m_n^2 \ .$$

The R's are the phenomenological parameters of the fits. The
reactions thus far fit with DP-OPE are listed in Table I
along with the best values of the parameters obtained in the
fits. A number between brackets means that particular parameter was fixed at that value in the fit or calculation.

6.   WOLF'S QUASI-TWO-BODY FITS

Wolf[12] simultaneously fit the dσ/dt distributions of
the first four quasi-two-body reactions listed in Table I,
thereby determining R_ρ, R_{N*} and R_n. He allowed for an additional degree of freedom in his fit using a form factor
$G(t)^2 = [(c - \mu^2)/(c + t)]^2$. The value of c = 2.3 which resulted from his fit makes $G(t)^2$ very weakly dependent on t in
the low t region of interest. Some of his fits are shown in
Fig. 7. Wolf[12] demonstrated for the reaction $\pi^+ p \to \rho^0 \Delta^{++}$
that the apparent shrinking of the forward peak in dσ/dt,
visible in Fig. 7, is of kinematical origin and arises because
of the finite mass selections for ρ^0 and Δ^{++} and the dependence of the Chew-Low boundary on beam momentum.

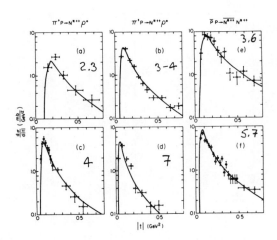

Fig. 7. dσ/dt distributions for $\pi^+p \rightarrow \rho^0\Delta^{++}$ and $\bar{p}p \rightarrow \overline{\Delta^{++}}\Delta^{++}$ from Wolf[12]. Beam momenta are indicated in Gev/c

7. $K^+p \rightarrow K^{*0}\Delta^{++}$ AND $K^-p \rightarrow K^{*0}n$

Trippe et al.[6] have fit the available dσ/dt data for the $K^{*0}\Delta^{++}$ final state from 3 - 13 GeV/c. In this fit R_{N*} and c were held fixed at Wolf's[12] values and R_{K*} was determined to be ~ 1.3 GeV^{-1}. The dσ/dt distributions for 3.0, 3.5, 5.0,[13] and 13[14] GeV/c are shown in Fig. 8 along with the curves calculated assuming the values shown in Table I. The 7.3 GeV/c data are shown in Fig. 18d. The broken line is the corresponding curve. The same apparent shrinking of the forward peak seen in the $\rho^0\Delta^{++}$ reaction is also seen here.

With R_{K*} determined, it is now possible to calculate predictions for the reaction

$$K^-p \rightarrow K^{*0}n \rightarrow K^-\pi^+n \ .$$

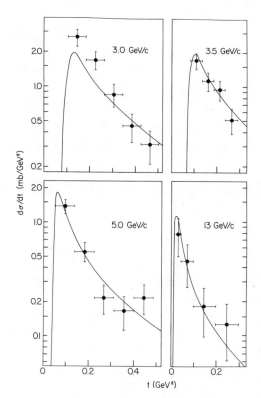

Fig. 8. dσ/dt for $K^+p \to K^{*0}\Delta^{++} \to K^+\pi^-\Delta^{++}$ with mass selec-
         tions .86-.94 and 1.16-1.29 Gev at 3, 3.5, 5 Gev/c[13]
         and .84-.96 and 1.12-1.36 Gev at 13 Gev/c[14]. Fits
         are from Trippe et al.[6].

These are shown in Fig. 9 with the 3.0 GeV/c data of Verglas[15]
and the 4.1 and 5.5 GeV/c data of Schweingruber et al.[16] The
curves fit well, thus suggesting that the $K^-\pi^+n$ reaction
should be amenable to the same type of detailed angular correlation analyses that have been performed on $\pi^-p \to \pi^-\pi^+n$.

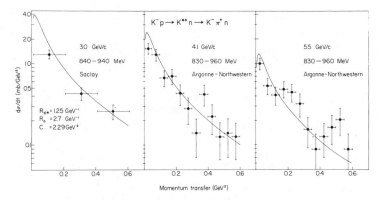

Fig. 9. dσ/dt for $K^-p \rightarrow K^{*0}n \rightarrow K^-\pi^+n$ at 3.0^{15}, 4.1 and 5.5^{16} Gev/c. Curves are calculated using R_{K^*} from Trippe et al.[6]. K* mass selections are shown.

8. $pp \rightarrow p\pi^-\Delta^{++}$, OPE, AND THE DECK EFFECT

Colton et al.[8] departed from the quasi-two-body work and have fit dσ/dm for an extended mass range at the upper vertex. Because the DP off-shell factors tend towards unity as m increases, for sufficiently large m no off-shell corrections are necessary at the upper vertex. Figure 10a shows the Chew-Low plot for $pp \rightarrow p\pi^-\Delta^{++}$ at 6.6 GeV/c from the earlier experiment of Gellert et al.[1] Figure 10b shows the $m(\pi^-p)$ projection for $t < 0.3$ GeV^2 of Colton et al.[8] and gives dσ/dm in absolute units (mb/GeV). The dashed curve is calculated using Wolf's[12] values for R_{N^*} and c with no off-shell corrections at the $p\pi^-$ vertex. The fit for $m \gtrsim 1.5$ GeV is

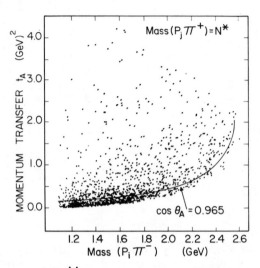

Fig. 10a. pp → pπ⁻Δ⁺⁺ at 6.6 Gev/c. Chew-Low plot from
         Gellert et al.[1]. Line of constant center-of-mass
         production angle cosine of 0.965 shown.

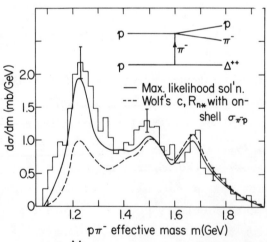

Fig. 10b. pp → pπ⁻Δ⁺⁺ at 6.6 Gev/c. dσ/dm(π⁻p) for momentum
         transfer to Δ⁺⁺, t<0.3 Gev² from Colton et al.[8].
         Absolute cross section units are shown. Curves are
         described in the text. Note the insensitivity of
         curves at large m to the value of c used(1.2,2.3 resp.)

quite good. For m $\lesssim$ 1.5 GeV, the four significant partial
waves $S_{1/2}$, $P_{1/2}$, $P_{3/2}$, $D_{3/2}$ are considered and are off-shell
corrected to give the solid curve. The procedure actually
corresponds to a successful inverse pole extrapolation. The
on-shell cross sections are input and the R parameters are
varied to give a best fit to the distribution $d^3\sigma/dtdmdM$ in
the physical region.

The relevance of this work to the Deck problem is the
following. Figure 11 from Colton et al.[8] shows the t-projec-
tion and the $\Delta^{++}\pi^-$ mass projections for the three indicated
m selections. The well-known N*(1400) effect is most striking
at the highest mass. The fact that the cross section for

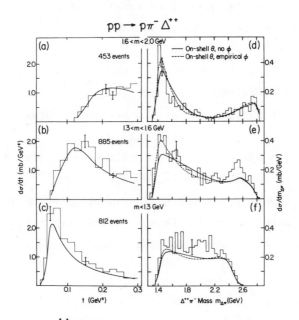

Fig. 11. pp → $p\pi^-\Delta^{++}$ at 6.6 Gev/c. (a-c) dσ/dt for the indicated mass selections. Curves are the t projections of
the same $d^2\sigma/dtdm$ used for the solid curve in Fig. 10b.
(d-f) dσ/dm($\Delta^{++}\pi^-$) for the same mass selections. Curves
are calculated from the same $d^2\sigma/dtdm$ as above in addition to the indicated assumptions for π^-p scattering
angular distribution. Colton et al.[8].

these events is understood in OPE terms within the large context of the DP-OPE work discussed here suggests that the OPE
version of $d^3\sigma/dtdmdM$ survives whatever additional complexi-
ties nature has invoked (e.g., $\pi^-\Delta^{++}$ final state scattering,
Reggeized exchange π, etc.).

Thus, there seems to be a duality of models. In the
reaction $pp \rightarrow \pi^-p\Delta^{++}$, as long as one looks at the distribution
in t and m, OPE (with the DP off-shell corrections) is suffi-
cient. If one wants to predict, e.g., the $\pi^-\Delta^{++}$ mass spectrum
or the π^-p CM scattering angular distribution at large m, then
one needs to Reggeize the exchange π [17] or put in a $\pi\Delta$ final
state interaction (in such a way that $d^2\sigma/dtdm$ is not disturbed,
however) or use the absorption model. This experimental result may be related to the Dolan-Horn-Schmidt[18] duality as
discussed by Chew and Pignotti.[19] The same tests should be
applied to the reactions $\pi^-p \rightarrow \pi^-p\rho^0$ and $K^-p \rightarrow \pi^-pK^{*0}$. That
is, with no additional free parameters, the same model can
predict the π^-p effective mass distribution when t < 0.3 GeV^2
to the ρ (or K*) is selected.

Figure 12 shows some predictions of Colton et al.[8] for
$p\pi^-\Delta^{++}$ up to 30 GeV/c and the good agreement with the data
points of the 28.5 GeV/c BNL experiment of Connolly et al.[20]
Figure 13 shows $d\sigma/dm$ for this experiment with the predictions
of Colton et al.[8] The agreement is quite good.

9. $pp \rightarrow (p\pi^+)n$

In a Michigan State-UCLA collaboration paper, Ma et
al.[21] have performed a pole extrapolation analysis of this
reaction at 6.6 GeV/c and obtained excellent results for the
π^+p elastic cross section in the Δ^{++} region. Figure 14 shows

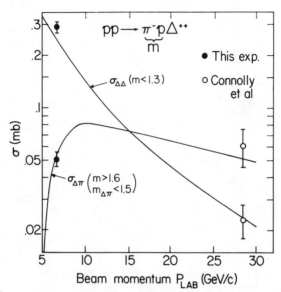

Fig. 12. Predicted P_{Lab} dependence of $\sigma_{\Delta\Delta}(pp \to \Delta^0\Delta^{++})$ and $\sigma_{\Delta\pi}(pp \to N^*_2(1400)p)$ for mass selections shown and for $t<0.3$ Gev^2 as in Fig. 10b from Colton et al.[8]. BNL 28.5 Gev/c points are from Connolly et al.[20].

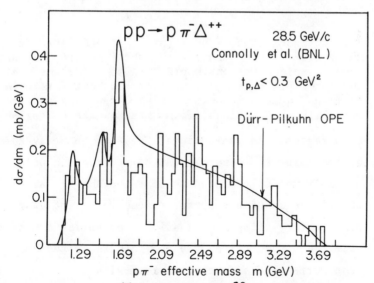

Fig. 13. $pp \to p\pi^-\Delta^{++}$ at 28.5 Gev/c[20]. $d\sigma/dm(\pi^-p)$ for $t<0.3$ Gev^2. Predictions are from Colton et al.[8]. and utilize the same $d^2\sigma/dtdm$ as above

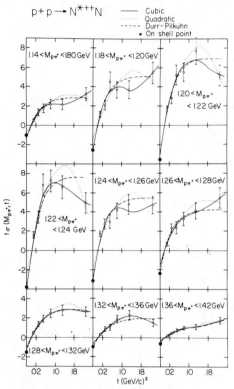

Fig. 14. Pole extrapolation of pp → (pπ⁺)n at 6.6 Gev/c from
Ma et al.[21]. The quantity tσ ,obtained from the data
and the pole equation is plotted vs. t for the nine
indicated pπ⁺ mass cuts. Curves are best fits using
cubic and quadratic power series expansions and the
Durr-Pilkuhn functional form with R_{N*} and R_n variable.

for nine mass regions the conventional Chew-Low quantity tσ
obtained by inserting the experimental dσ/dt into the pole
equation and solving for the product of t and the off-shell
cross section. The solid and dotted curves represent best
fits to this quantity using the classic power series expansion
method, while the dashed curves are the results of the best
fit using the Dürr-Pilkuhn functional form with

$$R_n \text{ and } R_{N*} \text{ as free parameters.}$$ Figure 15
shows the results for the extrapolated σ's for each of the

methods, compared with the known on-shell cross section. The
errors on the Dürr-Pilkuhn points are smaller because there
are fewer free parameters in that fit and thus it is more over-
constrained. The resulting values of R_n and R_{N*} agree with
those determined by Wolf.[12] There seems little doubt that the
Dürr-Pilkuhn functional form is a good representation of the
off-shell correction to the pole equation.

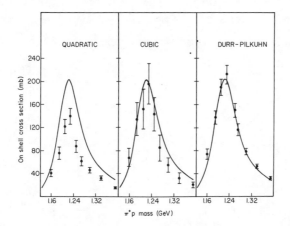

Fig. 15. Pole-extrapolated $p\pi^+$ cross sections for the three
          fits shown in Fig. 14 from Ma et al.[21]. Solid curve
          is the on-mass-shell cross section.

10. $\pi^- p \rightarrow (\pi^- \pi^+)n$

Malamud and I[22] have performed Dürr-Pilkuhn fits to
the Chew-Low distributions of the 2.1 - 3.1 GeV/c compilation
sample used earlier in our angular correlation analysis.
Figure 16 shows the $d\sigma/dm$ projections for these data divided
into three beam momentum regions. The curves shown are best
fits using the maximum likelihood method for three assumed

values of Γ_ρ, obtained using the DP-OPE functional form in
which R_n and R_ρ were varied. The corresponding $d\sigma/dt$ projections are shown in Fig. 17 in addition to predictions of the
same fit shown on published $d\sigma/dt$ distributions at 1.59, 4.0,
and 8.0 GeV/c. The excellence of fits in Figs. 16 and 17
represent a successful inverse pole extrapolation. Again,
it is possible to conclude that DP-OPE is a good representation of the off-shell corrections to the pole equation. Our
best value of Γ_ρ resulting from the detailed maximum likelihood fit after correcting for the experimental resolution
function is now about 135 ± 10 MeV.

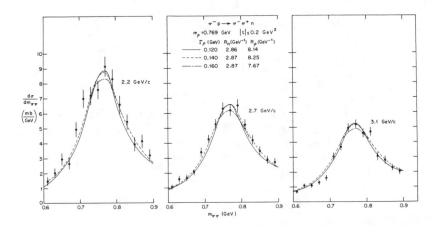

Fig. 16. $d\sigma/dm(\pi\pi)$ in $\pi^- p \rightarrow \pi^- \pi^+ n$ for momentum transfer t<0.3
Gev[2] from Malamud and Schlein[22]. Curves are the
result of maximum liklihood fits in which R_ρ and R_n
were variables.

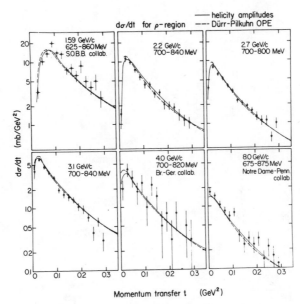

Fig. 17.   dσ/dt in $\pi^- p \to \rho^0 n$ from Malamud and Schlein[22]. The solid curves are determined by the helicity amplitudes obtained from fitting the 2.1-3.1 GeV/c data as in Ref. 4. A $1/P_{Lab2}$ dependence is then assumed to calculate the curves at 1.59, 4 and 8 GeV/c. The dashed curves are the t projections of the $d^2\sigma/dtdm$ distribution used to obtain the curves in Fig. 16.

11. $K^+ p \to K^+ \pi^- \Delta^{++}$ AND THE Kπ INTERACTION

We have seen that DP-OPE fits $K^+ p \to K^*(890)^0 \Delta^{++}$ from 3 to 13 GeV/c. The results of Colton et al.[8] which show that the DP-OPE prescription also leads to an acceptable description of $pp \to p\pi^- \Delta^{++}$ at 6.6 and 28.5 GeV for an extended mass range at the $p\pi^-$ vertex suggest that the $K^* \Delta^{++}$ analysis can be generalized to include an extended mass range at the Kπ vertex. Fig. 18 shows the results of the UCLA analysis of Trippe et al. of $K^+ p \to K^+ \pi^- \Delta^{++}$ at 7.3 GeV/c in which DP-OPE is used in a pole extrapolation analysis of the Chew-Low distribution to extract the s-wave Kπ interaction. The agreement of the relation $d\sigma/dm(K^+\pi^-) = 2\, d\sigma/dm(K^0\pi^0)$ supports the assumption of negli-

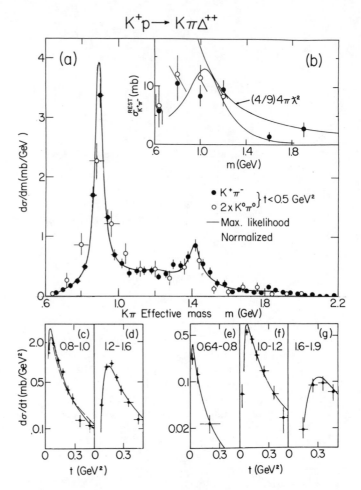

Fig. 18. $K^+p \rightarrow K\pi\Delta^{++}$ at 7.3 GeV/c from Trippe et al.[6] (a)
$d\sigma/dm(K\pi)$ for t<0.5 GeV^2. The solid curve here and those in
(c-g) below are calculated from the parameters resulting from
Fit B (t<0.5 GeV^2, m<1.9 GeV, see text) and are normalized to
the data thus masking a ~2.5σ difference between the calculated and experimental cross sections. The analogous curves for
Fit A (t<0.3 GeV^2, m<1.2 GeV), which has an overall χ^2 confidence level of 37%, fit the data well without normalization;
(b) $\sigma_{K^+\pi^-}^{rest}$ vs. m. Solid circles result from Fit B, open circles from Fit A. For m≲1.2 GeV, $\sigma_{K^+\pi^-}^{rest}$ represents the s-wave
$K^+\pi^-$ elastic scattering cross section. The curve labeled
$(4/9)4\pi\lambda^2$ is the unitarity limit. see text; (c-g) $d\sigma/dt$ for the
indicated m($K^+\pi^-$) selections. Broken curve in (c) is from the
same calculation as the curves in Fig. 8.

gible $T = 3/2$ Kπ interaction made in this analysis.

Trippe et al.[6] performed maximum likelihood and χ^2 minimization fits to $d^3\sigma/dtdmdM$ (see Sec. 5) independently for two different ranges of t and m. (Fit A: $t < 0.3$ GeV^2, $m < 1.2$ GeV and Fit B: $t < 0.5$ GeV^2, $m < 1.9$ GeV). In these fits the p-wave and d-wave Kπ interactions are assumed given by the K*(890) and K*(1400) Breit-Wigner amplitudes (a K*(1400) inelasticity of 0.5 is used). The parameters c and R_{N*} are fixed at Wolf's values (see Table I). R_{K*} and the non p- and d-wave cross section $\sigma^{rest}_{K^+\pi^-} = \sigma(m) - \sigma_p - \sigma_d$ at several values of m were left as variables.

Fit A has a χ^2 confidence level of 37%. The $\sigma^{rest}_{K^+\pi^-}$ values shown as the open circles in Fig. 18(b) and $R_{K*} = 1.0 \pm 0.5$ GeV^{-1} result from the fit. For Fit B, the confidence level drops to 0.5%, which is mainly accounted for by a cross section discrepancy due to the value of $R_{K*} = 2.3 \pm 0.5$ GeV^{-1}, needed to fit the t dependence out to $t = 0.5$ GeV^2. The $\sigma^{rest}_{K^+\pi^-}$ values for this fit are the solid circles in Fig. 18(b). It is found that the resulting $\sigma^{rest}_{K^+\pi^-}$ values are rather insensitive to changes in the fitting procedure because they are essentially determined in the fits with respect to $\sigma_p = (4/9)12\pi\lambda^2$ and $\sigma_d = (4/9)(.5)^2 \times 20\pi\lambda^2$ at the K*(890) and K*(1400) peaks, respectively.

Consider the $\sigma^{rest}_{K^+\pi^-}$ values in Fig. 18(b). For $m \lesssim 1.2$ GeV where the Kπ inelasticity is negligible and where only s-, p- and d-waves seem to be present, $\sigma^{rest}_{K^+\pi^-}$ is interpreted as the s-wave cross section. From the threshold value for Fit A, which is taken to be more reliable, Trippe et al.[6] obtain the T=1/2 s-wave Kπ scattering length as 0.34 ± 0.09 f. The point at 1.2 GeV is seen to meet the $4/9(4\pi\lambda^2)$ curve, indicating that the phase shift is $\sim 90°$ in this region. The resonant curve shown on the $\sigma^{rest}_{K^+\pi^-}$ points corresponds to the same calculation which pro-

duced the curves in Fig. 2c. As I indicated earlier in a
discussion of the moments, the Breit-Wigner s-wave assumption
does not seem quite correct, but it does give a rough agreement.

12.   INELASTIC $K\pi$ SCATTERING

In an attempt to measure the inelasticity for $K^+\pi^-$
scattering, Trippe et al.[6] have compared the spectra of the
missing mass above a peripherally produced Δ^{++} in reactions
of the type $K^+p \to \Delta^{++}x$. Shown in Fig. 19 are their spectra
for the final states $\Delta^{++}(K^0\pi^+\pi^-)$ and $\Delta^{++}(K^0\pi^0\pi^+\pi^-)$ compared
with the sum of the elastic and charge exchange reactions
$\Delta^{++}(K^0\bar{\pi^0})$. The solid curve corresponds to the dashed curve
in Fig. 18. Although there are several other inelastic
channels not plotted, it seems safe to conclude: (a) that
below 1.2 GeV the inelasticity is small; (b) the inelastic/
elastic ratio gets very large above 1.6 GeV and seems especially to be due to the $K3\pi$ reaction. This may be due to the
fact that 1.66 GeV is threshold for $K\pi \to K^*\rho$ and that the $K3\pi$
reaction is the first $K\pi$ inelastic channel which may proceed
through OPE. Above this threshold, the incoming K sees the
large pion cloud around the target π and the cross section
for this inelastic channel increases significantly.

As a means of testing whether π^-p inelastic cross sections may be in fact measured in this way, Colton et al.[23] have
compared $pp \to (p\pi^-)\Delta^{++}$, $pp \to (p\pi^-\pi^0)\Delta^{++}$, and $pp \to (n\pi^+\pi^-)\Delta^{++}$
at 6.6 GeV/c. Their observed ratios of $(p\pi^-\pi^0/p\pi^-)$ and
$(n\pi^+\pi^-/p\pi^-)$ are shown in Fig. 20 as a function of mass of the
systems and compared with the known on-mass-shell inelastic/
elastic π^-p ratios summarized by the shaded bands. The

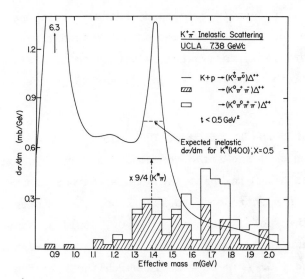

Fig. 19. $K^+\pi^-$ inelastic scattering from Trippe et al.[6]. Solid curve is identical to dashed curve in Fig. 18a. The histogram shows data for the two indicated reactions for the Δ^{++} and t<0.5 Gev^2 selections

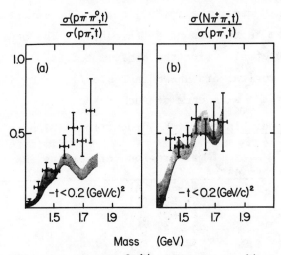

Mass   (GeV)

Fig. 20. Ratios $\sigma(pp \rightarrow p\pi^-\pi^0\Delta^{++})/\sigma(pp \rightarrow p\pi^-\Delta^{++})$ and $\sigma(pp \rightarrow n\pi^-\pi^+\Delta^{++})/\sigma(pp \rightarrow p\pi^-\Delta^{++})$ vs. mass of the non-Δ^{++} final-state system for $t(\Delta^{++})<0.2$ Gev^2 from Colton et al.[23]. Shaded bands represent summary of on-mass-shell cross sections $\sigma(\pi^-p \rightarrow \pi^-\pi^0p)/\sigma(\pi^-p \rightarrow \pi^-p)$ and $\sigma(\pi^-p \rightarrow n\pi^-\pi^+)/\sigma(\pi^-p \rightarrow \pi^-p)$.

agreement is generally good, and indicates that one may expect to be able, at low enough momentum transfer and with high
enough statistics, to eventually attain to complete multi-
channel partial wave analysis of $\pi\pi$ and πK scattering.

13.   SEARCH FOR K* BELOW Kπ THRESHOLD

Figure 21 shows the results of a Berkeley experiment
by Bland et al.[24] in which the bubble chamber was used as a
missing mass spectrometer to search for the existence of a K*
below Kπ threshold. Such a K*, if 0^+, would presumably decay
into K$\gamma\gamma$ and would appear among the two-prong events. Several
runs around 1 GeV/c were made in which the reaction (K$^+$p $\rightarrow$
p + missing mass) was studied. The missing mass for 4317
events is shown in the figure. The shaded events are those
with P_{proton} < 500 MeV/c. Seen are the large elastic peak
and, at higher mass, the K*(890) peak. The insert shows a
blowup of the region around Kπ threshold. The upper limits
set by Bland et al.[24] for the different runs and for the different mass regions are shown in Table II. They find no
evidence for the existence of such a K*.

Table II. Upper Limits for K$^*_S$ Production. (Bland et al.[24])

Incident laboratory momentum	μb/event	Mass region (Mev)	Upper limit to K$^*_S$ signal	
			all events (μb)	P_p 500<Mev/c (μb)
860 Mev/c	2.8	534-559 (A)	--	41
		559-584 (B)	62	45
		584-609 (C)	31	22
		609-634 (D)	26	22
960 Mev/c	4.9	534-559 (A)	--	58
		559-584 (B)	112	44
		584-609 (C)	39	28
		609-634 (D)	49	37
1.2 Gev/c	4.0	534-559 (A)	--	48
		559-584 (B)	68	23
		584-609 (C)	48	48
		609-634 (D)	40	36

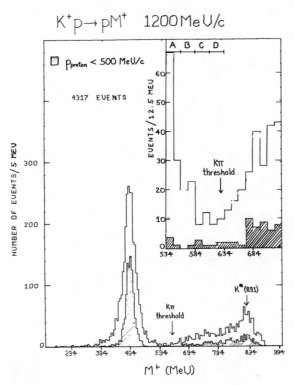

Fig. 21. Mass spectrum of M^+ in $K^+p \to pM^+$ from Bland et al.[24].

14.   CONCLUSIONS

The Durr-Pilkuhn vertex factors are seen to off-shell-correct the pole equations with a surprising degree of accuracy, thus giving us an extremely convenient functional form for pole extrapolation analyses.

The question of whether the difference in $K^+\pi^-$ and $K^o\pi^o$ moments in reactions (1a,b) for $m \gtrsim 1$ Gev is really evidence for $T = 3/2$ interaction, or whether the Deck production of $N^*(1400)$ is responsible, or whether there exists a duality in interpretation, is extremely important not only for an understanding of the KΠ interaction but also for strong

interaction dynamics in general. To this end, it will be
useful to compare the reactions

$$K^-p \rightarrow (K^-\pi^+)n$$
$$K^+n \rightarrow (K^0\pi^0)p$$

with reactions (1a,b).

Some elucidation of this problem has already resulted
from the analysis [8] of $pp \rightarrow p\pi^-\Delta^{++}$ which demonstrates that
even though there is considerable N*(1400) enhancement in the
$\pi^-\Delta^{++}$ mass spectrum for $m(p\pi^-)$ >1.6 GeV, the cross section
for these events is in excellent agreement with the OPE
expectation. This interesting result, if indeed an example
of a more general situation, would be expected to occur also
for related reactions

$$\pi^-p \rightarrow p\pi^-\rho^0$$
$$K^-p \rightarrow p\pi^-K^{*0}$$

where there occur A_1 and K*(1300) production. If the cross
section agreement is found to occur for these reactions also,
the result will be of fundamental importance in our understanding of the strong interaction dynamics of these processes. It has already been shown[12] that the πp CM angular
distributions are very similar to the corresponding on-shell
distributions. These results would suggest that the difference between $K^+\pi^-$ and $K^0\pi^0$ is due to a T = 3/2 Kπ interaction.

The above difficulty notwithstanding, the similarity
between reactions (1a,b) for $m \lesssim 1$ Gev suggests that in this
region, at least, a Kπ scattering interpretation is valid and
that $\delta_s^{1/2}$ does indeed increase smoothly from threshold and
reach $\sim 90°$ just above this region. This points to the exis-

tence of a broad s-wave T = 1/2 Kπ resonance centered at
∿ 1.1 - 1.2 GeV. The possible existence of such a state has
been mentioned earlier by Dalitz[25] on the basis of a quark
model discussion of other then-available 0^+ candidates.
Using the current best candidates for a 0^+ nonet, $\pi_v(1016)$,
$\eta_v(1070)$,[26] and $\eta_v'(730)$,[4] the Schwinger mass formula predicts $K_v(1100)$.

REFERENCES

*   Supported in part by the U. S. Atomic Energy Commission.

1.   Eugene Gellert, Gerald A. Smith, Stanley Wojcicki,
         Eugene Colton, Peter E. Schlein, and Harold K. Ticho,
         Phys. Rev. Letters 17, 884 (1966).

2.   B. C. Shen, G. Goldhaber, S. Goldhaber, and J. A.
         Kadyk, Phys. Rev. Letters 15, 731 (1965).

3.   Peter E. Schlein, Phys. Rev. Letters 19, 1052 (1967).

4.   Ernest Malamud and Peter E. Schlein, Phys. Rev.
         Letters 19, 1056 (1967).

5.   G. Bassompierre, et al., Study of Kππ Resonances Pro-
         duced in K^+p Interactions, CERN preprint 67-21 (sub-
         mitted to the Heidelberg International Conference on
         Elementary Particles, 1967).

6.   Thomas G. Trippe, Chih-Yung Chien, Ernest Malamud,
         Joel Mellema, Peter E. Schlein, William E. Slater,
         Donald H. Stork, and Harold K. Ticho, $K^+p \rightarrow K\pi\Delta^{++}$:
         OPE, Pole Extrapolation and the Kπ Interaction, Univer-
         sity of California, Los Angeles, Report No. UCLA-1024
         Rev. (to be published).

7.   C. Fu, A. Firestone, G. Goldhaber, G. H. Trilling, and
         B. C. Shen, The $K^+p \rightarrow K^+\pi^-\Delta^{++}$ Interaction at 4.6 and
         9 BeV/c, Lawrence Radiation Lab. Report No. UCRL-18201.

8.   Eugene Colton, Peter E. Schlein, Eugene Gellert, and
     Gerald A. Smith, pp $\to \Delta^{++} p \pi^-$: OPE, Pole Extrapolation
     and the Deck Effect, University of California, Los
     Angeles, Report No. UCLA-1023 Rev. (to be published).

9.   H. P. Dürr and H. Pilkuhn, Nuovo Cimento 40, 899 (1965).

10. See e.g., E. Ferrari and F. Selleri, Suppl. Nuovo
     Cimento 24, 453 (1962).

11. We use the metric in which t = $-\mu^2$ at the pole and is
     therefore positive in the physical region.

12. G. Wolf, Phys. Rev. Letters 19, 925 (1967), and private
     communication.

13. M. Ferro-Luzzi, et al., Nuovo Cimento 39, 417 (1965);
     R.° George, et al., Nuovo Cimento 49, 9 (1967).

14. J. C. Berlinghieri, et al., University of Rochester
     Report No. UR-875-218 (1967, unpublished).

15. Alain Verglas, Ph.D. thesis, Saclay, French Atomic
     Energy Commission Report No. CEA-R 3032 (1966, unpub-
     lished).

16. F. Schweingruber, et al., Phys. Rev. 166, 1317 (1968).

17. Edmund L. Berger, Eugene Gellert, Gerald A. Smith,
     Eugene Colton, and Peter E. Schlein, Phys. Rev. Letters
     20, 964 (1968).

18. R. Dolen, D. Horn, and C. Schmid, Phys. Rev. 166, 1768
     (1968).

19. G. F. Chew and A. Pignotti, Phys. Rev. Letters 20,
     1078 (1968).

20. P. L. Connolly, W. E. Ellis, P. V. C. Hough, D. J.
     Miller, T. W. Morris, C. Ouannes, R. S. Panvini, and
     A. M. Thorndike, Study of pp Interactions at 28.5 BeV/c
     in Two- and Four-Prong Final States, presented at the
     Third Topical Conference on Resonant Particles, at Ohio

University, Athens, Ohio, Nov. 22-24 (1967), and private communication.

21.   Z. M. Ma, G. A. Smith, R. J. Sprafka, E. Colton, and P. Schlein, The Reaction pp → pnπ^{+} : OPE and Pole Extrapolation (preprint, 1968).

22.   Ernest Malamud and Peter E. Schlein, Pole Extrapolation in πp → ππn and the Low Energy ππ Phase Shifts, University of California, Los Angeles, Report No. UCLA-1028

23.   Eugene Colton, Peter E. Schlein, Eugene Gellert, and Gerald A. Smith, Experimental Comparison Between On- and Off-Mass-Shell Inelasticities in π^{-}p Scattering, University of California, Los Angeles, Report No. UCLA-1027 (to be published).

24.   R. W. Bland, G. Goldhaber, B. H. Hall, and G. H. Trilling, A Search for a K* Below Kπ Threshold, Lawrence Radiation Laboratory Report No. UCRL-18206 (1968).

25.   R. H. Dalitz, Rapporteur Talks, Proceedings of the Oxford International Conference on Elementary Particles (1965), and the XIII International Conference on High-Energy Physics, Berkeley (1966).

26.   See e.g., the summary by A. H. Rosenfeld, et al., Rev. Mod. Phys. 39, 1 (1967).

METHOD FOR $\pi\pi$ OR $K\pi$ PHASE-SHIFT ANALYSIS*

Peter E. Schlein
University of California, Los Angeles, California
(Received 5 July 1967)

Based on the assumed dominance of one-pion exchange in the reaction

$$\pi^- + p \rightarrow \pi^- + \pi^+ + n, \qquad (1)$$

several analyses have been reported[1] in which the $T = 0$ s-wave $\pi\pi$ elastic-scattering phase shift (δ_s^0) was obtained over a range of $\pi\pi$ mass in the ρ region. These analyses generally fall into two classes: (i) those in which the effects of absorption are taken account of incompletely (or not at all), and (ii) those in which the analyses depend on the detailed validity of a theoretical treatment of the absorption. It is the purpose here to point out that the $\pi\pi$ phase shifts may be extracted from the data (at least in the region of the ρ resonance) without complete prior knowledge of the helicity amplitudes in Reaction (1), using therefore only a subset of the assumptions used in the absorption model,[2] all of which have observable consequences and which may be subjected to test. Furthermore, it is shown below that for data in a sufficiently narrow band of total center-of-mass energy E^* and production angle β (or momentum transfer t to the nucleon) in Reaction (1), empirical values of the helicity amplitudes may be extracted from the data. The arguments contained herein should apply equally to the reaction $\pi^+ p \rightarrow \pi^+ \pi^- N^{*++}$ and to the determination of the $K\pi$ phase shifts [at least in the $K^*(890)$ region] if the π-exchange dominated reaction $K^+ p \rightarrow K^+ \pi^- N^{*++}$ is used.

The fundamental assumption common to the one-pion-exchange models with and without absorption is that the amplitude, to reach the final state in (1) with given $\pi\pi$ relative orbital angular momentum l, can be factored into two parts, one of which is the amplitude for l-wave $\pi\pi$ scattering[3] $A_{\pi\pi}{}^l \sim \exp(i\delta_l) \sin\delta_l$. Thus we write $A_{\pi\pi}{}^l M_{l\mu}{}^{\lambda\lambda'}$ as the amplitude[4] to reach a final state containing a $\pi\pi$ system with internal angular momentum l and helicity μ and a nucleon with helicity λ from an initial state with nucleon helicity λ'. The helicity amplitudes $M_{l\mu}{}^{\lambda\lambda'}$ are in general functions of E^*, t, and the effective mass $m_{\pi\pi}$ of the $\pi\pi$ system. In the case of the one-pion-exchange Born amplitude without absorption, the $M_{l\mu}{}^{\lambda\lambda'}$ are well-defined, relatively real functions of these variables. The absorption model consists essentially of the detailed prescription for modifying the $M_{l\mu}{}^{\lambda\lambda'}$ from these well-known Born amplitudes. In the analysis proposed here, however, we consider the $M_{l\mu}{}^{\lambda\lambda'}$ as unknown parameters to be determined in fitting the data. We make only the tentative assumption (as in the absorption model) that their relative phases are not altered by the absorption; this point is discussed further below. The final-state $\pi\pi$ angular distribution in its rest frame can be written as

$$D(\hat{\pi}_{\text{out}}) = \sum_{\lambda'\lambda} | \sum_l A_{\pi\pi}{}^l \sum_\mu M_{l\mu}{}^{\lambda\lambda'} Y_l{}^\mu(\hat{\pi}_{\text{out}}) |^2 \, dt \, dm_{\pi\pi} \, d\Omega_{\hat{\pi}_{\text{out}}} \tag{2}$$

in which we assume production from an unpolarized target and sum over the final-state nucleon variable, and where the argument of the spherical harmonic $Y_l{}^\mu(\hat{\pi}_{\text{out}})$ is the outgoing π^- unit vector expressed in the $\pi\pi$ rest frame. Selecting a coordinate system in the $\pi\pi$ rest frame such that the $\hat{y}$ axis is along the normal to the production plane $\hat{n} \sim \hat{\pi}_{\text{in}} \times \vec{e}_z$, where $\vec{e}_z$ is a unit vector along the z axis which is taken to be the direction of motion of the $\pi\pi$ system, the consequence of parity conservation on the helicity amplitudes is the relation $M_{l,-\mu}{}^{-\lambda,-\lambda'} = (-1)^{\mu+\lambda+\lambda'} M_{l\mu}{}^{\lambda\lambda'}$, valid for any l.[5] This reduces the number of independent helicity amplitudes for each l from $4(2l+1)$ to $2(2l+1)$.

The $l = 0$ and 1 expansion of Eq. (2), appropriate to the experimental data[1] in the ρ region, can be simply expressed by considering the forms of the measurable $Y_L{}^M$ moments of $D(\hat{\pi}_{\text{out}})$. In writing these out, we consider the nucleon helicity-nonflip and -flip amplitudes for a given $\pi\pi$ helicity as the x and y components of a vector. Thus: $(M_{11}{}^{++}, M_{11}{}^{-+}) \equiv \vec{p}_1$, $(M_{1-1}{}^{++}, M_{1-1}{}^{-+}) \equiv \vec{p}_{-1}$, $(M_{10}{}^{++}, M_{10}{}^{-+}) \equiv \vec{p}_0$, and $(M_{00}{}^{++}, M_{00}{}^{-+}) \equiv \vec{s}$. With this notation the measured moments for data in the jth $\pi\pi$ mass bin have the forms

$$N = |A_{\pi\pi}{}^P|^2 \{ |\vec{p}_1|^2 + |\vec{p}_0|^2 + |\vec{p}_{-1}|^2 \} + |A_{\pi\pi}{}^S|^2 \{ |\vec{s}|^2 \}, \tag{3a}$$

$$N\langle Y_1{}^0 \rangle = 2(4\pi)^{-\frac{1}{2}} \operatorname{Re}(A_{\pi\pi}{}^S A_{\pi\pi}{}^{P*}) \{ \vec{p}_0 \cdot \vec{s} \}, \tag{3b}$$

$$N\langle \operatorname{Re} Y_1{}^1 \rangle = (4\pi)^{-\frac{1}{2}} \operatorname{Re}(A_{\pi\pi}{}^S A_{\pi\pi}{}^{P*}) \{ \vec{s} \cdot (\vec{p}_1 - \vec{p}_{-1}) \}, \tag{3c}$$

$$N\langle Y_2{}^0 \rangle = 2(20\pi)^{-\frac{1}{2}} |A_{\pi\pi}{}^P|^2 \{ |\vec{p}_0|^2 - \tfrac{1}{2}(|\vec{p}_1|^2 + |\vec{p}_{-1}|^2) \}, \tag{3d}$$

$$N\langle \operatorname{Re} Y_2{}^1 \rangle = (3/20\pi)^{\frac{1}{2}} |A_{\pi\pi}{}^P|^2 \{ \vec{p}_0 \cdot (\vec{p}_1 - \vec{p}_{-1}) \}, \tag{3e}$$

$$N\langle \operatorname{Re} Y_2{}^2 \rangle = (6/20\pi)^{\frac{1}{2}} |A_{\pi\pi}{}^P|^2 \{ -\vec{p}_1 \cdot \vec{p}_{-1} \}, \tag{3f}$$

where N is the intensity ($\pi\pi$ mass spectrum), and where we have suppressed the E^* and t dependence of the $\vec{p}_i$ and $\vec{s}$ vectors. Equations (3) are generalizations of the quantities[6] A_l used in conventional two-body scattering experiments and can be obtained experimentally for a discrete sample of events by evaluating[7]

$$N_j \langle Y_L^M \rangle_j = \sum_{i=1}^{N_j} Y_L^M (\theta_i, \varphi_i),$$

$$\delta(N_j \langle Y_L^M \rangle_j) \simeq N_j \delta\langle Y_L^M \rangle_j$$

$$= [\sum (Y_L^M)^2 - N_j \langle Y_L^M \rangle_j^2]^{\frac{1}{2}}, \qquad (4)$$

for the N_j events in the jth $m_{\pi\pi}$ bin. If we were performing a real-particle $\pi\pi$ scattering experiment describable by a plane-wave initial state e^{ikz}, the bracketed { } coefficients of $|A_{\pi\pi}^S|^2$ and $|A_{\pi\pi}^P|^2$ in Eq. (3a) and of $\mathrm{Re}(A_{\pi\pi}^S A_{\pi\pi}^{P*})$ and $|A_{\pi\pi}^P|^2$ in Eqs. (3b) and (3d) occur in the ratios of $1:3:\sqrt{3}:3$, respectively. In addition, $\langle Y_L^M \rangle = 0$ for $M \neq 0$. Here, however, all these coefficients are treated as unknown parameters.

Owing to the fact that the helicity amplitudes occur quadratically in the moment expressions for the quantities $N\langle Y_L^M \rangle$, averaging over E^* or t in any analysis destroys the relationships between the moments implied in the equations. Let us first consider an analysis in which such averages are made. It is expected that the helicity amplitudes depend very weakly on $m_{\pi\pi}$ compared, say, with the dependence on $m_{\pi\pi}$ of the resonant p-wave amplitude $A_{\pi\pi}^P$. Hence in the ρ region, or in general for a sufficiently small range of $m_{\pi\pi}$, helicity amplitudes may be assumed constant. (We consider below, however, how a moderate energy dependence may be allowed for and included in an analysis.) With this assumption, the entire $m_{\pi\pi}$ dependences of the $N\langle Y_L^M \rangle$ reside in the $\pi\pi$ scattering amplitudes. In this case, the following conditions result on the measurable $N\langle Y_L^M \rangle$ quantities of Eqs. (3): (a) $N\langle Y_2^0 \rangle$, $N\langle \mathrm{Re}(Y_2^1) \rangle$, and $N\langle \mathrm{Re}(Y_2^2) \rangle$ should have the same dependence on $m_{\pi\pi}$. (b) $N\langle Y_1^0 \rangle$ and $N\langle \mathrm{Re}(Y_1^1) \rangle$ should have the same dependence on $m_{\pi\pi}$. Note that (a) must be true even if the helicity amplitudes are not relatively real[8] and therefore tests the basic factorization assumption directly. However, (b) requires, in addition to the

factorization assumption, that $\vec{p}_0 \cdot \vec{s}$ and $\vec{s} \cdot (\vec{p}_1 - \vec{p}_{-1})$ be real. Thus, the success of (b) may be thought of as simultaneously testing both the factorization and the reality assumptions.

Agreement of experimental data with requirements (a) and (b) implies knowledge of the $m_{\pi\pi}$ dependences of $K_1 |A_{\pi\pi}^P|^2$, $K_2 \mathrm{Re}(A_{\pi\pi}^S A_{\pi\pi}^{P*})$, and $K_3 |A_{\pi\pi}^P|^2 + K_4 |A_{\pi\pi}^S|^2$, where K_1, K_2, K_3, and K_4 are unknown constants. Selection of a trial value for K_1 determines $A_{\pi\pi}^P$ as a function of $m_{\pi\pi}$.[9] (Note that in the ρ region $K_1 |A_{\pi\pi}^P|^2$ should have the dependence of a Breit-Wigner distribution without background and should provide a more reliable determination of the ρ parameters than a fit to the mass spectrum.) Subsequent selection of a trial value for K_2 then gives $A_{\pi\pi}^S$ as a function of $m_{\pi\pi}$.[10] K_1 and K_2 are determined by the requirement that some linear combination of these $|A_{\pi\pi}^P|^2$ and $|A_{\pi\pi}^S|^2$ fit the mass spectrum. In other words, for data at Q different $\pi\pi$ mass values, the determination of δ_S and δ_p at these Q energies is a $(Q-4)$-constraint problem. The resultant χ^2 probability is a test of the validity of the assumptions used. In the ρ region, an alternative fitting procedure could involve assuming a Breit-Wigner form for the ρ with E_ρ and Γ_ρ as free parameters. This would be a $(2Q-6)$-constraint fit. With the large number of constraints possible with even moderate statistics, it would also be possible to assume a second- (or even third-) order dependence of the multiplicative functions $\{\vec{p}_i, \vec{s}\}$ on $m_{\pi\pi}$. Thus, the fit could be extended over a larger range of $m_{\pi\pi}$.

Let us now consider that the experimental moments (3) have been obtained with sufficiently narrow E^* and t selections so that use may be made of the explicit functional dependence of the bracketed quantities in Eq. (3) and the helicity amplitude quantities $\vec{p}_i$ and $\vec{s}$ extracted from the data. Consider for purposes of illustration that δ_p and δ_s have been previously obtained from an analysis using E^*- and t-averaged data; in practice, however, they may also be variables in the fit along with the quantities $\vec{p}_i$ and $\vec{s}$ and any possible t dependence of δ_p and δ_s could be studied. Note that the functional form of the brackets in Eq. (3) is such that only dot products of the vectors occur. Thus the equations are invariant under rotations and reflections in the plane of the vectors and no generality is lost if we assume $\vec{s} = (|\vec{s}|, 0)$. In addition, the equations are in-

variant under the transformation $-\vec{p}_1 \rightarrow \vec{p}_{-1}$.
These invariances are due to the fact that no
polarizations are measured in the type of experiment discussed here. The following sev-
en quantities may be obtained from the exper-
imental $N\langle Y_L{}^M\rangle$ moments: $|\vec{s}|$, $|\vec{p}_0|$, $\vec{p}_0 \cdot \vec{s}$,
$|\vec{p}_1 - \vec{p}_{-1}|$, $(\vec{p}_1 - \vec{p}_{-1}) \cdot \vec{s}$, $|(\vec{p}_1 - \vec{p}_{-1}) - \vec{p}_0|$, and $(|\vec{p}_1|^2$
$+ |\vec{p}_{-1}|^2)$. There are seen to be five indepen-
dent variables[11] which determine the first six
experimental quantities and thus one constraint
exists between the experimental quantities.
The quantity $|\vec{p}_1|^2 + |\vec{p}_{-1}|^2$ simply requires the
vectors $\vec{p}_1$ and $\vec{p}_{-1}$ to originate at an arbitrary
point on a circle whose center is at the mid-
point of the vector $\vec{p}_1 - \vec{p}_{-1}$. Subject to the ambiguity in $\vec{p}_1$ and $\vec{p}_{-1}$ and the stated rotation
and reflection invariances, the helicity ampli-
tudes can be obtained as functions of E^* and
t, thereby allowing comparison with various
theoretical models.

An important test of the correctness of the
method of δ_S and δ_p determinations suggested here is whether or not independent analy-
ses at different E^* regions and in different
reactions will yield the same results. In par-
ticular, the reaction $\pi^+ p \rightarrow \pi^+\pi^- N^{+++}$ will be
of great interest in this respect, as it is known
that this reaction is dominated by $\rho^0 N^{+++}$ production via π exchange. This reaction is also
of interest in connection with the possibility
of utilizing the correlations[12] between the scattering angular distributions at the $\pi\pi$ vertex
and the $p\pi^+$ vertex. It is straightforward to
write down the joint distribution function starting from a form analogous to Eq. (2). Parity
conservation allows only correlation moments
of the form $N\langle \mathrm{Re}(Y_L{}^M)\mathrm{Re}(\mathcal{Y}_{\mathcal{L}}{}^{\mathfrak{M}})\rangle$ or $N\langle \mathrm{Im}(Y_L{}^M)$
$\times \mathrm{Im}(\mathcal{Y}_{\mathcal{L}}{}^{\mathfrak{M}})\rangle$ to occur in this joint distribution
function. There are 16 such independent mo-
ments all of which must have the $m_{\pi\pi}$ depen-
dence of $|A_{\pi\pi}{}^P|^2$ and ten independent moments
which must have the $m_{\pi\pi}$ dependence of $\mathrm{Re}(A_{\pi\pi}{}^S$
$\times A_{\pi\pi}{}^{P*})$. These arguments apply equally to
the use of the production reaction $K^+ p \rightarrow K^* N^{+++}$
and the study of $K\pi$ scattering.

Part of this work was done while the author
was a visitor at the Centre d'Etudes Nucléaires
de Saclay. He is grateful to J. Meyer for the
hospitality extended. Helpful comments by
J. D. Jackson and M. Jacob are also appreciated.

---

*Work supported in part by the U.S. Atomic Energy
Commission.

[1] L. Durand, III, and Y. T. Chiu, Phys. Rev. Letters
14, 329, 680(E) (1965); G. Wolf, Phys. Letters 19, 328
(1965); L. Jacobs, University of California Radiation
Laboratory Report No. UCRL-16877, 1966 (to be published); L. W. Jones et al., Phys. Letters 21, 590
(1966); Myron Bander and Gordon L. Shaw, Phys. Rev.
155, 1675 (1967); D. Griffiths and R. J. Jabbur, Phys.
Rev. 157, 1371 (1967); L. J. Gutay et al., Phys. Rev.
Letters 18, 142 (1967); W. D. Walker et al., Phys.
Rev. Letters 18, 630 (1967); J. P. Baton and J. Re-
gnier, Nuovo Cimento 36, 1149 (1965).

[2] K. Gottfried and J. D. Jackson, Nuovo Cimento 34,
735 (1964); L. Durand, III, and Y. T. Chiu, Phys. Rev.
Letters 12, 627 (1964); 13, 45(E) (1964); Phys. Rev. 139,
B646 (1965). M. H. Ross and G. L. Shaw, Phys. Rev.
Letters 12, 627 (1964); Myron Bander and Gordon L.
Shaw, Phys. Rev. 139, B956 (1965).

[3] We consider δ_I here as an effective phase shift to be
empirically determined as a function of momentum
transfer t. The observed (Ref. 1) Breit-Wigner shape
of the ρ peak in the $\pi\pi$ mass spectrum of Reaction (1)
and its weak dependence on t (if any) argue that the use
of $\sin\delta$ for the magnitude of $A_{\pi\pi}{}^l$ is a good approximation. See also Ref. 4. The near absence of events with
4π mass less than 1 GeV in the final state $n\pi^+\pi^-\pi^-\pi^-$
[S. U. Chung et al., Lawrence Radiation Laboratory Report No. UCRL-16881 (revised), 1967 (unpublished)]
supports the assumption of no inelasticity in the ρ region.

[4] Note here that any multiplicative off-mass-shell ef-
fects on $A_{\pi\pi}{}^l$ as, for example, the $(q_{\mathrm{off}}/q_{\mathrm{on}})^l$ factor
suggested by F. Selleri [Phys. Letters 3, 76 (1962)]
would be included in our definition of the $M_{l_\mu}{}^{\lambda\lambda'}$.

[5] M. Jacob and G. C. Wick, Ann. Phys. (N.Y.) 7, 404
(1959).

[6] The A_l's are defined by the expansion $d\sigma/d\Omega = \lambda^2 \sum_l A_l P_l$.

[7] φ is the conventional Treiman-Yang angle and θ is
the $\pi\pi$ rest frame scattering angle using the helicity direction and not the direction as the z axis. For discussions of the validity of these moment expressions, see
P. E. Schlein et al., Phys. Rev. Letters 11, 167 (1963),
and P. M. Dauber, thesis, University of California,
Los Angeles, 1966 (unpublished).

[8] If the $\vec{p}_i$ and $\vec{s}$ are not real, then the moments $N\langle Y_1{}^M\rangle$
and $N\langle Y_1{}^M\rangle$ in Eq. (3) have the forms $\sim |A_{\pi\pi}{}^P|^2 |\{\}|^2$ and
$\sim \mathrm{Re}(A_{\pi\pi}{}^S A_{\pi\pi}{}^{P*})$ $\mathrm{Re}\{\} + \mathrm{Im}(A_{\pi\pi}{}^S A_{\pi\pi}{}^{P*})$ $\mathrm{Im}\{\}$, respectively. In terms of the analysis described below, this
means that if averages are not made over E^* and t,
the moments $N\langle Y_1{}^M\rangle$ can be expressed as $\sim \sin\delta_p \sin\delta_S$
$\times |\{\}| \cos[\delta_p - (\delta_S + K)]$ and δ_S can still be determined to
within the unknown additive constant K, which is the
phase of $\{\}$.

[9] If the p wave is resonant, as it is in both the $\pi\pi$ and
$K\pi$ interactions, the association of the peak in $N\langle Y_1{}^M\rangle$
with $\delta_p = 90°$ determines K_1, and the Wigner condition
of counter-clockwise rotation with increasing energy
serves to uniquely determine δ_p at each $m_{\pi\pi}$ value.

[10] Actually, knowledge of $\mathrm{Re}(A_{\pi\pi}{}^S A_{\pi\pi}{}^{P*})$ and $A_{\pi\pi}{}^P$
yields, in general, two such solutions for $A_{\pi\pi}{}^S$. This
twofold ambiguity, as well as the determination of K_2,
should be resolved in the fit to the mass spectrum.

[11]These may be taken as $|\bar{s}|$, $|\vec{p}_0|$, $\theta_{s,\,p_0}$ (the angle between $\bar{s}$ and $\vec{p}_0$), $|\vec{p}_1-\vec{p}_{-1}|$, and $\theta_{p_1-p_{-1},\,s}$ (the angle between $\bar{s}$ and $\vec{p}_1-\vec{p}_{-1}$).

[12]See H. Pilkuhn and B. E. Y. Svensson, Nuovo Cimento 38, 518 (1965), who include references to earlier

work. The effects of absorption on correlation moments are discussed by B. E. Y. Svensson, Nuovo Cimento 39, 667 (1965); J. T. Donohue, thesis, University of Illinois, 1967 (unpublished); and J. D. Jackson et al., Phys. Rev. 139, B428 (1965).

$\pi\pi$ PHASE-SHIFT ANALYSIS FROM 600 TO 1000 MeV*

Ernest Malamud and Peter E. Schlein
University of California, Los Angeles, California
(Received 16 August 1967)

A method[1] has been proposed (referred to hereafter as I) for extracting the $\pi\pi$ elastic scattering phase shifts from data on $\pi N \to \pi\pi N$. It is shown in I that complete prior knowledge of the helicity amplitudes is not necessary in the analysis. Although some of these become additional free parameters in fitting the data, a large number of constraints remain which test the validity of the model. We present here an analysis of this type for $\pi\pi$ effective mass $0.6 < m_{\pi\pi} < 1.0$ GeV and $\cos\theta_{\text{c.m.}} > 0.9$ (nucleon momentum transfer $t \lesssim 0.175$ GeV^2), using a sample of data with beam momenta 2.1-3.2 GeV/c compiled from several laboratories[2]:

$$\pi^- + p \to \pi^- + \pi^+ + n \quad (6740 \text{ events}), \qquad (1)$$

$$\pi^- + p \to \pi^- + \pi^0 + p \quad (3656 \text{ events}), \qquad (2)$$

where the numbers of events are those remaining after the $m_{\pi\pi}$ and $\theta_{\text{c.m.}}$ selection. The detailed analysis, described below, is concerned mainly with Reaction (1), with Reaction (2) used to obtain independent information on the $T = 2$ s-wave interaction. Aside from demonstrating that the data satisfy well the tests suggested in I, the $T = 0$ s-wave phase shift ($\delta_s{}^0$) is shown to increase from ~60° to ~90° in the range $600 < m_{\pi\pi} \lesssim 730$. For 730 MeV $< m_{\pi\pi}$, $\delta_s{}^0$ most likely continues to increase, implying the existence of a $T = 0$ scalar meson $\sigma(730)$.

We show in Fig. 1 the spherical harmonic moments $\langle Y_l{}^0 \rangle$ of the $\pi_{\text{out}}{}^-$ angular distribution in the $\pi\pi$ rest frame of Reaction (1) for $l \leq 10$. As explained in I, the coordinate system used has its z axis along the direction of motion of the $\pi\pi$ system for reasons of simplifying the extraction of the helicity amplitudes in the subsequent analysis.[3] For both Reactions (1) and (2) (similar to Fig. 1, but not shown), small but significant (negative) moments exist for

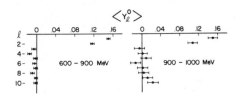

FIG. 1. Moments $\langle Y_l{}^0 \rangle$ of the outgoing π^- in the $\pi\pi$ rest frame of $\pi^- p \to \pi^- \pi^+ n$ with $\cos\theta_{\text{c.m.}} > 0.9$. The polar axis is the helicity axis of the $\pi\pi$ system. The moments are separately given for $0.6 < m_{\pi\pi} < 0.9$ and $0.9 < m_{\pi\pi} < 1.0$ GeV.

l as high as 8. We take these to be due to πN^* background[4] but henceforth ignore their presence compared with the large $l = 1, 2$ moments. As in earlier analyses,[5] we assume that only s- and p-wave scattering need be considered for the $\pi\pi$ interaction in this region.

The moments $N\langle Y_1{}^m \rangle$ and $N\langle Y_2{}^m \rangle$ (N is the $\pi\pi$ effective-mass spectrum) evaluated[6] every 20 MeV for $600 < m_{\pi\pi} < 1000$ MeV are given in Fig. 2 for Reactions (1) and (2). As shown in Eqs. (3a)-(3f) of I, these quantities have a dependence on the effective $\pi\pi$-scattering amplitude functions which is determined only by l. Thus, $N\langle Y_1{}^m \rangle \sim \{\ \} \text{Re}(A_{\pi\pi}{}^S A_{\pi\pi}{}^{P*})$ and $N\langle Y_2{}^m \rangle \sim \{\ \}|A_{\pi\pi}{}^P|^2$, where the brackets $\{\ \}$ denote functions of the helicity-amplitude vectors (defined in I) $\vec{p}_1$, $\vec{p}_0$, $\vec{p}_{-1}$, and $\bar{s}$. To the extent that these bracket quantities can be considered independent of $m_{\pi\pi}$, the data in Fig. 2 directly display the $m_{\pi\pi}$ dependence of the scattering-amplitude functions shown; the more rapidly varying the phase shifts, the better this approximation. Dirict tests of the fundamental factorization and reality assumptions of the formalism in I are that $N\langle Y_1{}^0 \rangle$ and $N\langle \text{Re}Y_1{}^1 \rangle$ have the same $m_{\pi\pi}$ dependence and that $N\langle Y_2{}^0 \rangle \sim N\langle \text{Re}Y_2{}^1 \rangle \sim N\langle \text{Re}Y_2{}^2 \rangle \sim$ (p-wave Breit-Wigner). Applying

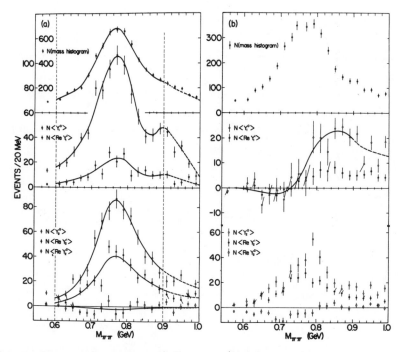

FIG. 2. Mass histograms (N) and moments $N \langle Y_l^m \rangle$ for (a) $\pi^- \pi^+ n$ and (b) $\pi^- \pi^0 p$ data with $\cos \theta_{c.m.} > 0.9$. Only the moments $N \langle Y_1^0 \rangle$ for $\pi^- \pi^0 p$ were used in the fits. The curves are calculated from the "Up-Up" solution; for the three moments $N \langle Y_2^m \rangle$, curves are those of a single Breit-Wigner function and differ only by multiplicative factors. The curves on N and $N \langle Y_1^m \rangle$ have been drawn smoothly to remove structure due to the fluctuations in δ_S seen in Fig. 3(d). Above 900 MeV the curves are drawn dashed to reflect the fact that the over-all fit is poor in this region.

these tests to the $\pi^+ \pi^- n$ data in Fig. 2(a), we find acceptable χ^2 confidence levels of 55 and 7 % for the $l = 1$ and $l = 2$ tests, respectively. For the $\pi^- \pi^0 p$ data, we find 98 and <0.01 %, respectively; excluding the $N \langle \mathrm{Re} Y_2^2 \rangle$ data from the $l = 2$ test improves the fit to CL = 2 %. This aspect of the $\pi^- \pi^0 p$ data suggests the presence of two exchange components (π and ω) which contribute differently to the $m = 0$ and $m = \pm 1$ ρ helicity states.

For purposes of fitting Eqs. (3) of I to the data, the $\pi^+ \pi^- n$ events were divided into three regions of $\cos \theta_{c.m.}$ containing approximately equal numbers of events (see Table II). There are $3 \times 20 \times 6 = 360$ independent $N \langle Y_l^m \rangle$ data points between 600 and 1000 MeV, in addition to the 20 moments[7] $N \langle Y_1^0 \rangle$ for the $\pi^- \pi^0 p$ events in Fig.

2(b). The $\pi^+ \pi^-$ elastic-scattering amplitudes are assumed to have the form[8] $A_{\pi^+ \pi^-}^S = \frac{1}{3} A(\delta_S^0) + \frac{1}{6} A(\delta_S^2)$ and $A_{\pi^+ \pi^-}^P = \frac{1}{2} A(\delta_p)$, where $A(\delta_l T) = \exp(i \delta_l T) \sin \delta_l T$. δ_S^0, δ_S^2, and δ_p were assumed independent of t (fits performed independently for each of the $\cos \theta_{c.m.}$ regions yielded phase shifts which were compatible with one another; thus the present data do not require a t dependence of these phase shifts). δ_S^0 was assumed unknown at each of the 20 $m_{\pi \pi}$ intervals. δ_S^2 was assumed unknown at seven different $m_{\pi \pi}$ values. δ_p was given by a p-wave Breit-Wigner amplitude[9] with $\cot \delta_p = [m_\rho^2 - m_{\pi \pi}^2][1 + (q/q_\rho)^2] / [2 m_\rho \Gamma_\rho (q/q_\rho)^3]$, where q_ρ and q are the $\pi \pi$ c.m. decay momenta for $\pi \pi$ systems of mass m_ρ and $m_{\pi \pi}$, respectively, and m_ρ and Γ_ρ are variables in the fit. The six indepen-

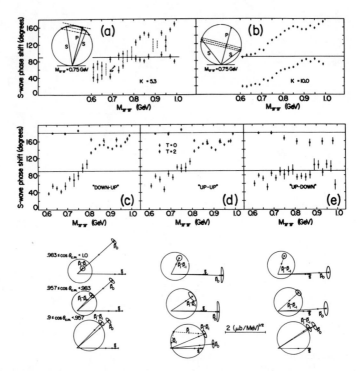

FIG. 3. (a), (b) Schematic diagrams showing how ambiguities in $\delta_S{}^0$ arise. δ_S is calculated from the moments $N\langle Y_1{}^0\rangle$ of Fig. 2(a) for the two indicated trial values of K in $N\langle Y_1{}^0\rangle = K\,\mathrm{Re}(A_{\pi\pi}{}^{S}A_{\pi\pi}{}^{P*})$. The unitarity circles show the projections of the complex S vectors on P at $m_{\pi\pi} = 750$ MeV. For $K = 5.3$ there exists poor separation between the two δ_S values at many $m_{\pi\pi}$ values, as demonstrated by the dotted lines. At 710 MeV the projection on P is 2σ outside the circle. (c)–(e) $\delta_S{}^0$, $\delta_S{}^2$, and the helicity-amplitude vectors for the solutions discussed in the text.

dent helicity-amplitude quantities discussed in I, namely $|\vec{s}|$, $|\vec{p}_0|$, $\theta_{\vec{p}_0,\vec{s}}$, $|\vec{p}_1 - \vec{p}_{-1}|$, $\theta_{\vec{p}_1 - \vec{p}_{-1},\vec{s}}$, and $(|\vec{p}_1|^2 + |\vec{p}_{-1}|^2)$, were assumed unknown in each of the three $\cos\theta_{\mathrm{c.m.}}$ regions, yielding 18 additional free parameters. $\{\vec{s}\cdot\vec{p}_0\}_{\pi^-\pi^0 p}$ was also a free parameter.

To demonstrate the nature of the $\delta_S{}^0$ ambiguities expected in the fits, we show in Figs. 3(a) and 3(b) the values of $\delta_S{}^0$ (we ignore $\delta_S{}^2$ for this purpose) obtained from the $N\langle Y_1{}^0\rangle$ data of Fig. 2(a) for two assumed trial values of the multiplicative helicity amplitude factor (call it K) in Eq. (3b) of I. The value $K = 5.3$ used in Fig. 3(a) is close to the preferred value in the actual fits. We refer to the set of larger δ_S values for all $m_{\pi\pi}$ as the "Up-Up"

branch and the set of smaller δ_S values as the "Down-Down" branch; the proximity of the two branches for small K also yields in this case the cross-over branches "Up-Down" and "Down-Up" as possible solutions.

Starting values for the χ^2-minimization search program[10] were chosen to correspond to the possible classes of solutions illustrated in Figs. 3(a) and 3(b) for a large range of K. These choices excluded rapid changes of $\delta_S{}^0$ with $m_{\pi\pi}$ which would result from jumping back and forth between the branches. Three of the four possible branches are obtained as convergence points (the "Down-Down" solution is never found). The resulting fits are summarized in Table I and the phase shifts and helicity-amplitude

Table I. Phase-shift solutions.

Solution	$m_{\pi\pi}$ range (GeV)	$m_{\pi\pi}$ dependence of $|\vec{s}|^2$, $|\vec{p}_i|^2$		χ^2	Constraints	Confidence level (%)	m_ρ (MeV)	Γ_ρ (MeV)
		Form[a]	Change, 0.6-1.0 GeV (%)					
"Down-Up"	0.6 - 0.9	constant	...	240	244	56	767±3	152±7
	0.6 - 1.0	constant	...	378	332	4	767±3	150±7
		$1-0.2\Delta-0.1\Delta^2$	-8	378	330	3	769±5	149±8
"Up-Up"	0.6 - 0.9	constant[b]	...	232	244	70	767±2	149±5
	0.6 - 1.0	constant	...	372	332	6	766±2	153±5
		$1-0.3\Delta-\Delta^2$	-16	370	330	6	769±3	157±7
"Up-Down"	0.6 - 0.9	constant	...	258	244	26	762±2	139±6
	0.6 - 1.0	constant	...	441	332	<0.01	761±2	136±6
		$1-\Delta-2.6\Delta^2$	-47	389	330	1	771±4	153±7

[a]$\Delta = m_{\pi\pi} - 0.75$ GeV.
[b]Accepting the validity of the "Up-Up" solution, the parameters of this fit should be the most reliable determination.

vectors for the best confidence limit fits for 600-1000 MeV shown in Figs. 3(c)-3(e) (confidence limits 4, 6, and 1%, respectively). It is important to note, however, that for all three solutions, neither the δ_S values nor the vectors $\vec{p}_i$, $\vec{s}$ obtained in the 600- to 900-MeV fits are significantly altered when the 900- to 1000-MeV data are added to the fit. However, the confidence limits decrease considerably, indicating that the formalism may be showing signs of breaking down when the fits are extended over the full 600- to 1000-MeV range. The "Down-Up" and "Up-Up" solutions are found to be extremely insensitive to the inclusion of the quadratic $m_{\pi\pi}$ dependence of $|\vec{s}|^2$ and $|\vec{p}_i|^2$ (shown in Table I) in the fit, whereas the confidence limit for the "Up-Down" solution improves from <0.01 to 1%; neither the phase-shifts nor the helicity-amplitude vectors change significantly in this process, however.

As shown in Figs. 3(c)-3(e), the three solutions have in common that $\delta_S^0 \sim 90°$ in the region $m_{\pi\pi} \sim 750$ MeV, a result which is thus independent of the following discussion. The "Down-Up" and "Up-Up" solutions differ essentially in their δ_S^0 values for $m_{\pi\pi} < 750$ MeV and in their helicity amplitudes. The smaller average contribution to the mass spectrum of the "Down-Up" solution in this $m_{\pi\pi}$ range causes $|\vec{s}|$ to be larger, resulting in $\theta_{p_0, s} \sim 45°$ in or-

der to retain approximately the same value for $\vec{p}_0 \cdot \vec{s}$. Since the absorption model predicts the ratio of nucleon helicity-flip/nonflip amplitudes to be the same for production of a zero-helicity $\pi\pi$ system of any l wave,[11] the "Up-Up" solution is preferred over the "Down-Up" solution on this basis.

The "Up-Up" and "Up-Down" solutions are nearly identical for $m_{\pi\pi} \lesssim 790$ MeV. Above this energy δ_S^0 increases fairly rapidly for the former solution while for the latter solution it remains near 90° up to 1000 MeV. Since for δ_S^0 slowly varying, the results of a fit are most sensitive to false assumptions concerning the $m_{\pi\pi}$ dependence of $|\vec{p}_i|^2$ and $|\vec{s}|^2$, it may be unreliable to rule out the "Up-Down" solution either on the basis of the large $\theta_{p_0, s}$ in Fig. 3(e) or because of the seemingly excessive fall-off of the $m_{\pi\pi}$ dependence of $|\vec{p}_i|^2$ and $|\vec{s}|^2$ shown in Table I for this solution. However, a relatively constant s-wave $\pi\pi$ cross section from 600 to 1000 MeV is not compatible with the experimental results of Corbett et al.,[12] Strugalski et al.,[13] and Wahlig et al.,[14] who present $\pi^0\pi^0$ mass spectra all of which show a significant drop-off in this region (although Wahlig et al. point out that uncertain background contributions may be in part responsible for their results).

For the preferred "Up-Up" solution, δ_S^0 passes through 90° at $m_{\pi\pi} \sim 730$ MeV implying the existence of a scalar meson $\sigma(730)$. The "Up-Up" solution for $600 < m_{\pi\pi} < 900$ MeV is not well fitted by a Breit-Wigner distribution, however, but requires $\cot\delta_S{}^0$ to be a more complex function of $m_{\pi\pi}$ with $d\cot\delta/dm_{\pi\pi}$ increasing as $\delta_S{}^0$ passes through 90° (the slope at the 90° point corresponds to $\Gamma \sim 150$ MeV). This fact, our large value ($\sim 60°$) of $\delta_S{}^0$ at 600 MeV, the value of $\delta_S{}^0 - \delta_S{}^2 = \pm(66 \pm 13)°$ at the K-meson mass deduced from $K \to 2\pi$ decay,[15,16] plus the absence of structure observed in $\pi\pi$ mass spectra between 400 and 600 MeV together suggest that $\delta_S{}^0$ is large ($\sim 60°-90°$ or so) throughout this region, perhaps being due to the simultaneous existence of the $\sigma(\sim 400)$ meson.

The measured helicity amplitude quantities are shown in Table II for the preferred "Up-Up" solution, normalized to unit $\cos\theta_{c.m.}$ interval, such that

$$d^2\sigma/dm_{\pi\pi}d\cos\theta_{c.m.}$$

$$= |A_{\pi\pi}{}^S|^2\{|\vec{s}|^2\} + A_{\pi\pi}{}^P|^2\{\sum_i|\vec{p}_i|^2\} \ \mu b/\text{MeV}. \quad (3)$$

In evaluating these numbers we use an approximate track length for the event sample of 5.3 events/μb ($\pm 10\%$ possible systematic uncertainty). Thus the $|\vec{s}|^2$ values of Table II can be used to predict $d^2\sigma/dm_{\pi\pi}d\cos\theta_{c.m.} = (|\vec{s}|^2/18) \times |\sin\delta_S{}^0 \exp(i\delta_S{}^2) - \sin\delta_S{}^2 \exp(i\delta_S{}^2)|^2 \ \mu b/\text{MeV}$ for the reaction $\pi^-p \to \pi^0\pi^0n$ near ~ 2.7 GeV/c, the average π^- beam momentum for our sample.

As discussed in I, the quantities in columns 4-7 of Table II may be compared with the ratios $1:3:\sqrt{3}:3$ expected for a real particle plane-wave initial state scattering experiment. The entries in columns 4-6 are seen to agree fairly well with these ratios, which is remarkable in view of the possible distortions due to absorp-

tion and the virtual nature of the exchanged pion. The similarity between the $\delta_S{}^0$ solutions presented here and those of earlier analyses[5] which ignored the effects of absorption must be related to this agreement. $|\vec{p}_0| - \frac{1}{2}(|\vec{p}_1|^2 + |\vec{p}_{-1}|^2)$ is most strongly affected by the absorption; the last column shows how the intensity ratio of ρ helicity states $(m = \pm 1)/(m = 0)$ varies with momentum transfer. A $\pi\pi$ phase-shift analysis[17] using the reaction $\pi^+p \to \pi^+\pi^-N^{*++}$ yields the same three $\delta_S{}^0$ solutions presented in this paper and therefore lends great support to the assumption that we are actually measuring properties of the $\pi\pi$ system rather than properties of the reaction as a whole.

We wish to express our appreciation to the groups who permitted us to use their data in this analysis and particularly to L. Jacobs, J. Kirz, and D. Miller (Berkeley); W. Selove (Pennsylvania-Saclay); F. Loeffler, D. Miller, and G. Tautfest (Purdue); and W. A. Cooper (Argonne-Toronto-Wisconsin) for their help.

*Work supported in part by the U.S. Atomic Energy Commission.

[1]Peter E. Schlein, preceding Letter [Phys. Rev. Letters 19, 1052 (1967)].

[2]The following laboratories and collaborations have generously contributed their data to this analysis: Argonne-Toronto-Wisconsin [D. R. Clear et al., Nuovo Cimento 49A, 399 (1967)], Pennsylvania-Saclay [V. Hagopian et al., Phys. Rev. 145, 1128 (1966); V. Hagopian and Y. Pan, Phys. Rev. 152, 1183 (1966)], Purdue [D. H. Miller et al., Phys. Rev. 153, 1423 (1967)], and Lawrence Radiation Laboratory [L. Jacobs, University of California Radiation Laboratory Report No. UCRL-16877, 1966 (unpublished)]. The average beam momentum for the entire sample is 2.69 GeV/c.

[3]The y axis is taken, as usual, to lie along the normal to the production plane $\hat{n} \sim \hat{\pi}_{in} \times \vec{e}_z$.

[4]The z-direction cosine of $\hat{\pi}_{out}{}^-$ in the coordinate system used is identical to the "longitudinal decay co-

Table II. Helicity quantities for the "Up-Up" solution.

$\cos\theta_{c.m.}$ interval	Approximate t interval (GeV^2)	No. of events 600-1000 MeV (600-900 MeV)	$|\vec{s}|^2$	$\Sigma|\vec{p}_i|^2$	$\vec{p}_0 \cdot \vec{s}$	$|\vec{p}_0|^2 - \frac{1}{2}(|\vec{p}_1|^2 + |\vec{p}_{-1}|^2)$	$\frac{|\vec{p}_1|^2 + |\vec{p}_{-1}|^2}{|\vec{p}_0|^2}$
						(μb/MeV)	
0.900-0.957	0.090-0.175	2225 (1894)	38± 5	132± 4	54± 4	51± 4	0.69±0.05
0.957-0.983	0.045-0.090	2224 (1940)	101±11	287±11	146± 9	174±10	0.35±0.03
0.983-1.000	0.010-0.045	2291 (2003)	166±21	448±18	246±16	324±16	0.23±0.03
0.900-1.000	0.010-0.175	6740 (5837)	76± 5	226± 5	110± 4	129± 4	0.40±0.03

sine" which scales linearly along a line of constant $\pi\pi$ mass on a Dalitz plot. Background due to crossing N^* bands will appear as localized distortions of the distribution due to $\pi\pi$ scattering alone. This situation becomes aggravated when several discrete beam momenta are used and can lead to the appearance of higher order moments.

[5]See Ref. 1 of the preceding Letter. L. Jacobs has a more complete summary of work on this subject. See also A. Rosenfeld et al., Rev. Mod. Phys. 39, 1 (1967).

[6]In the evaluation of these moments, we use the formula

$$N\langle Y_l^m\rangle = \sum_{i=1}^{N} Y_l^m (\hat{\pi}_{\text{out}}^{-})_i$$

and $\delta[N\langle Y_l^m\rangle] = \{[\sum (Y_l^m)^2 - N\langle Y_l^m\rangle^2][1+(2/\pi N)^{1/2}]\}^{1/2}$. We thank Derek Hudson for valuable discussions concerning this error expression. In evaluating the moments we find no evidence for the presence of any illegal moments $\langle\text{Im}\,Y_l^m\rangle$.

[7]The decision to use $N\langle Y_1^0\rangle$ and not $N\langle\text{Re}\,Y_1^1\rangle$ for this purpose was based on the assumption that ω exchange would contribute less to $m=0$ helicity states of the ρ than to the $m=\pm1$ states. The observed good compatibility between the moments $\langle Y_1^0\rangle$ and $\langle\text{Re}\,Y_1^1\rangle$ for $\pi^-\pi^0 p$ somewhat obscures the wisdom of this choice, however.

[8]See Refs. 4 and 5 of the preceding Letter.

[9]J. D. Jackson, Nuovo Cimento 34, 1644 (1964).

[10]Note that in constructing the χ^2, the strongly correlated quantities $N\langle Y_l^m\rangle$ are not used, but rather the quantities N and $\langle Y_l^m\rangle$. The searches were performed using the Berkeley program MINFUN; see W. E. Humphrey, Alverez Group Programmers Note No. P-6, 1962 (unpublished).

[11]We thank E. Abers and M. Parkinson for helpful discussions concerning this point.

[12]I. F. Corbett, C. J. S. Damerell, N. Middlemas, D. Newton, A. B. Clegg, W. S. C. Williams, and A. S. Carroll, Phys. Rev. 156, 1451 (1967).

[13]Z. S. Strugalski, I. V. Chuvilo, I. A. Ivanovska, L. S. Okhrimenko, B. Niczyporuk, I. Kanarek, B. Stowinski, and Z. Jabłonski; quoted by G. Goldhaber in Proceedings of the Thirteenth International Conference on High-Energy Physics, Berkeley, 1966 (University of California Press, Berkeley, California, 1967), p. 108.

[14]M. Wahlig, E. Shibata, D. Gordon, D. Frisch, and I. Mannelli, Phys. Rev. 147, 941 (1966).

[15]T. D. Lee and C. S. Wu, Ann. Rev. Nucl. Sci. 16, 530 (1966).

[16]δ_s^2 is determined to be small throughout the region considered in our analysis because of the characteristic interference with the ρ shown in Fig. 2(b) for $\pi^-\pi^0 p$, although it should be commented that the fits are rather insensitive to its inclusion; the absence of any explicit constraint on $\{\vec{s}\cdot\vec{p}_0\}_{\pi^-\pi^0 p}$ in the fits implies that the quoted errors on δ_s^2 in Fig. 3 may be somewhat underestimated.

[17]E. Malamud, P. E. Schlein, T. G. Trippe, D. Brown, and G. Gidal, in Proceedings of the International Conference on Elementary Particles, Heidelberg, Germany, 1967 (to be published).

K^* SPECTRUM AND DIFFRACTION DISSOCIATION EFFECTS (INCLUDING A_1)

Gerson Goldhaber

Department of Physics and Lawrence Radiation Laboratory
University of California, Berkeley, California

June 1968

My talk might be entitled "A Look at Bosons in a Strange Light, " by which I mean I shall concentrate on K^*'s. In this paper I will discuss the following:

By now SU(3) and its classification of particles into multiplets is very well established, and we all know and accept the scheme described by Gell-Mann and Ne'eman. For instance, we have an isovector, the π, two isosinglets, the η and η', and two isodoublets, the K and $\overline{K}$, all of which correspond to a single state split by SU(3) breaking. In order to study higher mass states one can study the isovectors, as has been done in the missing-mass-spectrometer experiments of Maglič, Kienzle, and coworkers. One can also look for any of the other I-spin multiplets; for

209

example, one can look for the isosinglets. However in this
case there is mixing between the two isosinglets (at least
this is the case for some of the nonets that are well established), so that the relation between the observed mass and
the center of the nonet is more complicated. The isovector
and the isodoublets on the other hand appear to be separated
by a quantity Δ, which appears to remain fairly constant,
and thus in the search for higher-mass bosons, one can
look either for the isovectors or for the isodoublets, the
K^*'s. Looking for bosons "in a strange light" thus corresponds to looking for the K^*'s.

I. A SURVEY OF THE K^*'s

There has been a considerable amount of work on
this subject, which I want to review and discuss. The K
and $K^*(890)$ are well established, so I will start by discussing the K^*'s beyond these. The $K^*(1420)$ is also well established, so I will only mention it to the extent that it relates
to the other nearby K^*'s.

A. REACTIONS LEADING TO K^* PRODUCTION. Let us
consider the type of experiment in which one observes the
higher K^*'s. These are primarily K^+p or K^-p reactions
giving four particles in the final state; for example, the
reactions $K^+p \rightarrow K^+\pi^-\pi^+p$ (see Fig. 1). Here one picks the
$K^+\pi^-$ to be in the $K^*(890)$, which thus gives three particles
effectively, $K^{*0}(890)\pi^+p$, and allows one to form a Dalitz
plot. In Fig. 2 we see the N^* band and a large $K^{*0}\pi^+$ enhancement along the horizontal axis. This consists of one
well-known feature, the $K^*(1420)$, for which the evidence
that it has $J^P = 2^+$ is rather good, and a broad enhancement
roughly from 1.1 to 1.4 BeV, the Q peak.

B. THE Q PEAK AND $K^*(1420)$. As may be noted on the
Dalitz plot, the entire $K^*\pi$ band runs into the N^* band. It
is general practice to cut out the N^* band and study the rest
of the Q enhancement. I have compiled some data on this
region with the help of Bronwyn H. Hall. See Figs. 3 to 5.
In Figs. 6 to 8 are some more recent contributions submitted at the time of the Meeting.

Let us first discuss the qualitative features: On the
right side of the Q peak is the $K^*(1420)$ decaying via the $K^*\pi$
or $K\rho$ mode. This is clearly discernible as a distinct feature in the three first momenta: the Wisconsin data at 3.5
BeV/c, our data (LRL) at 4.6 BeV/c, and in the Bruxelles-

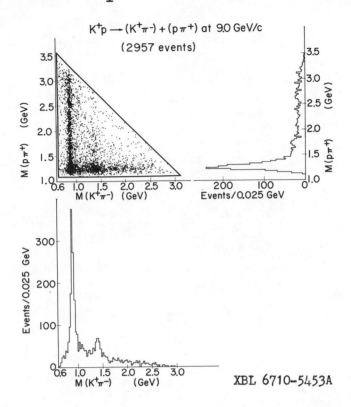

Fig. 1. Example of the triangle plot for the reaction $K^+p \rightarrow K^+\pi^-\pi^+p$. Data of Firestone et al. (LRL, 9 GeV/c).[1]

CERN data at 5.0 BeV/c in Fig. 3. For the higher momenta the $K^*(1420)$ is no longer clearly resolved unless one makes cuts in t; namely, $t > 0.3$ (BeV/c)^2. The same general features appear in the K^-p data in Fig. 5.

This behavior is readily understood as we can study the $K^*(1420) \rightarrow K\pi$ decay mode. The branching ratio of $K\pi/K\pi\pi \approx 1$ then allows one to estimate the $K\pi\pi$ contribution due to the $K^*(1420)$. This contribution decreases as the incident momentum increases, since $\sigma[K^*(1420)]$ is proportional to p_{lab}^{-2}, as Morrison has shown, while $\sigma(Q)$ appears to remain nearly constant with increasing p_{lab}. Furthermore the t distribution is wider for $K^*(1420)$ than for the Q peak.

C. THE STRUCTURE IN THE Q PEAK. There is every indication that the Q peak is not a single wide object but

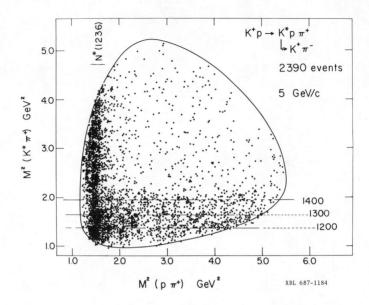

Fig. 2. An example of the Dalitz plot for the reaction
$K^+p \rightarrow K^*p\pi^+$. These events correspond to the K^* band on
a triangle plot similar to the one shown in Fig. 1. Data of
the Bruxelles-CERN-Birmingham collaboration.[2]

rather has more structure.

The question is: how much structure? How does it
vary with incident momentum and with t? What is the relation between the structure and alignment of the $K^*(890)$
which comes from the decay of the Q peak? And finally,
what is the behavior of the $K\rho$ decay mode? It is clear
from the present data that the Q-peak structure changes
with incident momentum, as can be noted by following the
vertical lines at 1.2, 1.3, and 1.4 BeV on Figs. 3 through 5.
Thus, for example, the 3.5- and 4.6-BeV/c K^+p data show a
single peak at 1300 to 1320 MeV (Fig. 3), while the 9- and
10-BeV/c data (Figs. 4 and 10) show two peaks at ~1250
MeV and 1360 to 1390 MeV.

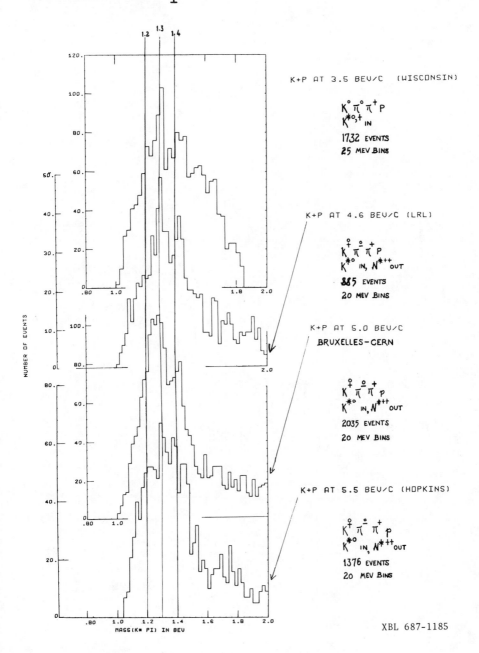

Fig. 3. Compilation of the K*π mass distributions from K⁺p interactions. Here K* refers to K*(890).

XBL 687-1185

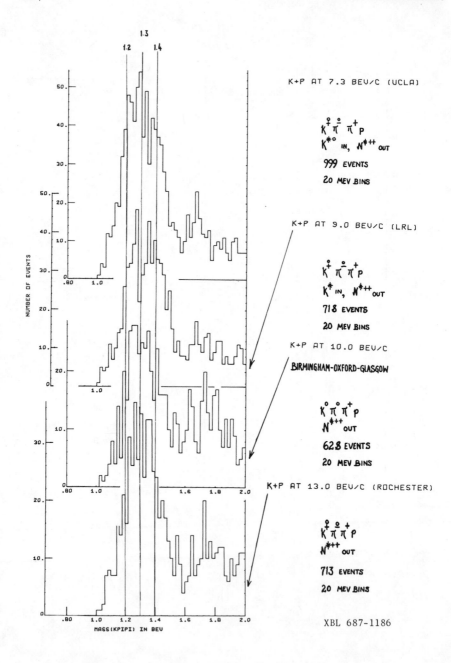

Fig. 4. Compilation of the $K^*\pi$ mass distributions from K^+p interactions.

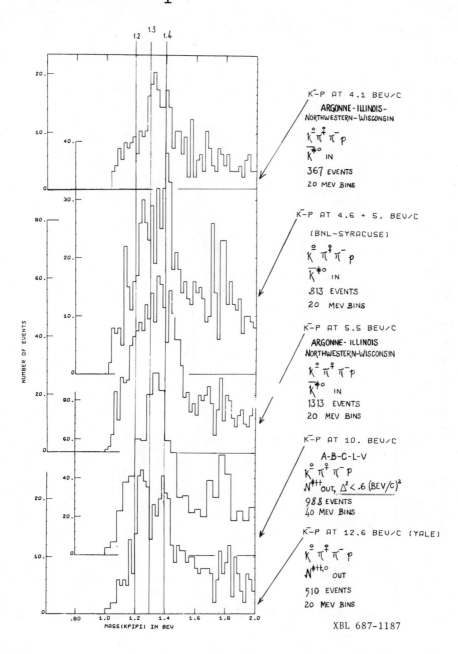

Fig. 5. Compilation of the K*π mass distributions from K⁻p interactions.

L. Eisenstein, O'Halloran et al.

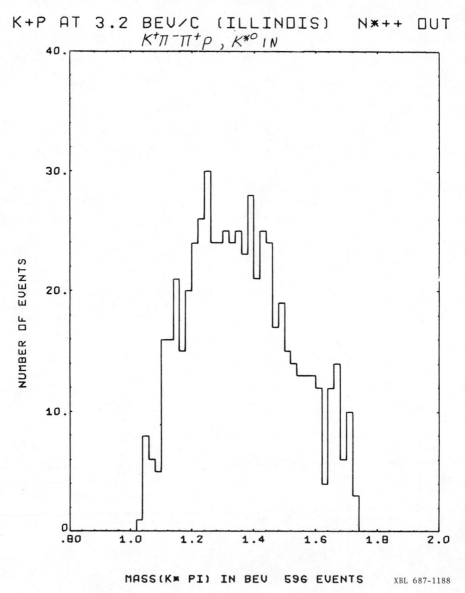

K+P AT 3.2 BEV/C (ILLINOIS)   N*++ OUT

$K^+\pi^-\pi^+P$, K^{*o} IN

MASS(K* PI) IN BEV 596 EVENTS   XBL 687-1188

Fig. 6. Additional data on the $K^*\pi$ mass submitted at the Conference.

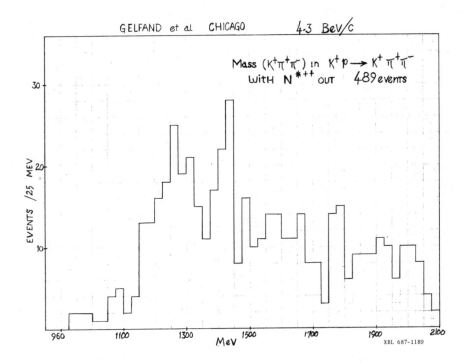

Fig. 7. Additional data on the Kππ mass submitted at the Conference.

Aside from the structure in the entire Q peak (without any cuts in t), a variation in structure is observed for cuts in t together with the selection of "polar" and "equatorial" alignment of the $K^*(890)$ from Q decay. In particular, the CERN-Bruxelles-Birmingham group (5-GeV/c K^+p) (see Fig. 9) suggest the presence of three distinct resonances, in addition to the $K^*(1420)$. This is however not observed by the Johns Hopkins group (5.5-GeV/c K^+p) or the ANL-Illinois-Northwestern-Wisconsin groups (5.5-BeV/c K^-p) (see Fig. 10). B. H. Hall and I have combined these three sets of data in Fig. 11. Some evidence for variation of the structure with t is shown in the LRL data (K^-p at 2.6 BeV/c), where the mass-squared distributions are shown for various cuts in the Kππ production angle (see Fig. 12).

D. SPIN AND PARITY OF THE Q PEAK. Figures 13 through 16 show three distinct attempts to get information on spin and parity in the various mass regions of the Q

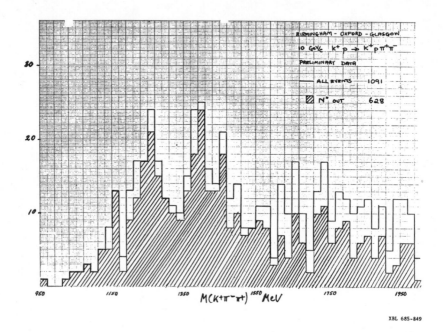

XBL 685-849

Fig. 8.   Additional data on the $K^*\pi$ mass submitted at the
Conference.

peak.   Chien, Slater, et al. at UCLA (K^+p at 7.3 GeV/c)
have studied the density distribution in the Dalitz plots for
the $K\pi\pi$ system (see Figs. 13 and 14).   They conclude
$J^P = 1^+$ with 2^- not ruled out.   In our own work at LRL
(K^+p at 9 GeV/c) we have studied various angular distributions described on Fig. 15 and conclude $J^P = 1^+$ or 2^-.   The
Johns Hopkins Group (Luste, Pevsner, et al., K^+p at 5.5
GeV/c) have carried out a Berman-Jacob analysis of the
two successive decays $Q \rightarrow K^*\pi$ and $K^* \rightarrow K\pi$.   They obtain
a weight function shown in Fig. 16 which corresponds to
$J^P = 1^+$ or 2^+.   From all these data, $J^P = 1^+$ appears
strongly preferred for all parts of the Q peak.

E.   COMPARISON WITH THE QUARK MODEL.   Let us
consider the situation of the possible 1^+ K^*'s, namely the
K^*'s which go with the A_1 and the B.   I am now assuming
that the A_1 and the B are reasonably well established; the
B will be discussed in another session, and I will say more
about the A_1 later in this session.   If we accept the A_1 and
B and that there are K^*'s which go with them (I think that
much we are likely to believe), there is a new phenomena

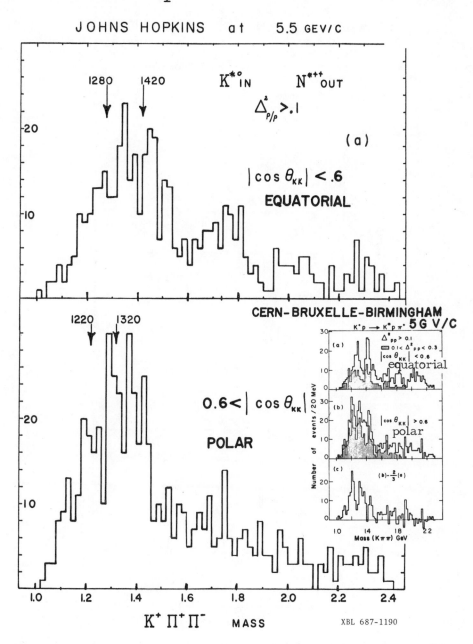

Fig. 9.   Search for additional structure in the Kππ mass
distribution for K$^+$p data with cuts in t and K* alignment
angle as indicated on the figure.[3,4]

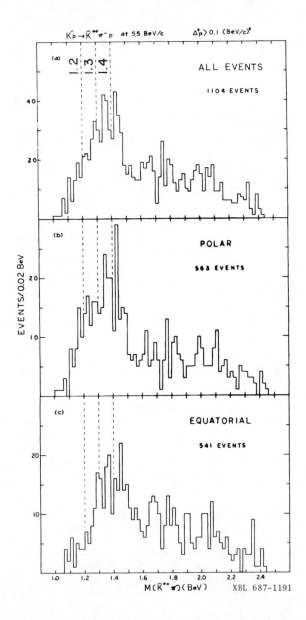

Fig. 10. Search for additional structure in the Kππ mass distribution for K⁻p data with cuts in t and K* alignment angle as indicated on the figure.[5]

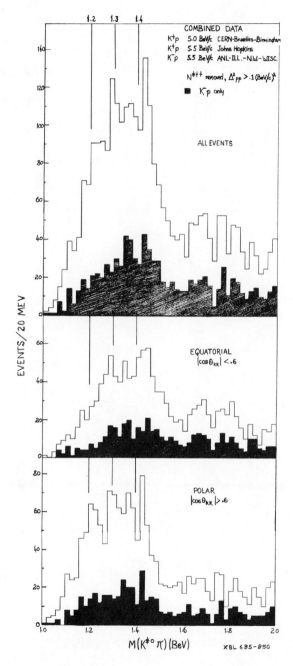

Fig. 11. Combination of the three sets of data in the previous two figures.

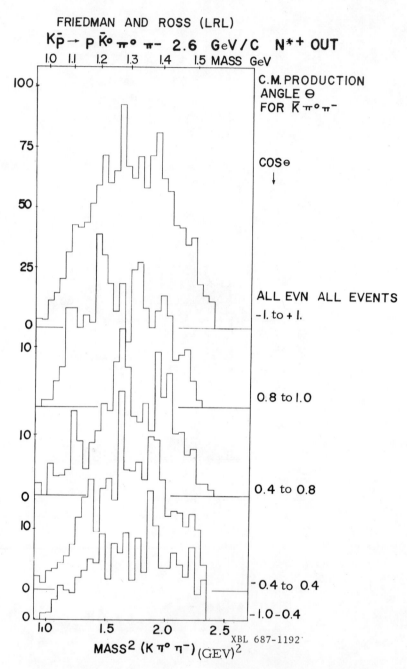

Fig. 12. Search for structure in the $K\pi\pi$ mass-squared distribution for various cuts in the K^* production angle.[6]

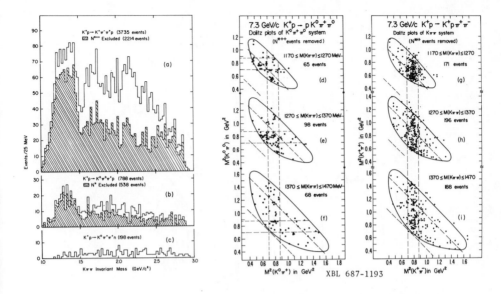

Fig. 13. Dalitz plots for the Kππ system with total mass as indicated on the figure for spin parity studies. Data of the UCLA group (Chien, Slater et al.). [7]

which can occur here; namely, the two K*'s can mix since the way these two K*'s differ is just that they belong to octets with different charge conjugations. We thus have two nonets of particles tied together. Gatto, Maiani, and Preparata have called this group of 18 particles an "octo-decimet" (see Fig. 17). [10]

Apart from the possibility of particle mixing, we can have interference effects between the two 1^+ K*'s which can occur in the mass distribution. Figure 17 shows the type of mass distributions which result from the introduction of a phase angle ϕ between the two amplitudes. [9] This problem is under investigation by a number of people, including Kane and Mani, [11] Altarelli, Gatto, and Maiani, [12,15] Harari and Quinn, [13] and Lipkin. [14]

So far there is not sufficient data to attempt a fit with this model. Furthermore, it is not clear at present whether the lack of structure in some of the experiments is real or due to resolution problems. In my opinion there is at present good evidence for at least two K*'s in the Q peak

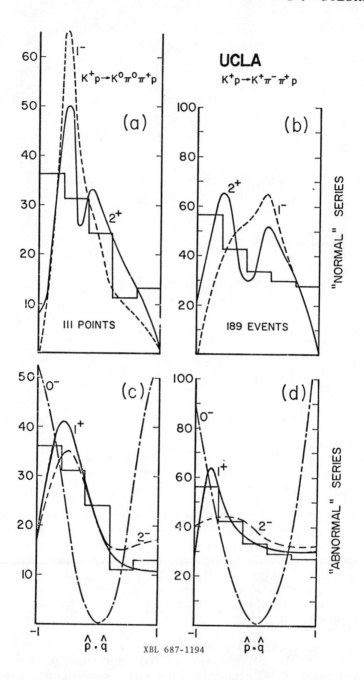

Fig. 14. Angular distributions related to spin parity determinations for the Kππ in the Q bump. Data from UCLA.

Fig. 15. The decay properties of the Kππ system shown
for five Kππ mass regions
I-V with N*++ band removed.
(a) M(Kπ)⁰; (b) M(ππ), the
shaded histograms for
events in the K*⁰(890) band
and for K*⁰(890) events;
(c) cos α, where α is the
angle between the outgoing
K and the incident K⁺ in
the (Kπ)⁰ rest frame;
(d) cos θ, where θ is the
angle between the odd π⁺
and the K⁺ in the (Kππ)⁺
rest frame; (e) cos ξ, where
ξ is the angle between the
outgoing K and the K*⁰(890)
flight direction in the
K*⁰(890) rest frame.

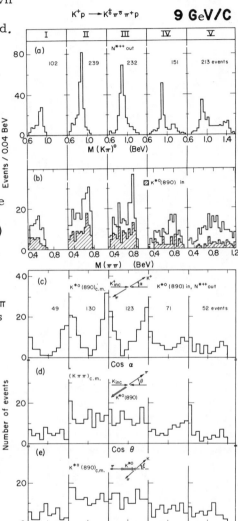

We show the decay
properties of the Kππ system as a function of the Kππ
mass for five mass regions
defined as (I) 1000-1180
MeV, (II) 1180-1280 MeV,
(III) 1300-1400 MeV, (IV)
1420-1500 MeV, and (V)
1600-1760 MeV. Regions
II, III, and IV correspond
to the (1250), (1360), and
(1420) mass bands, re-
spectively. Region I is a
control region, and Region
V corresponds to the L-
meson mass region. The
top two rows of five histograms each of Fig. 3
show, respectively, the
mass distributions of
(Kπ)⁰ and ππ systems. As may be noted, the main decay
mode of the K*(1250) and K*(1320) resonances is K*(890)+π;
however, the ρ+K decay mode is clearly present.

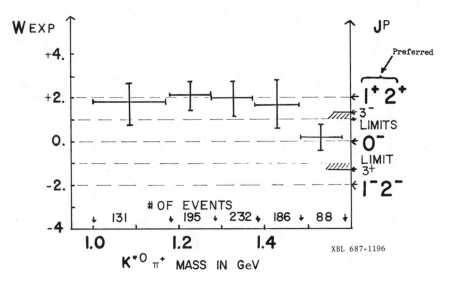

Fig. 16. Weight function deduced from Berman-Jacob analysis for the K*π mass peak. The corresponding theoretical spin parity values are shown on the right side of the figure. Data from the Johns Hopkins group. [3]

in addition to K*(1420) which lies above the Q peak. Comparable features now appear in the p̄p annihilation data at rest, the C and C'(see Fig. 18). The situation can of course be more complicated, although at present we are not forced to assume higher complexity.

There is one interesting test that can be made for the presence of K* mixing. As is well known, the coherent production of the Q peak on heavy nuclei and perhaps even on deuterium (see paper in these Proceedings by Pevsner) is expected to proceed via Pomeranchuk exchange. If in a good resolution experiment only a single peak--presumably the 1250-MeV K*--shows up, we have no K* mixing. If K* mixing occurs, and if the Pomeranchuk is a unitary singlet, then both the K*(1250) and K*($\sim$1320 and 1360) should be produced in the coherent peak.

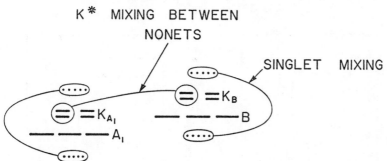

K* MIXING BETWEEN NONETS

SINGLET MIXING

Fig. 17.(a) Illustration of the octodecimet.
(Ref. 9)

Fig. 17.(b) Computation of the interference patterns in the $K\pi\pi$ mass distribution for two K^* resonances at 1250 and 1320 MeV added coherently and a third at 1420 MeV added incoherently. The computation was done for a series of values of the phase angle φ between the two coherent amplitudes as described in the text, and is shown in parts a to j. In part k the incoherent sum of the three resonances is shown.

THE TWO I^+ NONETS

I^{++} $^3P_1$ I^{+-} $^1P_1$

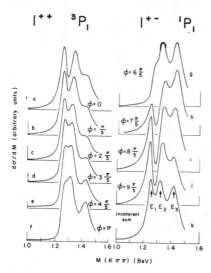

$d\sigma/dM$ (arbitrary units)

$\phi = 6\frac{\pi}{5}$ g

$\phi = 0$ a

$\phi = \frac{\pi}{5}$ b $\phi = 7\frac{\pi}{5}$ h

$\phi = 2\frac{\pi}{5}$ c $\phi = 8\frac{\pi}{5}$ i

$\phi = 3\frac{\pi}{5}$ d $\phi = 9\frac{\pi}{5}$ j

$\phi = 4\frac{\pi}{5}$ e   Incoherent sum E_1 E_2 E_3

$\phi = \pi$ f   k

1.0   1.2   1.4   1.6 1.0   1.2   1.4   1.6

$M(K\pi\pi)$ (BeV)

Let $B_k = \frac{1}{2}\Gamma_k/(E_k - E - i\frac{1}{2}\Gamma_k)$, with $k = 1$, 2, and 3, correspond to the Breit-Wigner amplitude for each of these resonances; then the resulting mass distribution can be expressed as

$$d\sigma/dM \propto (|a_1 B_1 + B_2 e^{i\varphi}|^2 + |a_3 B_3|^2)P,$$

where E_k and Γ_k are the resonant masses and widths, respectively, φ is a relative phase angle, and a_1 and a_3 relative amplitudes, all of which must be determined from experiment, and P is a phase-space factor. As an illustration, this expression was evaluated for E_1 = 1250 MeV, Γ_1 = 50 MeV; E_2 = 1320 MeV, Γ_2 = 80 MeV; E_3 = 1420 MeV, Γ_3 = 90 MeV; $a_1 = 1$; $a_3 = 2^{-1/2}$; and values of φ from 0 to $9\pi/5$ in ten equal steps.

XBL 687-1197

C AND C' MESONS

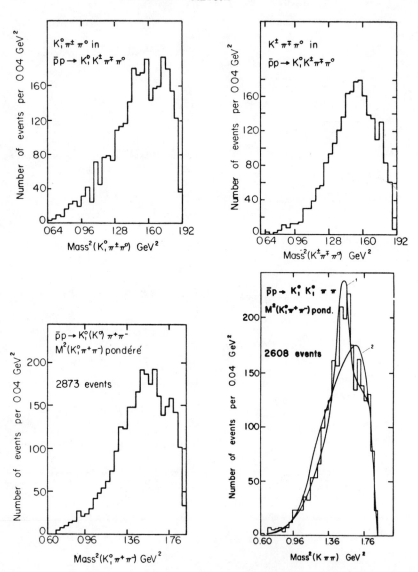

Fig. 18. **Mass squared plots of** K$\pi\pi$ **in** p$\bar{\text{p}}$ → K$\bar{\text{K}}\pi\pi$ **at rest, from the CERN-Paris-Liverpool Collaboration:**

a) K$_1^0\pi^{\mp}\pi^0$ from p$\bar{\text{p}}$ → K$_1^0$K$^{\pm}\pi^{\mp}\pi^0$;

b) K$^{\pm}\pi^{\mp}\pi^0$ from p$\bar{\text{p}}$ → K$_1^0$K$^{\pm}\pi^{\mp}\pi^0$;

c) K$_1^0\pi^+\pi^-$ from K$_1^0$(K^0)$\pi^+\pi^-$;

d) K$_1^0\pi^+\pi^-$ from K$_1^0$K$_1^0\pi^+\pi^-$.

XBL 687-1198

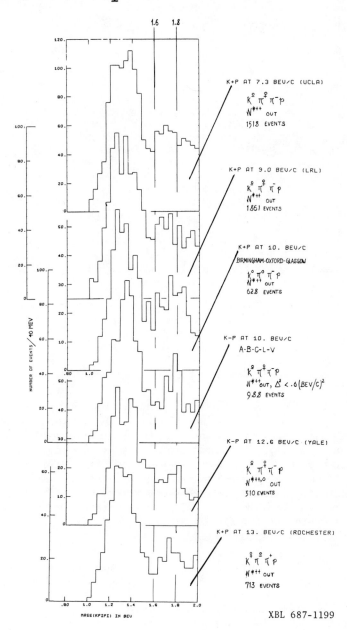

Fig. 19. Compilation of data on the Kππ mass distribution to show the evidence of a second boson cluster in the mass region 1.6 to 1.8 BeV, the L-meson region.

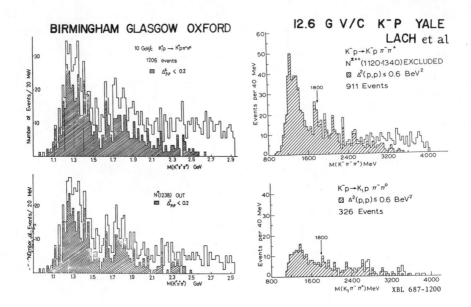

Fig. 20.   More detailed Kππ mass distributions.[16, 17]

II. THE NEXT K* CLUSTER

The ABCLV collaboration have observed a high-mass K*, the L(1790), in the 10-GeV/c K⁻p experiment. This is now confirmed in most of the high-energy K⁺p and K⁻p experiments. A compilation is shown in Fig. 19, and some further details in Figs. 20 and 21, and Table I. As may be noted, there may actually be an entire cluster of K*'s from 1.6 to 1.8 GeV. So far no additional structure has been clearly identified, although some evidence has been presented by the CERN-Bruxelles-Birmingham Group for a possible peak at 1660 MeV (see Fig. 22).

On the quark model we might expect the four L = 2 K*'s corresponding to the nonets with $J^{PC} = 1^{--}, 2^{--}, 2^{-+}, 3^{--}$

III. EVIDENCE FOR AN ENHANCEMENT IN THE $\overline{\Lambda}$N MASS DISTRIBUTION

We have investigated the $\overline{\Lambda}$N channel in the reactions $K^+p \rightarrow \overline{\Lambda}pp$ and $K^+p \rightarrow \overline{\Lambda}NN\pi$. Here the $\overline{\Lambda}$N system can have the quantum numbers of a K*. This is thus an interesting channel in which to investigate the mass region > 2055 MeV,

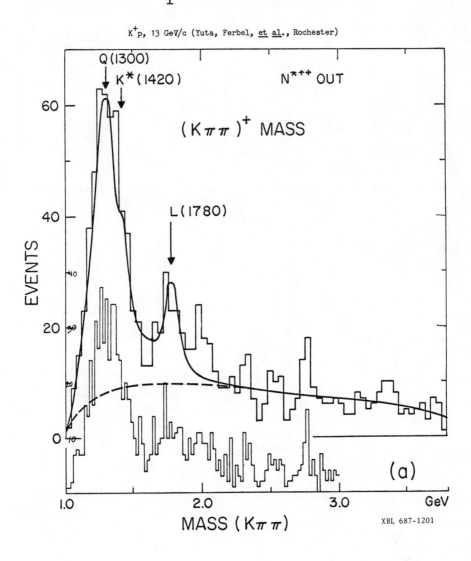

Fig. 21. More detailed Kππ mass distributions.[18]

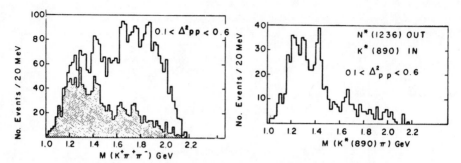

Evidence for K*(1660) from the CERN-Brussels-Birmingham study of K$^+$p interactions at 5 GeV/c. K$\pi\pi$ and K*π when N* is removed.

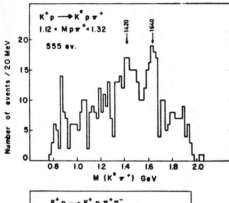

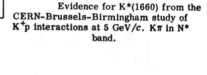

Fig. 22.
(Ref. 19)

Evidence for K*(1660) from the
CERN-Brussels-Birmingham study of
K$^+$p interactions at 5 GeV/c. Kπ in N*
band.

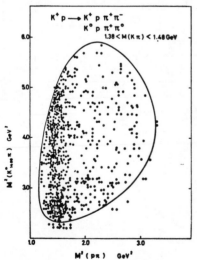

Evidence for K*(1660) from the CERN-
Brussels-Birmingham study of K$^+$p interactions
at 5 GeV/c. K*(1400) πp Dalitz plot.

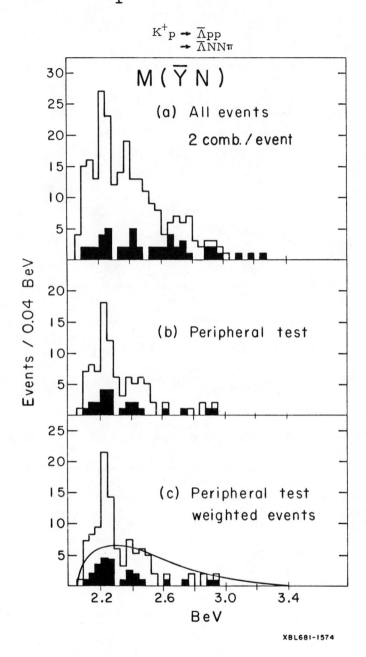

Fig. 23. The $\overline{\Lambda}$N mass enhancement. Data of Alexander et al., 9 GeV/c.[20]

Table I. Summary of properties for L-meson
(ABCLV Collaboration)

Mass: 1785 ± 12 MeV
Width: 127 ± 43 MeV
J^P: $\neq 0^-$, could be $1^+, 2^-$

Branching ratios	Events	%
$K\pi\pi$	194.6	44.5 ± 15
$K\rho$	43.2	9.9 ± 6
$K^*(890)\pi$	106.4	24.4 ± 8
$K^*(1430)\pi$	71.9	16.4 ± 8
$K\omega$	21.0	4.8 ± 2
$K\pi$	<10	<2.3

as it is not expected to suffer from the severe background
problems of the $K\pi\pi$ channel in this mass region. Also the
comparison with the corresponding $\bar{p}p$ and $\bar{p}n$ channels, in
which evidence for possible boson peaks in σ_{tot} have been
observed by Abrams et al., will be of interest.

In our own work (Alexander et al., K^+p at 9 GeV/c)
we have observed a strong enhancement near the threshold
for $\bar{\Lambda}N$ production. Aside from a clear broad enhancement
there is a suggestion of structure at a mass of 2240 MeV
(see Fig. 23). The Birmingham-Oxford-Glasgow collabora-
tion (K^+p at 10 GeV/c) has studied the channel $K^+p \to \bar{\Lambda}np\pi^+$
and observes a similar behavior for the $\bar{\Lambda}n$ mass distribution on the very limited data available so far (see Fig. 24).
The Rochester Group (Ferbel et al., K^+p at 12.6 GeV/c)
again observe the low-mass $\bar{\Lambda}N$ enhancement but do not see
any clear indication of structure (see Fig. 25).

More work will be needed on the investigation of this
enhancement before its properties can be definitely established.

IV. THE A_1 AND THE GENERAL A ENHANCEMENT

This seems to be the Conference at which more
structure is reported. In Figs. 26 to 33 I show some
recent results on the $\pi\rho$ or $\pi\pi\pi$ mass distributions from

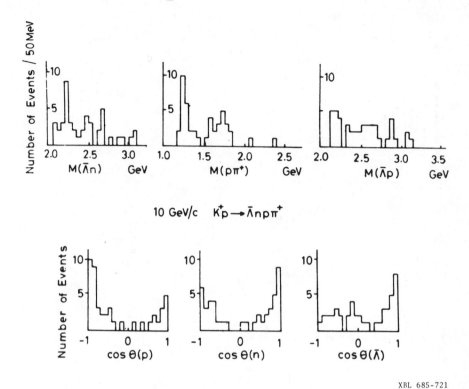

Fig. 24. The Ān mass enhancement. Data of Birmingham-
Oxford-Glasgow at 10 GeV/c. [16]

various experiments. It would appear that some structure
in addition to the A_1 peak--the so-called $A_{1.5}$ peak--keeps
showing up near 1.2 BeV in a number of experiments.
There is the disturbing feature that the $A_{1.5}$ peak is not
always at the same mass. It occurs at 1.17 BeV in the 5-
GeV/c data of the University of Illinois and at 1.2 to 1.22
BeV in the Wisconsin data (7 GeV/c) and Notre Dame data
(18.5 GeV/c) respectively. We can thus take three approaches to these data: (a) We add up the data from the experiments at the various momenta á la Ferbel and then the
effect disappears--and in fact so does the conventional relatively narrow A_1. (b) We assume a mechanism which can
give rise to some motion of the peak with incident momentum. Interference effects with a coherent background could
be such a mechanism, for example. (c) We can assume that
we are all victims of large statistical fluctuations.

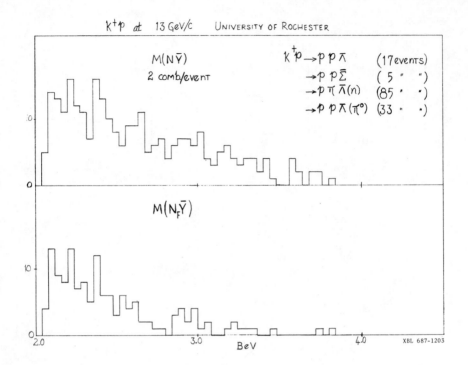

Fig. 25. The $\bar{\Lambda}N$ mass enhancement. Data of Rochester at 12.6 GeV/c. [18]

I am afraid it will take much more data and several further conferences before we can settle this point.

A. IS THE A_1 PRODUCED OUTSIDE A DIFFRACTION DISSOCIATION PEAK AS WELL? As we all know, in most experiments the A_1 is produced in association with a very large diffraction dissociation peak. The question is then to find out whether it is also produced in other reactions? There are a number of such examples in the literature illustrated in Figs. 34 and 35. Whether the effects observed are indeed the manifestations of the A_1 is perhaps somewhat in doubt as yet.

In the case of the Q bump, evidence for $K^*(1300)$ has been seen in a non-Deck-type reaction $\pi^- p \to \Lambda K \pi \pi$ by Crennell et al. at 6 GeV/c (Brookhaven).

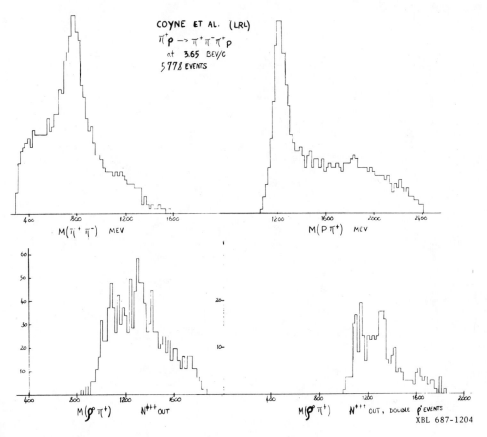

Fig. 26. The πρ mass distribution. [21]

B. RESONANCES VERSUS DIFFRACTION DISSOCIATION
OR DECK EFFECT. At present we know of three well-
documented cases of diffraction dissociation effects:
      (a) the A peak in πρ (discussed here)
      (b) the Q peak in πK*(890) (discussed here)
      (c) the baryon peak in πΔ (discussed in Schlein's
           paper in these Proceedings).
All three have the feature of nearly energy-independent
cross sections characteristic of Pomeranchuk exchange.
Furthermore they all have good evidence for additional
structure indicative of resonance formation. Whether the
resonances are produced by the diffraction dissociation--or
are equivalent to it, as Chew and Pignotti have recently
suggested[28]--is still under debate. To my mind, the evidence that there is some resonance structure present in

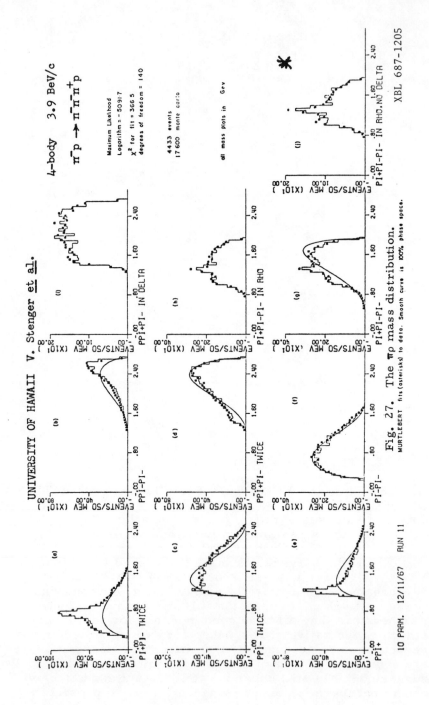

Fig. 27. The πp mass distribution.
MURTLEBERT fits (asterisks) to data. Smooth curve is 00% phase space.

10 PARM. 12/11/67   RUN 11

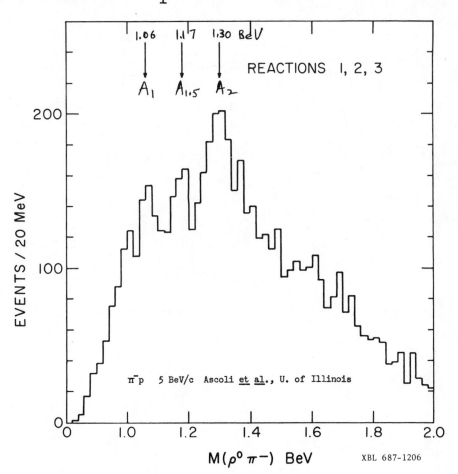

Fig. 28. The πρ mass distribution.[23]

each case looks very convincing.

I wish to thank G. Alexander, A. Firestone, C. M. Fu, and C. Wohl for helpful discussions and C. Frank, B. H. Hall, and H. J. Rice for help in preparing this article.

This work was done under the auspices of the U. S. Atomic Energy Commission.

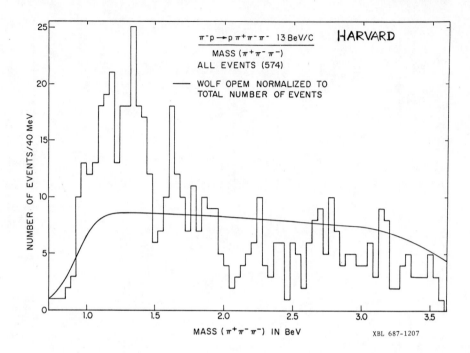

Fig. 29. The πρ mass distribution.[24]

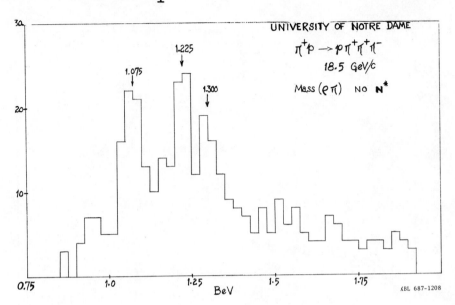

Fig. 30. The πp mass distribution. [25]

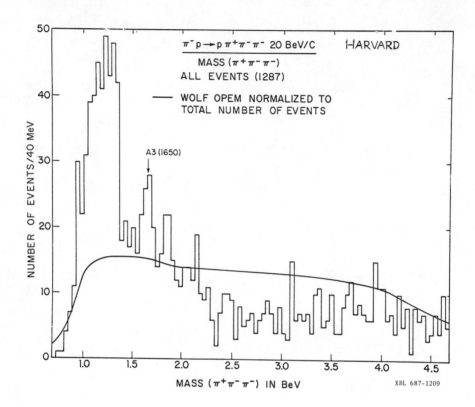

Fig. 31.   The πρ mass distribution.[24]

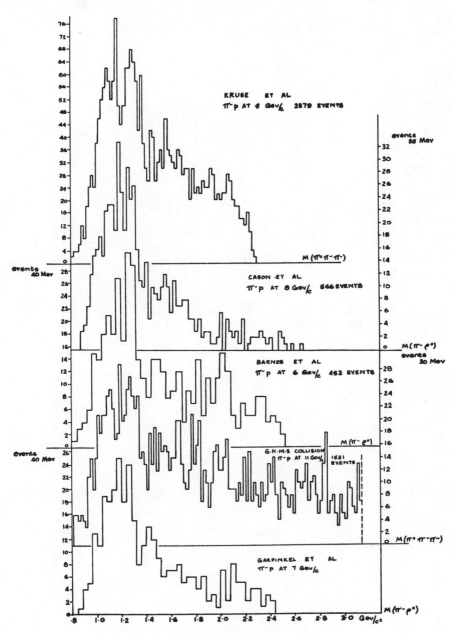

Fig. 32.   Compilation of data relevent to A$_{1.5}$,
by I. Butterworth.[19]

XBL 687-1210

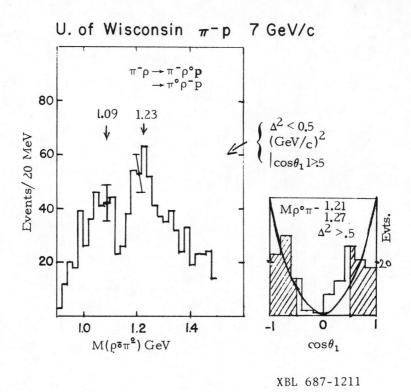

XBL 687-1211

Fig. 33. The $\pi\rho$ mass distribution.[26]

K* SPECTRUM AND A$_1$ 245

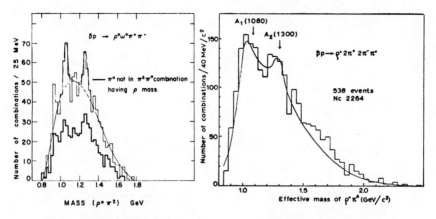

$M(\rho\pi)$ in $\bar{p}p \rightarrow 3\pi^+3\pi^-\pi^0$ containing non-interfering combinations of the $\pi^+\pi^-$ and $\pi^+\pi^-\pi^0$ in the ρ^0 and ω^0 region respectively. The thick line is for events where the π^0 is not in a $\pi^\pm\pi^0$ combination having a mass in the $\rho^\pm$-region. The reaction is studied at 3 GeV/c by Danysz et al.

$M(\rho^0\pi^\pm)$ for $\bar{p}p \rightarrow 3\pi^+3\pi^-\pi^0$ at 5.7 GeV/c, reported by Fridman et al.

Fig. 34

(Ref. 19)

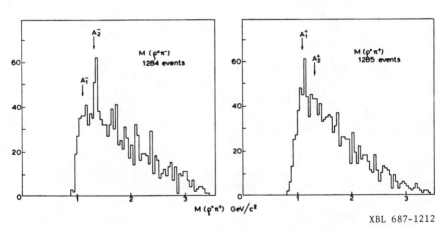

XBL 687-1212

$M(\rho^0\pi^\pm)$ for $\pi^-p \rightarrow n\pi^+\pi^+\pi^-\pi^-$ at 11 GeV/c reported by the GHMS Collaboration, a) $\rho^0\pi^-$ b) $\rho^0\pi^+$.

OXFORD-MUNICH-BIRMINGHAM-GLASGOW
RUTHERFORD LAB - I.C. (LONDON).[27]

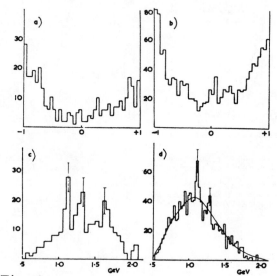

Fig. 35.

a) $\cos \theta_\Lambda^*$ for reaction (1),
b) $\cos \theta_\Lambda^*$ for reaction (2),
c) Mass of $(\pi^+\pi^+\pi^-)$ for reaction (1) with $\cos \theta_\Lambda^* > 0$,
d) Mass of $(\pi^+\pi^+\pi^-)$ for reaction (2) with $\cos \theta_\Lambda^* > 0$
    (the phase space prediction is given by the curve).
(These plots are corrected for losses due to the finite
        fiducial volume and short decays).

XBL 687-1213

(1) $K^-p \to \Lambda\, \pi^+\pi^-\pi^+\pi^-$ 301 events
(2) $K^-p \to \Lambda\, \pi^+\pi^-\pi^+\pi^-\pi^0$ 1266 events

(1) $M(\pi^+\pi^+\pi^-) = 1117 \pm 30$ MeV $\Gamma = 50 \pm 50$ MeV
(2) $M(\pi^+\pi^+\pi^-) = 1111 \pm 10$ MeV $\Gamma = 50 \pm 25$ MeV

(1) $\sigma(\Lambda A_1^+ \pi^-)$ $= 9 \pm 3\,\mu b$
(2) $\sigma(\Lambda A_1^+ \pi^-\pi^0) = 15 \pm 5\,\mu b$

REFERENCES

1. A. Firestone, C. M. Fu, G. Goldhaber, and B. C. Shen, submitted to the Conference.

2. Bruxelles-CERN-Birmingham Collaboration, submitted to the Conference.

3. F. Bomse, S. Borenstein, A. Callahan, J. Cole, B. Cox, D. Ellis, L. Ettlinger, D. Gillespie, G. Luste, R. Mercer, E. Moses, A. Pevsner, and R. Zdanis, Phys. Rev. Letters 20, 1519 (1968); also contribution to this Conference.

4. G. Bassompierre et al., Phys. Letters 26B, 30 (1967).

5. J. Park, S. Kim, G. Chandler, E. L. Goldwasser, T. P. Wangler, M. Derrick, J. G. Loken, F. Schweingruber, R. Ammar, R. Davis, J. Mott, and B. Werner, contribution to this Conference.

6. J. H. Friedman and R. R. Ross, LRL, contribution to this Conference.

7. C. Y. Chien, P. M. Dauber, E. I. Malamud, D. J. Mellema, P. E. Schlein, P. A. Schreiner, W. E. Slater, D. H. Stork, H. K. Ticho, and T. G. Trippe, Spin and Parity of the T = 1/2 Kππ System near 1.3 GeV, UCLA preprint UCLA-1020, 1967.

8. G. Goldhaber, A. Firestone, and B. C. Shen, Phys. Rev. Letters 19, 972 (1967).

9. G. Goldhaber, Phys. Rev. Letters 19, 976 (1967).

10. R. Gatto, L. Maiani, and G. Preparata, Nuovo Cimento 39, 1192 (1965).

11. G. L. Kane and H. S. Mani, University of Michigan preprint; Phys. Rev., in press.

12. G. Altarelli, R. Gatto, and L. Maiani, Istituto di Fisica dell'Universita Firenze preprint TH. 68/3.

13. H. Harari and H. Quinn, private communication.

14. H. J. Lipkin, Princeton University preprint PUC 937-323 June 1968.

15. R. Gatto and L. Maiani, Phys. Letters 26B, 95 (1967).

16. Birmingham-Oxford-Glasgow, 10-GeV/c K⁺p, contribution to the Conference

17. T. Ludlam, J. Lach, J. Sandweiss, and H. D. Taft, contribution to this Conference.

18. J. C. Berlinghieri, M. S. Farber, T. Ferbel, B. E. Forman, A. C. Melissinos, P. F. Slattery, T. Yamanouchi, and H. Yuta, University of Rochester, contribution to the Conference.

19. Quoted by I. Butterworth, Rapporteur's talk, in Proceedings of the Heidelberg International Conference on Elementary Particles (North-Holland Publishing

Company, Amsterdam, 1968).
20. G. Alexander, A. Firestone, G. Goldhaber, and B. C.
    Shen, Phys. Rev. Letters 20, 755 (1968).
21. D. G. Coyne, W. R. Butler, P. J. Gaposchkin, G.
    Goldhaber, J. A. Kadyk, J. N. MacNaughton, and
    G. H. Trilling, contribution to the Conference.
22. V. Stenger et al., University of Hawaii, contribution
    to the Conference.
23. G. Ascoli, H. B. Crawley, U. Kruse, D. W. Mortara,
    E. Schafer, A. Shapiro, and B. Terreault, Univer-
    sity of Illinois preprint COO-1195-121 (March 1968).
24. M. L. Ioffredo, G. W. Brandenburg, A. E. Brenner,
    B. Eisenstein, L. Eisenstein, W. H. Johnson, Jr.,
    J. K. Kim, M. E. Law, B. M. Salzberg, J. H.
    Scharenguivel, and J. J. Szymanski, Harvard
    University, contribution to the Conference.
25. N. M. Cason et al., University of Notre Dame, con-
    tribution to this Conference.
26. W. D. Walker et al., University of Wisconsin, con-
    tribution to this Conference.
27. W. W. M. Allison, A. Cruz, W. Schrankel, M. M.
    Haque, S. K. Tuli, P. J. Finney, C. M. Fisher,
    J. D. Gordon, R. M. Turnbull, R. Erskine, K.
    Sisterson, K. Paler, P. Chaudhuri, A. Eskreys,
    and S. J. Goldsack, Phys. Letters 25B, 619 (1967).
28. G. F. Chew and A. Pignotti, Phys. Rev. Letters 20,
    1078 (1968).

Coherent Production of Resonances

A. Pevsner

The Johns Hopkins University

An important new way for the study of high energy
mechanisms and resonances is "coherent production" from
nuclei. I report here the results of several laboratories
where deuterium and neon were used as targets. The existance
of copious production of resonances by coherent production
is of interest in itself. In the study of resonances
isotopic spin can clearly be determined. Some spin parity
assignments are overwhelmingly favored over other assignments
on the basis of copious production alone. Further there
seems to be little background present so that further
detailed analysis is of more significance than in the
usual situation.

The presence of coherent production is shown in the
first two figures. For figure 1 the B.N.L., Milan, Orsay,
Berkeley collaboration[1], B.M.O.B., measured three prong
events which are assumed to have an invisible recoil at
incident K^- energies of 5.5 and 12.7 BeV/c using the 80"
B.N.L. chamber partially filled with neon. The smaller

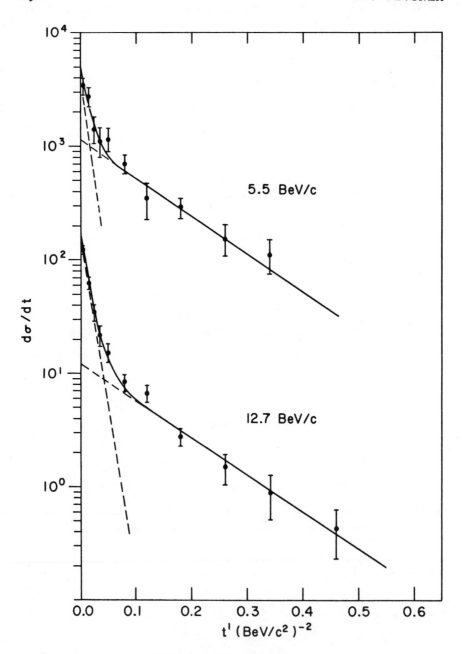

Figure 1 B. M. O. B.   Neon Data

slope is exactly that expected for production off single
nucleon on the basis of hydrogen experiments. The higher
slope is then interpreted as originating in production off
the entire nucleus. Similar results are obtained for such
slopes in the Johns Hopkins[2] deuterium data. The numerical
values of the slopes are consistent with coherent model calculations. Furthermore for deuterium the presence of the
deuteron can be directly shown in 4-c fits as indicated in
the upper curves of figure 2 from Johns Hopkins. The lower
curves in figure 2 from Johns Hopkins, figure 3 from
B.M.O.B., and figure 5 from Argonne-Northwestern[3] show the
strong presence of the $K^*(890)$ and some $K^*(1400)$ in the
Hopkins data. These resonances are actually not directly
produced but most likely are the daughters of higher three
body $(K^-\pi^+\pi^-)$ resonances. The $(K^-\pi^+\pi^-)$ mass distribution
are shown in figure 4 from B.M.O.B., figure 5 from Argonne-
Northwestern, and figure 6 from Hopkins. In this figure
from Hopkins it may be seen how the $K\pi\pi$ spectrum peaks in
the Q-region around 1300 Mev, as well as the L-region around
1730 Mev.

It may further be seen in this figure that the
Q-region decays mainly into the $K^*(890)$ and that the
L-region is associated with both $K^*(890)$ and $K^*(1420)$.

Since the isotopic spin of the deuteron is zero,
the $K\pi\pi$ system and resonances within it necessarily have
isospin one-half.

The upper graph in figure 6 shows for the same
amount of film two body coherent production. Clearly, such
production, which represents the main decay mode of the
1^- $K^*(890)$, and the 2^+ $K^*(1400)$, is suppressed by an order
of magnitude.

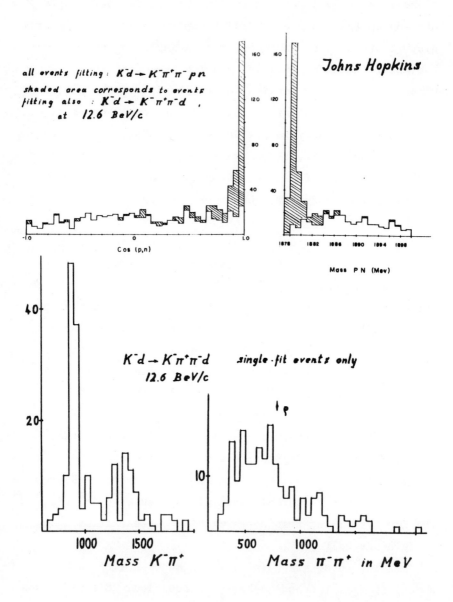

Figure 2

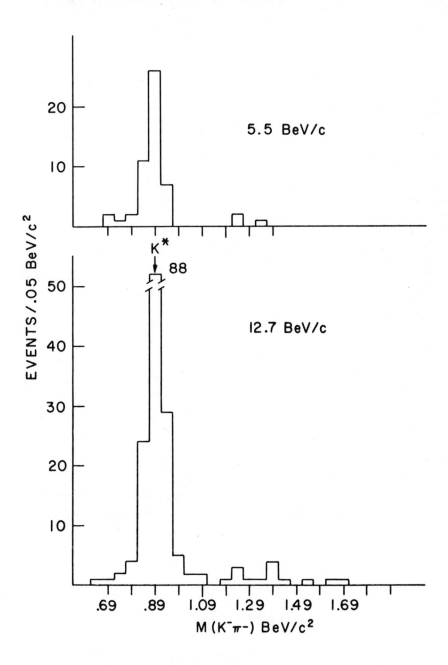

Figure 3   B. M. O. B.

A. PEVSNER

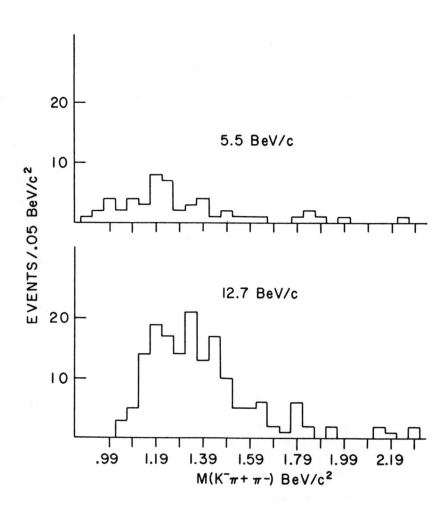

Figure 4   B. M. O. B.

Argonne - Northwestern

$K^-d \rightarrow K^-d\pi^+\pi^-$ 5.5 GEV/c

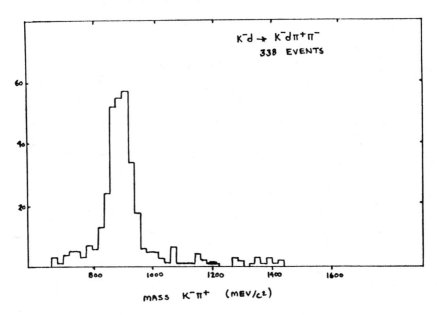

$K^-d \rightarrow K^-d\pi^+\pi^-$

338 EVENTS

MASS $K^-\pi^+$ (MEV/c²)

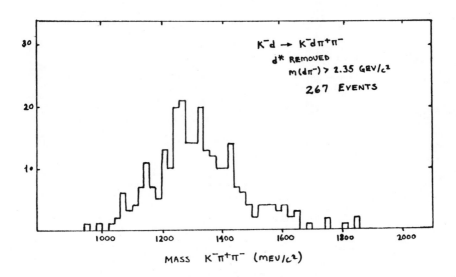

$K^-d \rightarrow K^-d\pi^+\pi^-$

d* REMOVED

m(dπ⁻) > 2.35 GEV/c²

267 EVENTS

MASS $K^-\pi^+\pi^-$ (MEV/c²)

Figure 5

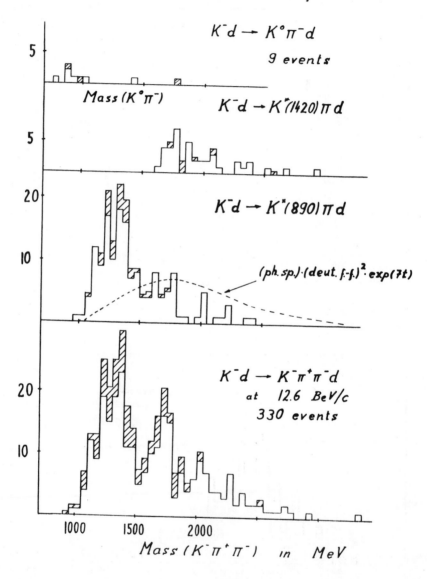

Figure 6

The coherent model indeed suppresses production of the 1^-, 2^+, ... series of particles relative to the 1^+, 2^-, ... series. Thus we believe that the Q and L regions most likely are in the spin parity sequence, 1^+, 2^-, ...

A direct spin parity analysis for the Q is shown in part in figure 7. A 1^+ assignment with s-wave decay is completely consistent with the data while a 0^- is completely incompatible. The 1^+ prediction is favored over a 2^- p-wave by the absence of events at $\cos \chi = 0$. This demonstrates the importance of minimal background.

The direct study of the L region is consistent with the 1^+, 2^- assignment but statistics do not yet allow differentiation between these possibilities.

Concerning Professor Goldhaber's previous talk I would like to reemphasize the need for many more statistics especially if we are to resolve the Q region into several resonances. As there exist many experiments each of which tries a myriad of cuts there can be many fluctuations. What will be necessary is a detailed study of these curves as a function of energy since there may be coherent interaction with background. I would like to illustrate the difficulties in figure 8 by comparing the two experiments with the highest available statistics here, a K^+-p experiment at 5 Gev from CERN, and at 5.5 Gev from Johns Hopkins University. With the same cuts in the data it is seen that the clear splitting of the Q region in the CERN data is not repeated in the Hopkins data.

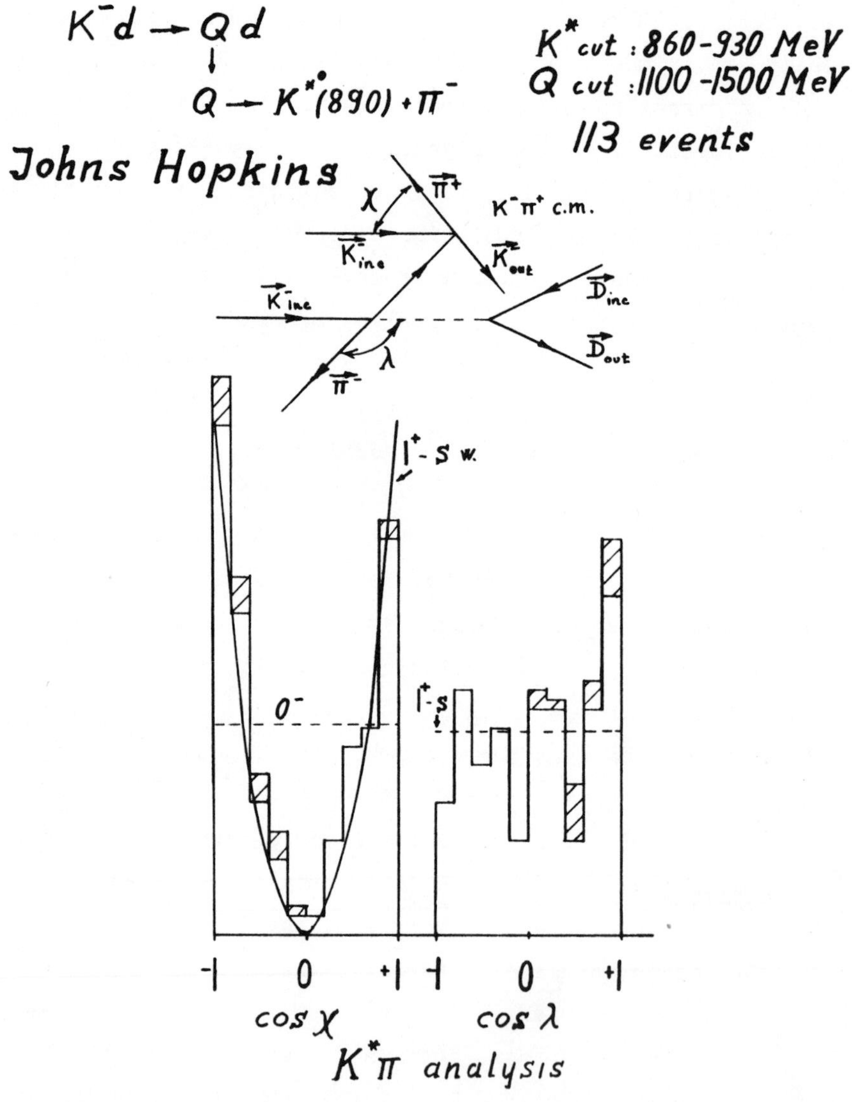

K⁻d → Qd
Q → K*⁰(890) + π⁻
K* cut : 860-930 MeV
Q cut : 1100-1500 MeV
113 events
Johns Hopkins
χ
π⁺
K⁻π⁺ c.m.
K_inc
K_out
K⁻_inc
D_inc
D_out
λ
π⁻
1⁺-S w.
0⁻
1⁺-S
-1
0
+1
-1
0
+1
cos χ
cos λ
K*π analysis

Figure 7

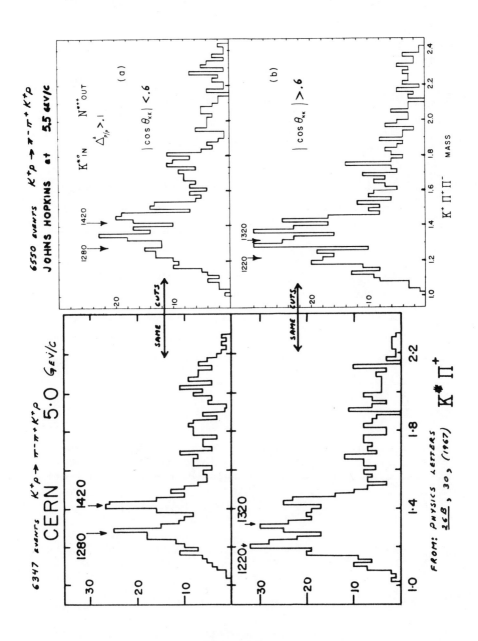

Figure 8

Professor Schlein mentioned that the kappa meson has been killed. When Art Rosenfeld last slew the kappa he predicted that a 3 standard deviation kappa would reincarnate itself at least once a year. Figure 9 shows this in the current 5.5 Gev Hopkins experiment as the shoulder below the $K^*(890)$.

Lastly, I want to comment on attempts to explain resonances by the use of models, some of the more popular ones being shown in figure 10. Figure 11 compares some of these models to our data. The total data is shown as well as a shaded region with reduced data after common cuts. A given model predicts all the results in a given row as well as a mass plot. All of these should be compared with the data.

Attention must be given to the sensitivity of a prediction to a particular cut in the data. If this is done none of the proposed models to date fit all the data very well.

[1] B.N.L.: W. B. Fowler, F. R. Huson, R. I. Louttit, D. J. Miller, J. S. O'Neall; MILAN: G. Bellini, M. di Corato, E. Fiorini, K. Moriyasu, E. Muggia, P. Negri, M. Rollier; ORSAY: B. Daugeras, D. Fournier, W. B. Fretter, J. Hennessy, J. Six, J. J. Veillet; UC-BERKELEY: H. H. Bingham, C. Farwell, G. Irwin, A. Lu .

[2] JOHNS HOPKINS: M. Sacchi-Bosco, A. Callahan, D. Denegri, L. Ettlinger, D. Gillespie, G. Goodman, R. Mercer, E. Moses, A. Pevsner, R. Zdanis, B. Cox, R. Carson, D. Ellis, D.Feiock. G. Luste.

[3] ARGONNE: J. Phelan, Y. Cho, M. Derrick, J. Loken, B. Musgrave, F. Schweingruber, T. Wangler; NORTHWESTERN: R. Ammar, R. Davis, W. Kropac, J. Mott, D. Slate, B. Werner.

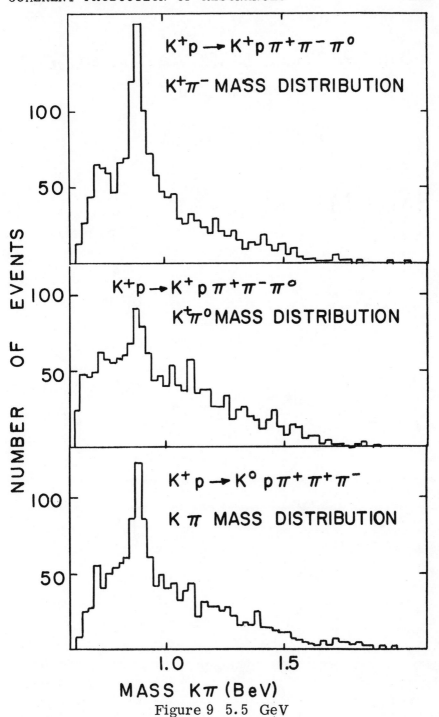

Figure 9 5.5 GeV

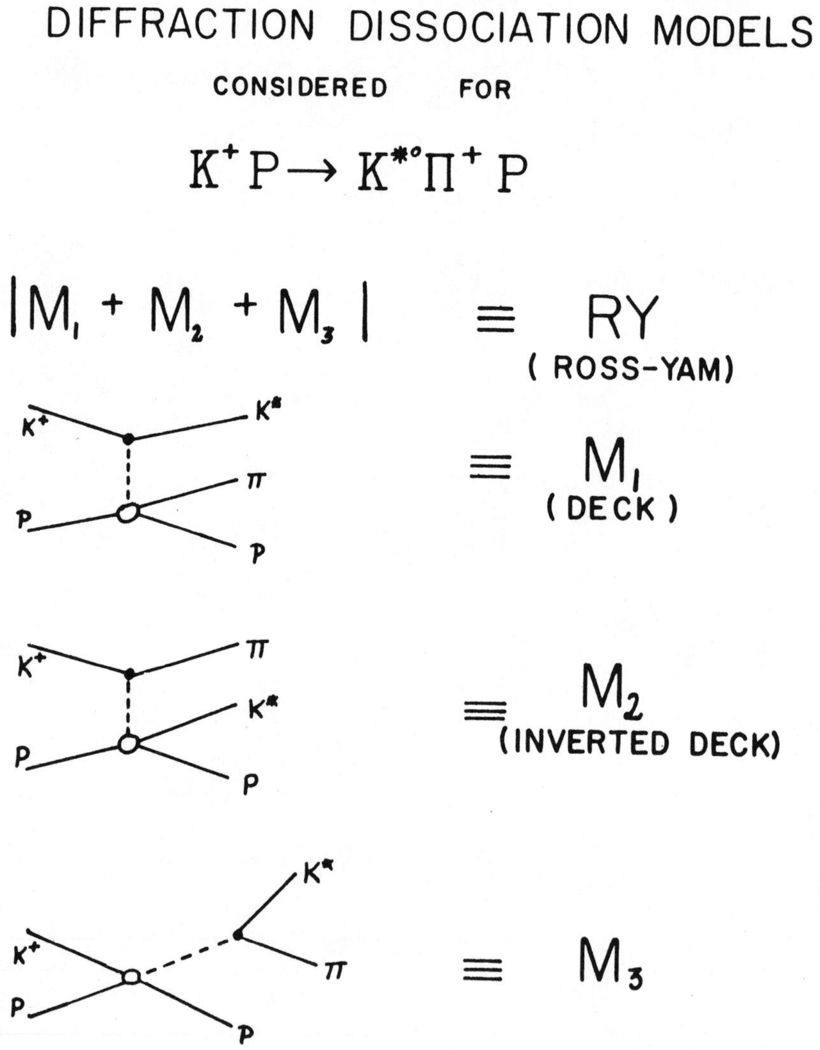
DIFFRACTION DISSOCIATION MODELS
CONSIDERED FOR
K+P → K*0π+ P
|M1 + M2 + M3| ≡ RY
(ROSS-YAM)
K+
K*
π
P
P
≡ M1
(DECK)
K+
π
K*
P
P
≡ M2
(INVERTED DECK)
K*
K+
π
P
P
≡ M3

Figure 10

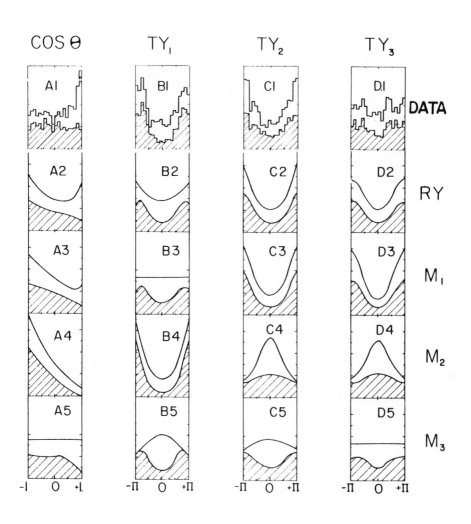

Figure 11

COMPILED EVIDENCE

FOR A SPLITTING OF THE

A2 MESON

W. Kienzle
CERN, Geneva, Switzerland

This is a summary of the present knowledge about the A2 mass spectrum, specifically with respect to the question: "Is the A2 split?" This question originates in spark chamber work done at CERN; therefore the evidence for a two-peak structure will be presented in the following order:

I)   Missing-mass Spectrometer, CERN

II)   Boson Spectrometer, CERN

III)   Bubble-Chamber Data from BNL

Speculative interpretations of the splitting will be mentioned at the end.

I) MISSING-MASS SPECTROMETER, CERN (MMS)

The first indication that the A2 meson may consist of two nearby peaks was obtained with the MMS at CERN in 1965. The MMS produced A2 mesons in the reaction

$\pi^- p \rightarrow p\ X^-$, where the Mass spectrum M_X of the meson X^- (equal to the missing-mass of the proton) is

$$M_X^2 = (E_1 + m_2 - E_3)^2 - p_1^2 - p_3^2 + 2p_1 p_3 \cos \Theta \quad (1)$$

with definitions

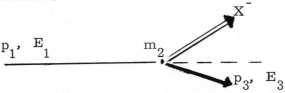

As illustrated in Fig. 1, the MMS was operating in the "Jacobian peak" region (I), i.e. the recoil protons were selected by a rough momentum measurement in the maximum lab angular region such that $dM_X/dp_3 \approx 0$, i.e. M_X is only a function of the lab angle Θ. Therefore a precise lab angle measurement is important; no magnet is needed. This method was originally proposed by Maglić and Costa in 1963[1]. The operation of the MMS system, which is shown in Fig. 2 (photograph in Fig. 3) has been described in detail[2]. It consists essentially of a proton telescope, movable on a rail around the H_2 target, with four acoustic spark chambers to measure Θ, and a range interval to stop the protons.

In the original version of the MMS the range interval was made up simply by a block of aluminium, spaced between the counters R2 and R3. In this way the first A2 spectra have been measured.[3]

The first data, shown in Fig. 4a, were obtained

in May 1965 at a beam momentum of 6.0 GeV/c. "Tapered
absorber" means, that during this run the aluminium
block had a Θ dependent thickness such that for each mass
the protons were at the Jacobian peak = maximum angle.
Then the system was somewhat modified, i.e. different
beam with p_1 = 7.0 GeV/c, different central angle of the
p-telescope, new spark chambers, and this time a flat,
i.e. constant thickness proton absorber was used. Both
samples, Figs. 4a and 4b, show a dip in the A2 centre.
The sum (Fig. 4c) has been published in the "Compiled
boson-spectrum", 1966[4].

In January 1967 the subject was taken up again,
with the MMS basically modified[5]. Wide-gap wire
chambers were introduced in the forward direction to
measure the decay products of X^-. During a test run
for these chambers, the p-telescope was running during
six days full-time on A2 production at 7.0 GeV/c again,
resulting in a huge A2 peak as shown in Fig. 5. But
now also the range interval was much improved: instead
of an aluminium block, five thin (15 mm) scintillators
were taken, such that the momentum could be determined
to within 30 MeV/c by knowing inside which scintillator
the proton stopped; this is shown in Fig. 6a. The mass
resolution Γ_{exp}, turns out to be very sensitive to how
far the protons are from the Jacobian peak and it varies
nearly by a factor of two, depending on p_3, as seen in
Fig. 6a. Therefore we broke up the total A2 of Fig. 5

into five sub-samples according to the five range
intervals. These sub-samples are shown together with
the mass resolutions Γ_{exp} in Figs. 6b to f. Sharp dips
occur in the A2 centre for the finest resolution samples,
intervals 3 and 4. The sum of the best resolution data
is shown in Fig. 7.

A total MMS A2 has then been obtained by adding
the data from the 1965 runs (Fig. 4c) to those from 1967
(Fig. 7). The sum is shown in Fig. 8. (Before adding it
was necessary to centre the over-all A2 peaks of 1965
and 1967 on each other, since due to uncertainty in the
absolute beam momentum the absolute mass value is only
known to within ±16 MeV).

The splitting of the total A2 is clearly significant.
The parameters of the various fits are given in Table 1.
It should be pointed out that:

    i) if Fig. 8 were plotted in 20 MeV bins, no
       splitting would be seen, and

    ii) if the mass resolution was twice as large the
       splitting would not be resolved.

At this point the MMS experiment came to an end and an
entirely new experiment started.

II.   CERN BOSON SPECTROMETER (CBS) (For authors
                                    see Ref. 6)

The mode of operation of the CBS is illustrated in
Fig. 1. It is contrary to the MMS in that it operates in

region II where the mass M_X is only a function of proton
momentum, and therefore a magnetic analysis of recoil
protons has to be done. It is seen that, for a given beam
momentum, one achieves higher masses than with the
MMS, each mass being measured at the lowest momentum
transfer.

A scale drawing of the layout is shown in Fig. 9.
A photograph of the CBS as of January 1968 is seen in
Fig. 10. Recoil protons are selected through a lead
collimator near 0° lab angle and momentum analysed to
within about $\pm 1\%$ by magnetic spectrometer which consists
of two pairs of $(1.5 \times 1.5 \text{ m}^2)$ wide gap wire chambers
and a wide-gap $(1.5 \times 0.5 \text{ m}^2)$ magnet. In addition the
momentum is measured by time-of-flight. The proton
telescope moves on rails around the magnet centre to
select the proper mass-bite. The mass resolution is 15
MeV (FWHM) at the A2. Figure 11 shows that protons
are clearly identified against π^+ and K^+ background, using
magnetic deflection and time-of-flight. The CBS is (as
was the MMS), a fully automatic system with an on-line
computer. This system was built as a high-mass spectrometer, capable of searching for bosons up to M_X = 5 GeV.

The CBS was run in and tested in a low energy
pion beam, with energy just high enough to reach the A2
mass region. The kinematical condition at p_1 = 2.65 GeV/c,
where most of the new A2 data were taken, is illustrated
in Fig. 12. It is seen that the CBS operation at such low
masses is quite difficult due to the following reasons:

i) the end of phase space limits the spectrum already
   at 1460 MeV and

ii) there is a sharp drop of efficiency just below
    1200 MeV, since there the protons are so slow
    that they stop in the target; this, in fact, fixed
    p_1 at 2.65 GeV/c.

However, between these limits, the detection efficiency
is practically 100%. Given such a low beam momentum,
the A2 is produced barely above threshold, i.e. with
very low total cross-section, as seen in Fig. 13; this
situation has however the advantage that the c.m. energy
is now as different as possible from the one where the
MMS data were obtained.

   The first A2 spectra, obtained in January 1968,
are shown in Fig. 14. The A2 region, sitting on top of
a broad maximum of the phase space, shows again a
two-peak structure. Note that the top histograms are
obtained from magnetic momentum measurement, the
lower from p_3 through time-of-flight. Histograms to the
left show the total spectra, those to the right only those
spectra where X^- goes into three charged particles. The
over-all A2 occurs now with a signal to background ratio
of only 1:5 as compared to 1:1.5 in the MMS data.

   Having seen that the double peak structure repeats
we dismantled the CBS entirely in February 1968 and
reassembled it differently in such a way, that the solid
angle was increased by a factor 2, and with a modified
magnetic optics such that now all events, independent of

mass, fall into one and the same c.m. interval.

In March 1968 the system was running again at p_1 = 2.65 GeV/c; the results are shown in Fig. 15. Again the A2 appears as a double bump in all selections. Note that in all CBS data the A2's are produced between 0 and 3.5° c.m.

The sum of January and March 1968 data is shown in Fig. 16, the statistics being now the same as in the former total MMS data (Fig. 8). Also the statistical significance of the hole is similar. We have finally fitted the total new A2 data from CBS to various one- and two-peak hypotheses (Fig. 17) and a quantitative comparison of the parameters is given in Table 1.

The conclusion is that both the new CBS data near A2 threshold and the earlier MMS data at high energy have in common that they reject the one-peak hypothesis [P (X) < 0.1%]. They are well fitted with double peaks, which appear equal in height and width (25-30 MeV) and have essentially the same positions (~1270 and 1320 MeV) in the old and new data.

It should be pointed out that the CBS data are only a few weeks old and they are to be considered as still preliminary, a more detailed analysis being under way at present.

III. BUBBLE CHAMBER DATA FROM BNL[7]

A great surprise came from a bubble chamber

experiment at BNL$^{(7)}$. 60,000 two-prong events were analysed of the reaction $\pi^- p \rightarrow p\, \pi^- +$ neutral MM at $p_1 = 6.0$ GeV/c. The missing-mass spectrum of the recoil proton, after applying the same angular and momentum cuts ($485 < p_3 < 660$ MeV/c, $45^o < \Theta_{lab} < 65^o$) as in the May 1965 6 GeV/c data of the MMS (fig. 4a) is shown in Fig. 18. There is a sharp dip centred around 1295 MeV and with an appearance very much like in the total MMS data. The numbers above the A2 region in Fig. 18 indicate the MMS two-peak parameters.

It is important to note, however, that no structure is seen in the low |t| data, i.e. for $p_3 < 485$ MeV/c (for the high |t| sample, i.e. $p_3 < 660$ MeV/c the statistics are so low, that no statement can be made). The BNL group quotes 14 ± 3 MeV, 10 ± 2 MeV and 12 ± 2 MeV as the FWHM resolutions for the low, medium and high |t| samples, respectively. In view of the uncertainties of these numbers it is not clear, whether the disappearance of the splitting at low |t| values is due to a broadening of resolution, as it seems in the MMS data, or a physical effect. In addition the authors point out that they find the η signal, seen in neutral MM, to be equal whether they take the events of the lower half A2 or of the upper half.

In conclusion it seems, that the compiled evidence for a two-peak structure in the A2 meson is convincing.

To find out, however, what goes on behind the scenes, a spin parity analysis of separate Dalitz-plots for the two halves of A2 is needed[8].

SPECULATIVE INTERPRETATIONS

1) Two independent resonances with the same $J^P = 2^+$, one being the "real A2" (i.e. L = 1 in $q\bar{q}$ model), the other belonging to the L = 3 supermultiplet of the $q\bar{q}$ system and falling due to spin-orbit splitting into the A2 region. Both states could go into $\rho \pi$ and they would interfere.

2) A double pole with $J^P = 2^+$; as suggested, for example, by J. S. Bell (CERN) [consequence: look for more double poles, e.g. K* (1400) and f^o].

3) One peak is the real A2 with $J^P = 2^+$; the other is the isotriplet state of the first radial excitation of the 0^- nonet in a $q\bar{q}$ model (Zweig, Philadelphia Conference 1968).

REFERENCES

1.   B. Maglic and G. Costa, "A Method for the search for unstable particles using Jacobian peaks in angular distribution," Physics Letters 18, 185 (1965)

2.   H. R. Blieden, D. Freytag, J. Geibel, A. R. F. Hassan, W. Kienzle, F. Lefebvres, B. Levrat, B. Msglic, J. Seguinot and A. J. Smith,

"Observation of ρ^- meson with a missing-mass spectrometer operating in region of 'Jacobian peaks'," Physics Letters **19**, 444 (1965).

3. B. Levrat, C. A. Tolstrup, P. Schubelin, C. Nef, M. Martin, B. Maglic, W. Kienzle, M. N. Focacci, L. Dubal and G. Chikovani, "Structure within the R (1675) boson and possible structure within the A2 (1290)," Physics Letters **22**, 714 (1966).

4. M. N. Focacci, W. Kienzle, B. Levrat, B. Maglic, and M. Martin, "Mass spectrum of bosons from 500 to 2500 MeV in the reaction $\pi^- + p \; p + X^-$ observed by a missing-mass spectrometer," Physics Letters **17**, 890 (1966).

5. G. Chikovani, M. N. Focacci, W. Kienzle, C. Lechanoine, B. Levrat, B. Maglic, M. Martin, P. Schubelin, L. Dubal, M. Fischer, P. Grieder, H. A. Neal and C. Nef, "Evidence for a two-peak structure in the A2 meson," Physics Letters **25B**, 44 (1967).

6. G. Chikovani, R. Baud, H. Benz, B. Bosnjakovic, G. Damgaard, M. N. Focacci, W. Kienzle, R. Klanner, C. Lechanoine, M. Martin, C. Nef, P. Schubelin and A. Weitsch, "Confirmation of a two-peak structure in the A2 meson produced in $\pi^- p \rightarrow pA2^-$ at 2.65 GeV/c," Preliminary results of the CERN Boson Spectrometer, presented at this conference.

7.   D. J. Crennell, K. W. Lai, J. M. Scarr, U.
      Karshon and I. O. Skillicorn, "Confirmative
      evidence for an A2 splitting with the 80 in. HBC
      of the BNL, " Preliminary results   submitted to
      this Conference (courtesy Dr. Kwan Lai).

8.   When this report was finished, the BNL data
      appeared in publication: D. J. Crennell, U.
      Karshon, K. W. Lai, J. M. Scarr, I. O.
      Skillicorn, Phys. Rev. Letters $\underline{20}$, 1318 (1968).
      Parameters of their two peaks: M_1 = 1269 ($\pm$5)
      MeV, Γ_1 = 24 ($\pm$10) MeV, M_2 = 1315 ($\pm$5) MeV,
      Γ_2 = 12 ($\pm$10) MeV. The interesting new results
      compared to the data shown at the Philadelphia
      Conference are the narrow width of the $K_1^0 K_1^0$
      peak and the fact that it falls nearly on the
      higher of the two A2 peaks; therefore the authors
      suggest that there are two difference resonances
      ($A2^{high}$ being the conventional A2, $A2^{low}$ being a
      candidate for J^P = 1^-, 3^-, ...). The $K_1^0 K_1^0$ peak
      has the parameters M = 1311 ($\pm$5) MeV, Γ = 21
      ($\pm^{10}_{6}$) MeV. This result would rule out the double-
      pole hypothesis.

Table 1

A comparison of parameters for one Breit–Wigner resonance, two incoherent Breit Wigner resonances and double pole fits to the A2 region.

Instrument	P_1 (GeV/c)	One Breit-Wigner resonance			Two incoherent Breit Wigner resonances			Double pole		Significance of hole
		$\bar{M}$ (A2) (MeV)	Γ_{tot} (MeV)	Confidence level	M_1 (MeV) Γ_1 (MeV)	M_2 (MeV) Γ_2	Confidence level	$\bar{M}$ (MeV) Confidence level		
CERN Missing Mass Spectr. (1965–67)	6.0 7.0 7.0	1297 ± 12	95 ± 15	0.1%	1274 ± 12 29 ± 8	1320 ± 12 35 ± 8	15%	1296 ± 12 30 ± 8 (70%)		5.5 stan. dev.
CERN Boson Spectr. (1968)	2.65	1292 ± 8	75 ± 10	0.1%	1266 ± 8 28 ± 5	1319 ± 8 28 ± 5	50%	1291 ± 8 30 ± 8 (70%)		4.5 stan. dev.
BNL 80" Bubble Ch. Crennell et al. (1968)	6.0 $\pi^- p$	1287 ± 10	94^{+30}_{-20}		1269 ± 5 24 ± 10	1315 ± 5 12 ± 10				> 5 stan. dev.

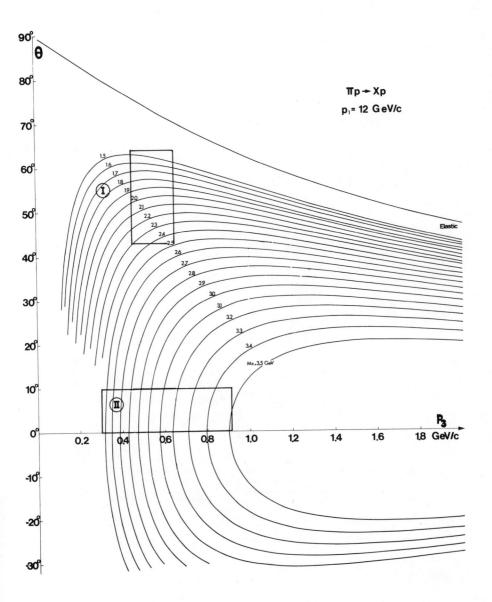

Fig. 1: Kinematics of the reaction $\pi^- p \to p \, X^-$ for an arbitrarily
chosen beam momentum p_1 = 12 GeV/c. This is to illustrate
the region of operation of:

I) the Missing-mass Spectrometer ("Jacobian peaks"), MMS
II) the CERN Boson Spectrometer ("0° method"), CBS

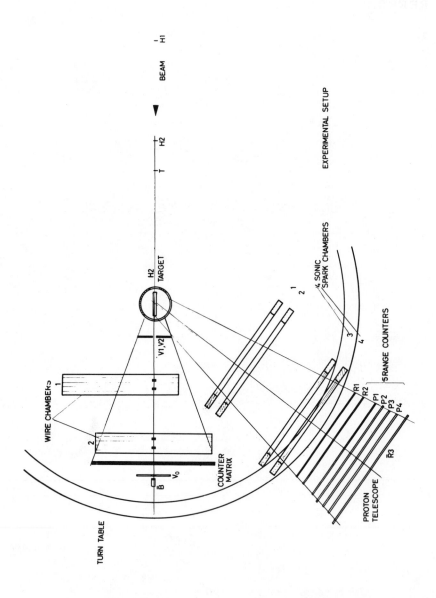

Fig. 2:   CERN Missing-mass Spectrometer, layout 1967.

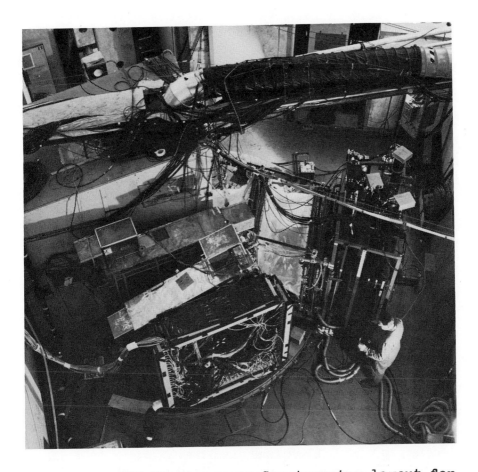

Fig. 3: CERN Missing-mass Spectrometer layout for
A2 runs 1967. Proton telescope on the
right, decay analyser below, beam comes
from left on top.

W. KIENZLE

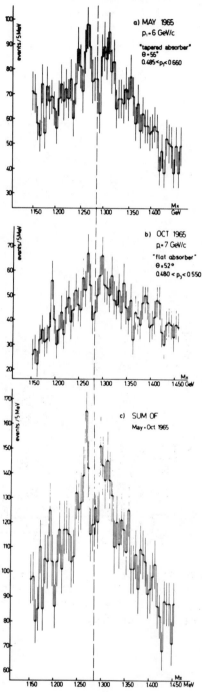

Fig. 4: Earliest results on A2 (1965).

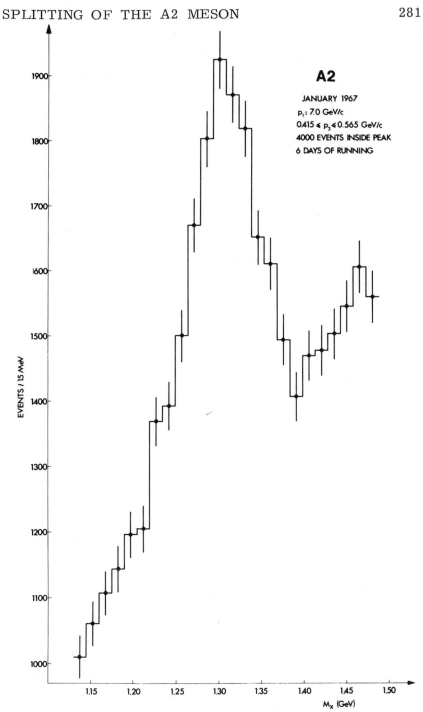

Fig. 5: Total A2 obtained with improved Missing-mass Spectrometer 1967.

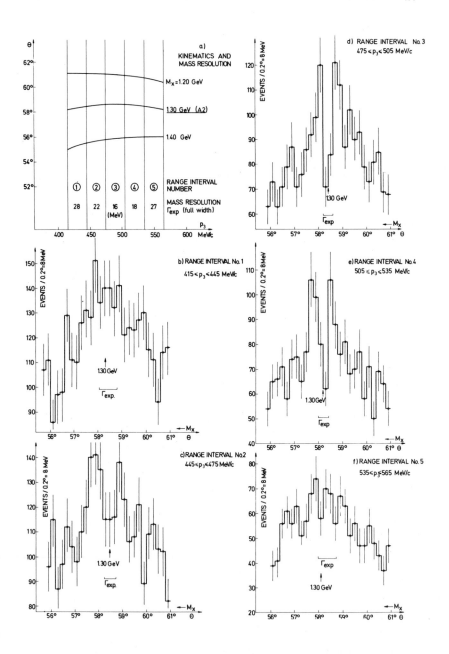

Fig. 6: (a) Kinematics. (b) - (f) Mass spectra in the A2 region
in fine bins for sub-samples with varying resolutions $\Gamma_{exp.}$,
as obtained with the improved MMS, 1967.

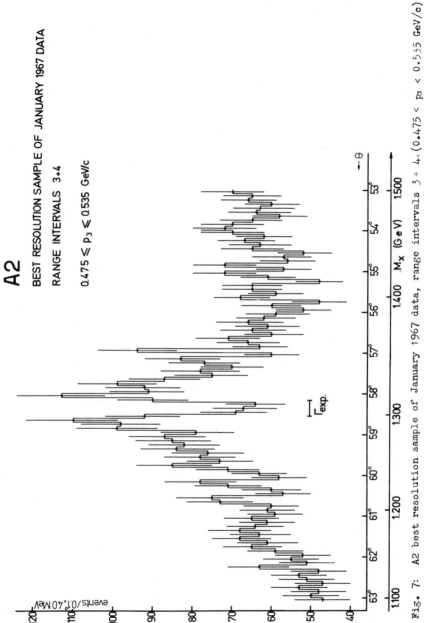

Fig. 7:   A2 best resolution sample of January 1967 data, range intervals 3 + 4. (0.475 < p_3 < 0.535 GeV/c)

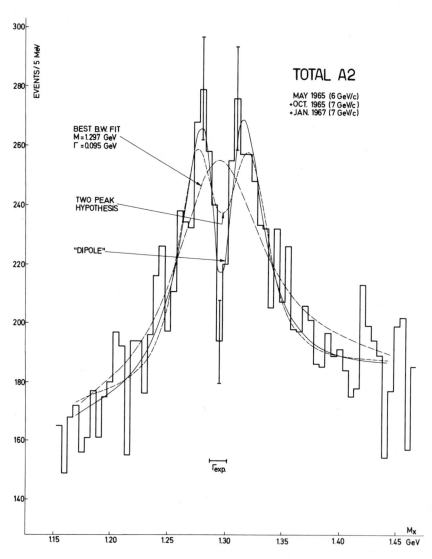

Fig. 8:   Total A2.   (May 1965 + October 1965 + January 1967).
          The following fits were obtained:

              i) a single Breit-Wigner curve (dash-point line);
             ii) two incoherent Breit-Wigner curves (dashed line);
            iii) a "double pole" (full line).
            (For parameters see Table 1.)

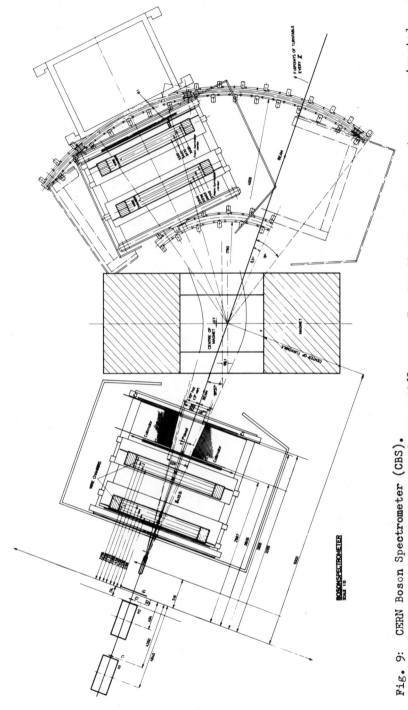

Fig. 9: CERN Boson Spectrometer (CBS).
Experimental set-up for the January 1968 run. For the March run, the system was contracted
in order to gain solid angle and change magnetic optics.

Fig. 10:   Boson Spectrometer (q5 beam, South Hall).
           Experimental set-up as of January 1968.
           The beam comes from the upper left side,
           proton telescope on the right.

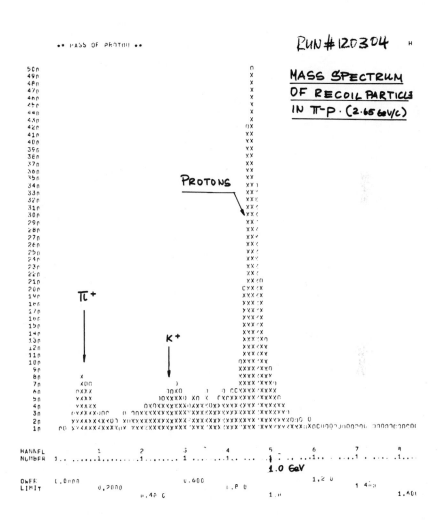

Fig. 11: Mass spectrum of recoil particles in π^-p collisions at 2.65 GeV/c.
The mass is obtained by dividing the momentum measured by the
magnet by $\beta\gamma$ obtained from time-of-flight from T_2 to R_1

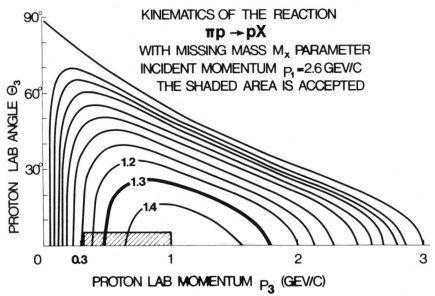

Fig. 12: Kinematical condition in which the CBS A2 data were taken, i.e. lab angle   versus lab
momentum p₃ for recoil protons in π⁻p → pX⁻ at 2.65 GeV/c.   The region covered in the
January run is shaded.

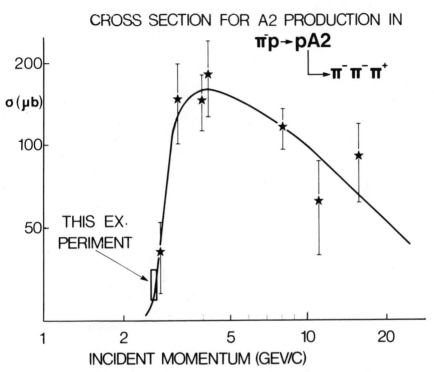

CROSS SECTION FOR A2 PRODUCTION IN
$\bar{\pi}p \rightarrow pA2$
$\hookrightarrow \pi^- \pi^- \pi^+$

σ(μb)

THIS EX·
PERIMENT

INCIDENT MOMENTUM (GEV/C)

Fig. 13:   Excitation curve for A2 production in $\pi^- p \rightarrow pA2^- (A2 \rightarrow \pi^- \pi^- \pi^+)$.
(Compilation by D.R.O. Morrison, CERN TC Division).   This is to
illustrate the difference in c.m. energy between the MMS and the CBS data.

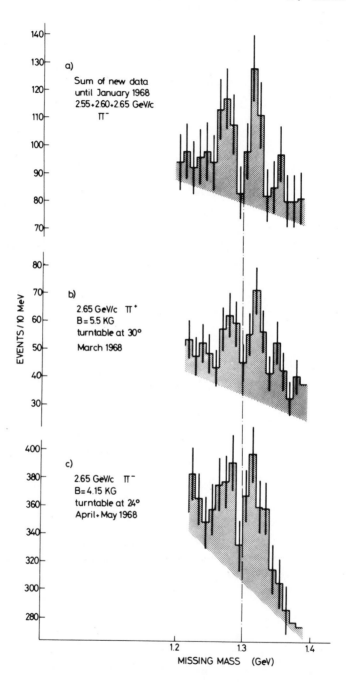

FIG. 14: Appearance of the splitting under different experimental conditions
CERN Boson Spectrometer 1968

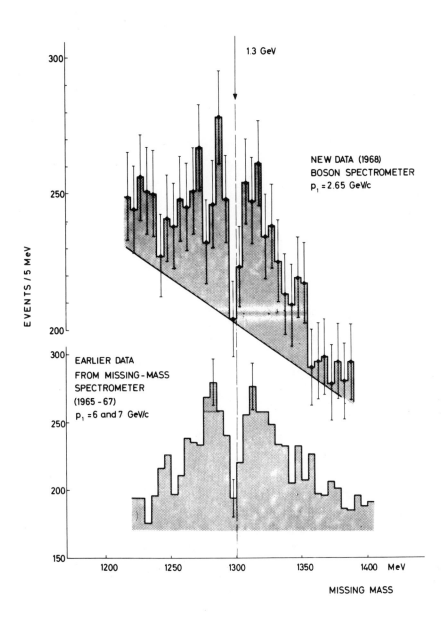

FIG. 15

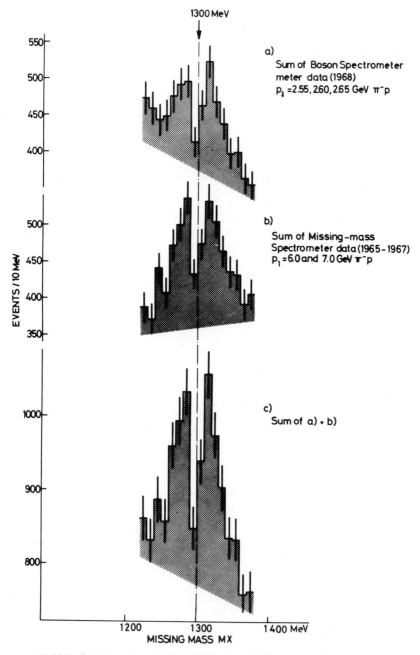

FIG.16: Compilation of the total A2 data from CERN Boson Spectrometer(0°method) 1968, and CERN Missing - mass Spectrometer (Jacobian peak method) 1965-67

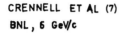

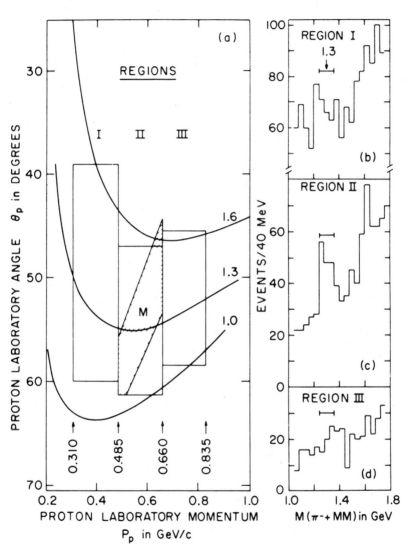

FIG. 17

CRENNELL ET AL (7)

BNL, 6 GeV/c

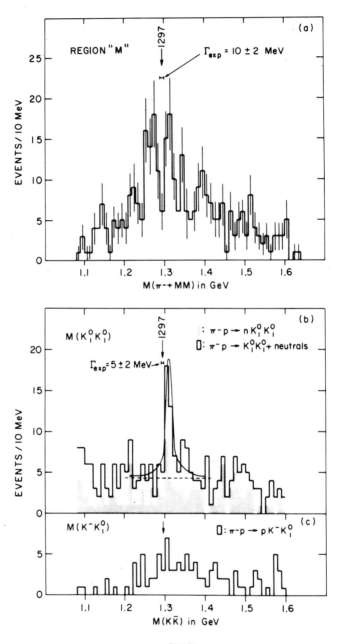

FIG.18

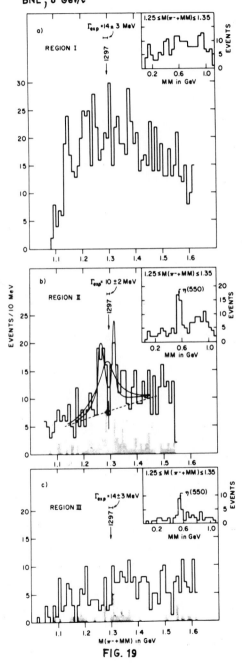

FIG. 19

DOUBLE POLES

Alfred S. Goldhaber
State University of New York
  at Stony Brook,
Stony Brook, New York 11790

The symmetrical split peak shown by Kienzle leads one to speculate on several possible explanations. Let us consider here the possibility that the split peak comes from a coherent effect in a state of definite spin-parity.

Ignoring the spin of the ρ, we can write the elastic scattering amplitude for ρ on π as

$$T = \sum_{\ell} (2\ell + 1)\, T_{\ell}\, P_{\ell}\, (\cos \theta)$$

$$T_{\ell} = \frac{1}{2i} (e^{2i\delta_{\ell}} - 1) \tag{1}$$

For a single Breit-Wigner resonance, T_{ℓ} has a pole at $E = M - \frac{i}{2}\Gamma$, so, near the pole,

$$e^{2i\delta} \approx \frac{E - M - \frac{i}{2}\Gamma}{E - M + \frac{i}{2}\Gamma} \tag{2}$$

We assume purely elastic scattering, and therefore

$$\left| e^{2i\delta} \right| = 1 \tag{3}$$

This automatically requires the form (2) up to a slowly varying phase factor $e^{2i\nu}$, but ν must be small if T_ℓ is small outside the resonance region.

Suppose two resonances are found in the same partial wave. This is most naturally described by making $e^{2i\delta}$ the product of two factors like (2):

$$e^{2i\delta} = \frac{E-M-\frac{i}{2}\Gamma}{E-M+\frac{1}{2}\Gamma} \cdot \frac{E-M'-\frac{i}{2}\Gamma'}{E-M'+\frac{i}{2}\Gamma'} \tag{4}$$

If the two resonances have the same width, this expression becomes symmetrical about the mean mass $\overline{M} = \frac{1}{2}(M+M')$:

$$T_\ell = \frac{-(E-\overline{M})\Gamma}{(E-\overline{M})^2 - \frac{\Gamma^2}{4} - \Delta^2 + i(E-\overline{M})\Gamma} \tag{5}$$

where $\Delta = \frac{1}{2}(M'-M)$. This expression vanishes at $E = M$ and has resonant peaks at

$$E-\overline{M} = \pm\sqrt{\frac{\Gamma^2}{4} + \Delta^2}; \quad T_\ell = i.$$

Clearly, in the case at hand $\Delta \lesssim \frac{\Gamma}{2}$ if we want to fit the split A_2; a tempting choice is $\Delta = 0$. Now T_ℓ has a second-order pole, or double pole, at $E = M - \frac{i}{2}\Gamma$. Our way of reaching this result suggests a general conclusion, that double poles result from a degeneracy of two ordinary poles. The example discussed has the disadvantage that there is no direct way to verify that the double pole comes from degeneracy because it is seen only in a single channel of an elastic scattering process. One could call this an "intrinsic" double pole.

A simple alternative picture has been suggested by Lassila and Ruuskanen. Suppose that there are two mesons, A_2 and A_2', of the same quantum numbers, and coupled to each other by virtual interactions. The amplitude for production of a particular multimeson state μ in πp collisions is given by

$$A(\mu) = \sum_{i,j=1}^{2} \mu_i \, D_{ij} \, a_j \tag{6}$$

Here a_j is the amplitude for producing meson $j\,(A_2$ or $A_2')$ in πp collisions, D_{ij} is the propagator for the two coupled resonances, and μ_i is the coupling constant for decay of meson i to the state μ. Time reversal invariance is well known to require symmetry of scattering amplitudes for a given partial wave under interchange of initial and final states. One may show by similar arguments that the propagator D_{ij} is a symmetric matrix. By analogy with a single channel propagator we write $D = (E - \mathcal{M})^{-1}$ with

$$E - \mathcal{M} = \begin{pmatrix} E-M + \frac{i}{2} \Gamma & X \\ \\ X & E-M' + \frac{i}{2} \Gamma' \end{pmatrix} \qquad (7)$$

where X can be taken real by a suitable choice of A_2 and A_2'. The reality of X means that A_2 and A_2' decay into orthogonal states. If we want a double pole in $A(\mu)$, we must ask that Det (D) have a double pole, i.e., that Det $(E-\mathcal{M})$ have a double zero,

$$\text{Det}(E-\mathcal{M}) = (E - \overline{M} + \frac{i}{2} \overline{\Gamma})^2. \qquad (8)$$

The necessary conditions for (8) to hold are

$$(M - M')(\Gamma - \Gamma') = 0 \qquad (9a)$$

and

$$\frac{(\Gamma - \Gamma')^2}{4} - (M - M')^2 = X^2 \geq 0 \qquad (9b)$$

thus, we have

$$\overline{M} = M = M', \quad \overline{\Gamma} = \frac{1}{2}(\Gamma + \Gamma'), \quad X = \pm (\Gamma - \Gamma') \qquad (9c)$$

To choose the right value of X, we write

$$D = \left(\frac{1}{E-\overline{M}+ \frac{i}{2}\overline{\Gamma}} \right)^2 \begin{pmatrix} E-M+ \frac{i\Gamma'}{2} & -X \\ \\ -X & E-M+ \frac{i\Gamma}{2} \end{pmatrix} \qquad (10)$$

yielding

$$A(\mu) = \left(\frac{1}{E-\overline{M}+ \frac{i}{2}\overline{\Gamma}} \right)^2 \left[(E-M)(\mu_1 a_1 + \mu_2 a_2) \right.$$

$$+ \frac{i\Gamma'}{2} \mu_1 a_1 + \frac{i\Gamma}{2} \mu_2 a_2 - X(\mu_1 a_2 + \mu_2 a_1) \Big] \qquad (11)$$

This will give a split peak only if the last three terms in (11) add up to zero. Lassila and Ruuskanen achieve this by setting $\Gamma' = 0$ and $\mu_2 = a_2 = 0$. In other words A_2' is degenerate in mass with A_2, does not decay, and is not produced in $p\pi$ collisions. It has a strong virtual coupling to A_2, so that an A_2 which is produced can turn into an A_2', just as a K^0 meson can turn into a $\bar{K}^0$. However, the A_2' has to turn back into an A_2 before decaying. It is this peculiar virtual coupling to A_2' which leads to the double pole. Relaxing the conditions $\Gamma' = 0$, etc., we see that there might exist a very narrow (few MeV) resonance degenerate in mass with A_2 and decaying to different channels, e.g. $K\bar{K}$ or $\eta\pi$. One simple possibility would be that the dominant channel for A_2 decay is $\rho\pi$ in a P wave, and for A_2' is $\rho\pi$ in a F wave.

In any case, this example makes clear that a symmetrical split peak is a very special effect, which requires more than the existence of a double pole in the S-matrix, namely the dominance of a single channel of the resonant system.

I thank R.F. Peierls for a helpful comment.

REFERENCES

M.L. Goldberger and K.M. Watson, Collision
Theory, Wiley (1964), Ch. 8, (especially 8.6);
Phys. Rev. 136, B1472 (1964).

J.S. Bell and C.J. Goebel, Phys. Rev. 138,
B1198 (1965).

K.E. Lassila and P.V. Ruuskanen, Phys. Rev.
Let. 17, 490 (1966), 19, 762 (1967).

Experimental Review of Meson Resonances Decaying into (K$\overline{\text{K}}$) States *

Kwan Wu Lai

Brookhaven National Laboratory

Upton, New York

There are four isosinglet mesons (φ, S*, f^o, f*) and three isotriplet mesons (π_V, A_2, g_1) having K$\overline{\text{K}}$ decay mode as shown in Table I.

I shall review the ones which either are less well established or have significant recent developments (since the 1966 Berkeley International Conference on High Energy Physics).

1) φ: no new information.

2) S*:

a) <u>Recall the situation of the S* at the 1966 Berkeley Conference</u>.[1]

The S* has been observed mainly from the reaction

$$\pi^- p \to n K_1^0 K_1^0 \tag{1}$$

as well as

$$\bar{p} p \to \pi^+ \pi^- K_1^0 K_1^0 \text{ in flight at 1.2 GeV/c} \tag{2}$$

Fig. 1 is a plot of the $K_1^0 K_1^0$ mass distribution as

TABLE I

Meson Resonances Decaying into $(K\bar{K})$ System

(April, 1968)

	(m, Γ)	$(_I{}^G J^P)$	Observed Decay Mode	πN	$\bar{K}N$	$\bar{p}N$
isosinglet	ϕ (1020, 3)	$0^-\ 1^-$	$\underline{K_1^0 K_2^0}$, K^+K^-, $\rho\pi$(?)	π (~2 GeV/c)	yes	yes
	s^* (1068, 80)	$0^+\ 0^+$	$\underline{K_1^0 K_1^0}$, $\pi\pi$(?)	yes	no	yes
	f^0 (1270,120)	$0^+\ 2^+$	$K_1^0 K_1^0$ (?), $\underline{\pi\pi}$	yes	yes	yes
	f^* (1515, 80)	$0^+\ 2^+$	$\underline{K_1^0 K_1^0}$, K^+K^-, $\pi\pi\pi$(?), $K^*\bar{K}$(?), $\eta\eta$(?)	π^- (6 GeV/c)	yes	no
isotriplet	π_v (1016, 25)	$1^-\ 0^+$	$\underline{K^\pm K^0}$, $\eta\pi$(?)	no	no	at rest
	A_2 (1300, 80)	$1^-\ 2^+$	$K^\pm K^0$, $K_1^0 K_1^0$, $\rho\pi$, $\underline{\eta\pi}$	yes	yes	yes
	g_1 (1630,150)	$1^+ {\geq}3^-$	$K^\pm K^0$, $K_1^0 K_2^0$ (?), $\underline{\pi\pi}$	$\pi^\pm$ (6 GeV/c)	K^- (4.2 GeV/c) ?	no

___ : main decay mode.

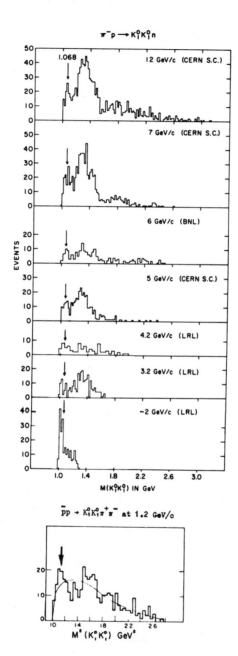

Fig. 1   Compilation of data on the $K_1^O K_1^O$
         mass distribution.
         (Ref. 2,3,4,5)

a function of the incident π^- momentum in reaction
(1).[2,3,4] It is evident that a marked low mass
enhancement centered about 60 MeV from the threshold is seen in all experiments except the experiment at the incident momentum of about 2 GeV/c
which shows a peak at the threshold.[3] I will
return to this point later. Also in Fig. 1 the
$K_1^0 K_1^0$ mass spectrum from reaction (2) at 1.2 GeV/c
shows a peak at the S* mass.[5]

The evidence for:[2]

(1) <u>I = 0</u> comes from the absence
of an enhancement near the S* region in the $(K^\pm K_1^0)$
system from the reactions:

$$\pi^+ p \to pK^+ K_1^0 \qquad (3)$$

$$\pi^- p \to pK^- K_1^0 \qquad (4)$$

as shown in Fig. 2(a). If the isospin of the S*
is one, one expects at least 29 ± 5 $K^\pm K_1^0$ events
in the corresponding region (below 1140 MeV) from
charge independence. The observation of only four
events implies the I = 0 assignment for the S*.

(2) <u>C = P = +1</u> comes from its
$K_1^0 K_1^0$ decay mode which is allowed only for states
with $J^P = 0^+, 2^+$, etc.

(3) <u>J = 0</u> is shown in Fig. 2(e).
The $K_1^0 K_1^0$ scattering angular distribution agrees
well with isotropy. This evidence coupled with
the low Q-value (72 MeV) of the decay into $K_1^0 K_1^0$

favors zero spin for the S*.

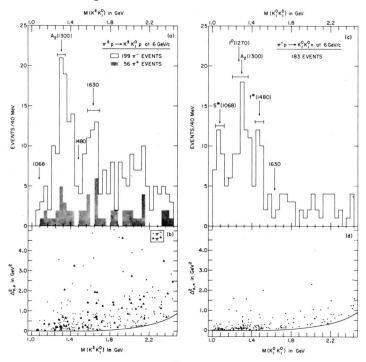

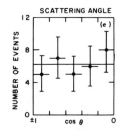

Fig. 2 (a) and (c) mass spectra of $K^{\pm}K^O$ and $K_1^O K_1^O$, and (b) and (d) Chew-Low plots of the $t_{p \to p}$ vs $M(K^{\pm}K_1^O)$ and $t_{p \to n}$ vs $M(K_1^O K_1^O)$ for reactions (1)(3) and (4). (e) the scattering angle $\cos\theta$ (folded about zero) of one K_1^O relative to the incident pion in the S* rest frame. The distribution is consistent with "isotropy" (solid curve) as expected for $J^P = 0^+$. (Ref. 2)

(4) <u>G = +1</u> for the S* because the G-parity of a neutral $K\bar{K}$ state is related to J and I by $G = (-1)^{J+I}$; the I = J = 0 of the S* requires G = +1 for the S*. Thus the S* can be produced by one pion exchange

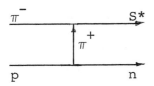

Fig. 2(d) shows the Chew-Low plot for reaction (1) from the BNL data. The $t_{p \to n}$ distribution of the events in the S* region is extremely peripheral (most of the events are below 0.1 GeV^2). The excitation function of the S* production cross section from reaction (1) is shown in Fig. 3.

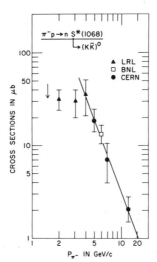

Fig. 3 Compilation of S* production cross
sections in the $K\bar{K}$ system only.
(Ref. 2,3,4)

The cross section behavior of S* production is consistent with the $(\frac{1}{p_\pi^2})$ dependence. At 6 GeV/c, $\sigma(\pi^- p \to n S^*_{\ \hookrightarrow K\bar{K}})$ is about 13μb. The quantum numbers of the S* allow the $(2\pi)^0$ decay mode, however, the detection is made difficult due to copious production of the ρ^0 (~1mb) and f^0 (0.5mb) at this energy region.[6] This can be seen in Fig. 4(a), and only an upper limit was available ($\frac{\pi\pi}{K\bar{K}} \leq 2.5$ with 90% confidence).[2] Based on the phase space consideration alone $\frac{\pi\pi}{K\bar{K}}$ rate should be 2.7 for a spin zero assignment. However, a marked change occurs in

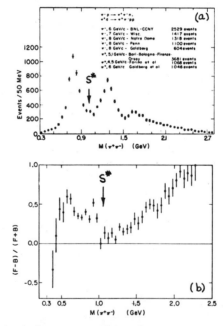

Fig. 4 (a) A compilation by Lai and Samios of the available data on $\pi^+\pi^-$ distribution (1966). See Ref.1,page 131. (b) A compilation by Veillet on the (F-B) / (F+B) ratio as a function of $\pi^+\pi^-$ mass distribution. (Ref. 1)

the $\pi^+\pi^-$ angular distribution at M($\pi^+\pi^-$) $\sim$ 1 GeV in the $\pi\pi$ rest frame from the reaction $\pi^- p \rightarrow \pi^+ \pi^- n$ as shown in Fig. 4(b). This effect has been only observed 'in the I_z = 0 $(\pi\pi)^o$ state. I will return to this point later.

Interpretation of any enhancement near a threshold is always difficult; possibilities are an S-wave resonance or S-wave complex scattering

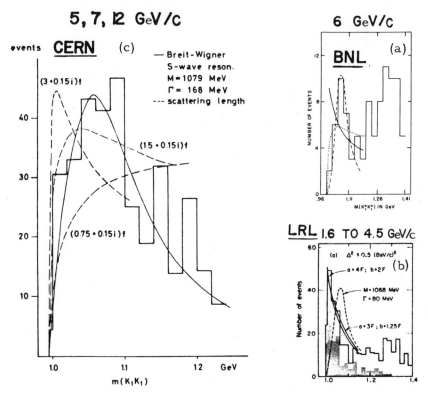

Fig. 5 (a) An S-wave resonance curve (dashed) and constant S-wave scattering length fits (dotted ±1.4 + 0.2 i F and solid ±4 + 0.2 i F) are shown. (Ref. 2)
(b) and (c) are similar fits from Ref. 4 and Ref. 3 respectively.

length (±a+ib) effect, and the S* is no exception.
Available data were fitted by both interpretations
(See Fig. 5), and an S-wave resonance fit to the
data is strongly favored with only one exception
(Berkeley low energy data,[3] see Fig. 5(b)).

   b) New Developments since the 1966
Berkeley Conference -

      (1) S* → K$\overline{\text{K}}$: A recent counter
spark chamber experiment by Argonne, University
of Illinois (Chicago Circle) and Notre Dame collaboration[7] has also shown evidence for the S* from
reaction (1) with good statistics. Fig. 6 is the
uncorrected data at 4 GeV/c and 5 GeV/c. The S*
enhancement is again peaked about 60 MeV from
the threshold.

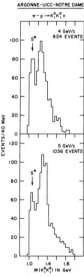

Fig. 6 Uncorrected data on the $K_1^0 K_1^0$ mass
        distribution from a counter spark chamber
        experiment. (Ref. 7)

(2) $\underline{S^* \rightarrow \pi^+ \pi^-}$: There are three experiments in which some evidence for the $S^* \rightarrow \pi^+ \pi^-$ are seen.

(i) $\underline{\overline{p}n \rightarrow \pi^+ \pi^- \pi^- \pi^o}$ at rest (Syracuse University and Rome collaboration):[8] A $\pi^+ \pi^-$ enhancement centered about 1.1 GeV is seen in this final state, and no other charged counterpart ($\pi^- \pi^o$, $\pi^- \pi^-$, $\pi^+ \pi^o$) is seen at this mass (Fig. 7).

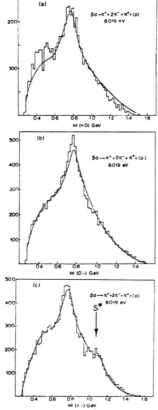

Fig. 7 Dipion mass spectra from $\overline{p}n \rightarrow \pi^- \pi^- \pi^+ \pi^o$ at rest. (Ref. 8)

This observation suggests an I = 0 assignment for this $\pi^+\pi^-$ enhancement which may be associated with the $S^* \to \pi^+\pi^-$. Search for $K\bar{K}$ decay mode is in progress in the similar final state

$$\bar{p}n \to \pi^-\pi^- S^*$$
$$\llcorner K_1^0 K_1^0$$
$$K^+ K^-$$

(ii) $\underline{\pi^-p \to n\pi^+\pi^-}$ at 3.1 to 3.6 GeV/c (Rutherford Lab.): A counter spark chamber experiment (Harwell, Southampton, U.C. London)[9] also observed a similar $\pi^+\pi^-$ enhancement about 1.1 GeV (see Fig. 8(a)). A compiled $\pi^+\pi^-$ mass spectrum from various bubble chamber data [10] in this same energy region also gave indication of a small fluctuation at this $\pi^+\pi^-$ mass (Fig. 8(b)).

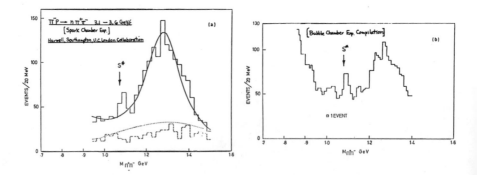

Fig. 8 (a) and (b) Mass spectra of the $\pi^+\pi^-$ from Ref. 9 and 10 respectively.

However, the apparent width of this enhancement from both spark chamber data and bubble chamber compiled data is of the order of 30 MeV. Because of the large background, a reliable estimation of the width is difficult, if not impossible.

(iii) $\underline{\pi^- p \to n \pi^+ \pi^-}$ at 6 GeV/c (Brookhaven National Laboratory): We have also examined our data in the reactions $\pi^- p \to n \pi^+ \pi^-$ as well as $p \pi^- \pi^o$ at 6 GeV/c. Dalitz plots for these two final states are shown in Fig. 9(a) and (b).

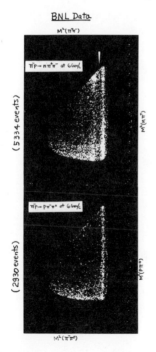

Fig. 9 (a) BNL data. Dalitz plot for $\pi^- p \to n \pi^+ \pi^-$. Structure in the $\pi^+ \pi^-$ mass band centered at 1 GeV^2 is indicated by an arrow, and (b) Dalitz plot for $\pi^- p \to p \pi^- \pi^o$.

As usual, strong ρ^0 and f^0 as well as some g^0
(Fig. 9(a)), and strong ρ^- and some g_1^- (Fig. 9(b)
formation are evident. There is, however, some
structure in the $\pi^+\pi^-$ mass band as indicated by
an arrow between the ρ^0 and the f^0. This $\pi^+\pi^-$
structure centered about 1 GeV, again, has no
charged counterpart as seen in Fig. 9(b). Strong
concentrations of events in low $(\pi N)^+$ mass ($\sim$1.1
to 1.5 GeV), such as π^+n in the $n\,\pi^+\pi^-$ and $\pi^0 p$
in the $p\,\pi^-\pi^0$ final states complicate the $\pi\pi$
analysis, in particular, in the forward hemisphere
of the $\pi\pi$ system. This complication may be due
to the proton dissociation effect (without form-
ing any $N^*_{1/2}$'s), which gives qualitative agreement with our observation; namely, the ratio of
the intensities $\frac{\pi^+n}{\pi^0 p} \simeq 2$. To see a weak $\pi^+\pi^-$ effect
such as the $S^*{\to}\pi^+\pi^-$, we therefore have to select
events in the backward hemisphere of the $\pi^+\pi^-$
system in order to reduce the background. This
is shown in Fig. 10.

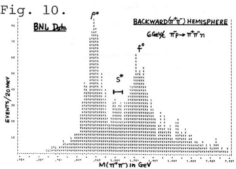

Fig. 10   BNL data. Mass spectrum of $\pi^+\pi^-$
events in the backward $\pi^+\pi^-$ hemisphere.

A marked $\pi^+\pi^-$ enhancement is clearly seen in the
mass region of the S*. We have tried to obtain
a limit for the branching ratio of $(\frac{\pi\pi}{K\bar{K}})^\circ = 1^{+0.6}_{-0.3}$.
Large errors on this value are due to our in-
adequacy of understanding of the $\pi\pi$ background
near the S* mass region. This similar $\pi^+\pi^-$ effect
was also observed in a compilation of high energy
πp experiments (4-8 GeV/c) in the same final state
by Veillet et al.,[11] when a selection of events
in the $\pi\pi$ backward hemisphere has been made.
(See Fig. 11).

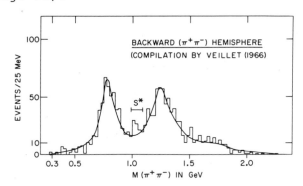

Fig. 11 Mass spectrum of $\pi^+\pi^-$ events in
the backward $\pi^+\pi^-$ hemisphere. Data
from a compilation by Veillet. (Ref. 11)

Additional evidence for resonance behaviors
in the I = 0 $\pi\pi$ state at the S* mass region comes
from a careful analysis of the $\pi\pi$ moments by
L. Gutay.[12] The details of this analysis can be
found in Appendix I.

Questions have been raised concerning the absence of the S* production in K^-N interaction as shown in Table I. For the $I^G = 0^+$ and $J^P = 0^+$ S*, the only exchange particles from $\pi^- p \to nS^*$ and $K^- p \to \Lambda S^*$ are π and K mesons respectively. It is well known that the cross section induced by a strangeness exchange in the t-channel is, in general, an order of magnitude suppressed from that of a non-strangeness exchange (for example:

$$\sigma(\pi^- p \to K^*(890)\Lambda)/\sigma(K^- p \to K^*(890)p) \sim \frac{1}{10}).\ [13]$$

To be more specific for the case of this isosinglet, the ratio of coupling constants $g^2_{pK\overline{\Lambda}} / g^2_{p\pi n}$ is ~1/2 if one uses the recently determined $\frac{F}{D+F}$ ratio to be 0.41.[14] Therefore, a suppression in the cross section of the S* production of a factor two to ten is expected in the $\overline{K}$ induced reaction in comparison with that from the π induced reaction. At the present level of bubble chamber experiments in $K^- p$ interactions[15] one expects, at best, ten visible $K^o_1 K^o_1$ events between the threshold and 1.14 GeV.

In summary, the existence of this $I^G = 0^+$, $J^P = 0^+$ S* is confirmed by numerous experiments in various reactions. The peak of this enhancement is ~60 MeV from the threshold and the resonance interpretation is strongly favored over the scattering length interpretation. In view of the mounting evidence for the $S^* \to \pi^+ \pi^-$, it is reasonable to

state that we now have an isosinglet scalar meson
together with other well established $J^P = 0^-$, 1^-,
2^+ mesons.

      3) f^0: no new information. Only
the mass of the f^0 meson is creeping up to 1270 ±
5 MeV if one uses only results from high energy
πp interactions (≥4 GeV/c).

      4) f*: recent results from a BNL
and Syracuse collaboration[16] showed some evidence
for the f*→η(550) $\pi\pi$, together with the results
of the K̄K moment analysis, ruling out the $J^P = 0^+$
assignment for the f*. The width of the f* obtained from the same experiment is 86 ± 23 MeV
whereas a similar experiment performed at Argonne
by Argonne and Northwestern collaboration[17] gave a
width of 35 ± 25 MeV with about one-fifth of the
events of the BNL and Syracuse experiment.

      5) π_V: This enhancement has been
only observed in the $\bar{p}p \to (KK)^{\pm} \pi^{\mp}$ reaction at rest.[18]
A fit to the whole Dalitz plot (see Fig. 12(a))-
including the K*(890), the K̄K at 1280 as well as
the π_V(1016) amplitudes - gives a satisfactory
complex scattering length for the π_V:
$a = +2.0 \begin{smallmatrix} +1.0 \\ -0.5 \end{smallmatrix}$ or $-2.3 \begin{smallmatrix} +0.3 \\ -4.0 \end{smallmatrix}$ and $b = 0 \begin{smallmatrix} +0.5 \\ -0 \end{smallmatrix}$ fermi.
If the sign of the "a" is negative it implies a
bound state below the K̄K threshold with a mass
$975 \begin{smallmatrix} +15 \\ -10 \end{smallmatrix}$ MeV and a width consistent with zero
(b ≈ 0). The quantum numbers ($I^G = 1^-$ and $J^P = 0^+$)

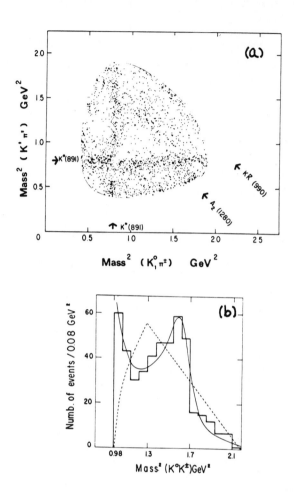

Fig. 12 (a) Dalitz plot for the reaction
$\bar{p}p \to K_1^0 K^\pm \pi^\mp$ at rest. (b) Mass squared
distribution of $K^\pm K_1^0$ with K*(890) removed.
Solid curve is a best fit to the data when
$\pi_V(1016)$, $K\bar{K}(1280)$ are included. The
dotted curve is phase space. (Ref. 18)

of the π_V may suggest a narrow resonance at ∼975

MeV with possible η(550) π decay mode which is in

remarkable agreement with the mass and width of

the recently discovered δ^-(965) peak.[19] Search

from the same experiment gives a negative result
for the $\pi_V \to \eta(550)\ \pi$ with an upper limit of $\frac{\eta\pi}{K\bar{K}} < 5$.
Assuming the π_V is in an SU_3 octet with symmetric
coupling to pseudo scalar mesons, one gets $\frac{\eta\pi}{K\bar{K}} \simeq 2$.

It is interesting to note, in this respect,
that an $\eta\pi$ enhancement of about 1.02 GeV was reported by Alliti et al.[20] from the reaction
$\pi^{\pm}p \to p\eta\pi^{\pm}$ as shown in Fig. 13. However, in the
$\pi^-p \to pK^-K^o$ there is no threshold K^-K^o enhancement.[2,3]

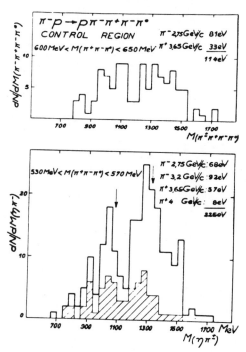

Fig. 13 Mass spectra for $\eta(550)\pi$ from the
reaction $\pi^{\pm}p \to p\eta\pi^{\pm}$. (Ref. 20)

There might be a contradiction in the rate of
$\pi_V \to \frac{\eta\pi}{K\overline{K}}$ if one identifies the $\pi_V(1016)$ observed in
the $\overline{p}p$ at rest with the $\eta\pi$ enhancement near 1020
MeV from the $\pi^- p$ interactions.

6) "A_2": In view of the evidence
for the splitting of the "A_2" from the CERN missing mass experiment [21] and from our bubble chamber
experiment at 6 GeV/c, [22] any serious discussion
concerning the "A_2"$\to K\overline{K}$ rate is irrelevant. However, one can examine the excitation function
of

$$\pi^- p \to p "A_2^-" \qquad \text{vs.} \qquad \pi^- p \to p "A_2^-"$$
$$\qquad \ \ \llcorner_{(K^- K_1^0)} \qquad \qquad \qquad \llcorner_{(\rho^0 \pi^0)} \ \text{and}$$

$$\pi^- p \to n "A_2^0" \qquad \text{vs.} \qquad \pi^+ n \to p "A_2^0"$$
$$\qquad \ \ \llcorner_{(K_1^0 \overline{K}_1^0)} \qquad \qquad \qquad \llcorner_{(\rho^{\mp} \pi^{\pm})} \ \text{as}$$

shown in Fig. 14. The production for the charged
"A_2" does not fall off as fast as that of the
neutral "A_2" for increasing energy. This observation suggests that the production mechanisms
for the charged and neutral "A_2" are different
and the I = 0 exchange in the t-channel may be
dominant at high energies. We note that the
branching ratio for the charged "A_2"$\to \frac{K\overline{K}}{\rho\pi}$ ~5% (also
in $\overline{p}p$ at rest) and for the neutral "A_2"$\to \frac{(K\overline{K})}{\rho\pi}$ ~10%.
This difference could be in some way due to the
underestimation of the $f^0 \to K_1^0 K_1^0$ rate. The excitation curve of the $f^0 \to (\pi\pi)^0$ production is also

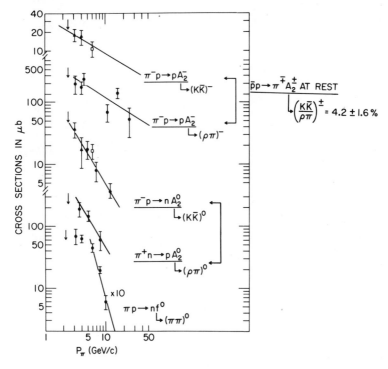

Fig. 14 Compilation of "A$_2$" and f^o
        production cross sections as a
        function of incident momentum.

shown for this comparison purpose.

_____

NOTE: Analysis of the K$_1^o$K$_1^o$ mass spectrum from
our BNL 6 GeV/c data reveals a narrow K$_1^o$K$_1^o$ peak
centered at 1311 ± 5 MeV which is in remarkable
agreement with the higher part of the split A$_2$.
Absence of a K$_1^o$K$_1^o$ in the lower A$_2$ mass peak
suggests that there are two different resonances
in the "A$_2$" mass region. Details will be published in Phys. Rev. Letters, June 3, 1968.

7) g_1: Possible evidence for a K̄K decay mode for this $I^G = 1^+$ and $J^P = 3^-$ (favored) meson [6] comes from two experiments $K^-p \rightarrow \Lambda K_1^o K_2^o$ at 4.2 GeV/c [23] and $\pi^{\pm}p \rightarrow pK^{\pm}K_1^o$ at 6 GeV/c. Limited statistics in the first experiment shed very little light on this enhancement. The results from our $\pi^{\pm}p$ experiment at 6 GeV/c are shown in Fig. 15.

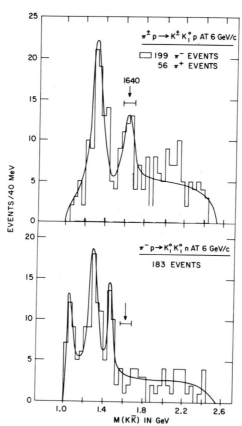

Fig. 15   BNL data (also shown in Fig. 2(a) and (c)). K̄K mass distribution from reactions (1), (3) and (4).

The presence of an enhancement in the $(K\bar{K})^{\pm}$ system centered at 1630 MeV, in addition to the charged "A_2" meson, is evident in Fig. 15(a). The neutral $K_1^o K_1^o$ mass projection shows marked enhancements centered at 1068, 1311 and 1480 MeV corresponding to S*, combination of f^o and "A_2^o", and f* respectively. We note that there is an absence of $K_1^o K_1^o$ events in the mass region of 1630 MeV. This observation suggests, not proves, that the charge conjugation and parity for the 1630 $K^{\pm} K_1^o$ mass state are odd. Limited statistics in the 1630 mass region precludes a spin determination, however, the moment analysis of the decay angular distributions of the $(K^{\pm} K_1^o)$ system shows structures in the high moments, and it is consistent with a high spin (J = 3) assignment for this $K^{\pm} K_1^o$ object. If we assume that this $K^{\pm} K_1^o$ object is an alternative decay mode of the $g_1(1630)$, one obtains a branching ratio $g_1^- \to \dfrac{K^- K^o}{\pi^- \pi^o}$ = 12 $^{+5}_{-3}$ %.

I wish to thank Dr. Uri Karshon for reading the manuscript.

---
*
Work performed under the auspices of the U.S. Atomic Energy Commission.

REFERENCES

1. G. Goldhaber, in Proceedings of Thirteenth International Conference on High-Energy Physics, Berkeley, 1966 (University of California Press, Berkeley, 1967), p. 123.

2. D.J. Crennell, G.R. Kalbfleisch, K.W. Lai, J.M. Scarr, T.G. Schumann, I.O. Skillicorn and M.S. Webster, Phys. Rev. Letters 16, 1025 (1966).

3. R.I. Hess, O.I. Dahel, L.M. Hardy, J. Kirz, and D.H. Miller, Phys. Rev. Letters 17, 1109 (1966) and R.I. Hess (Ph.D. Thesis) UCRL-16832, June 24, 1966.

4. W. Beusch, W.F. Fischer, B. Gobbi, M. Pepin, E. Polgar, P. Astbury, G. Brauti, G. Finocchiaro, J.C. Lassalle, A. Michelini, K.W. Terwilliger, D. Websdale, C.H. West, Phys. Letters 25B, 357 (1967).

5. J. Barlow, E. Lillestol, L. Montanet, L. Tallone-Lombardi, C. D'Andlau, A. Astier, L. Dobrzynski, S. Wojcicki, A.M. Adamson, J. Duboc, F. James, M. Goldberg, R.A. Donald, R. James, J.E. Lys, T. Nisar, Nuovo Cimento 50A, 701 (1967).

6. D.J. Crennell, P.V.C. Hough, G.R. Kalbfleisch, K.W. Lai, J.M. Scarr, T.G. Schumann, I.O. Skillicorn, R.C. Strand, M.S. Webster, P. Baumel, A.H. Bachman, and R.M. Lea, Phys. Rev. Letters 18, 323 (1967).

7. Argonne, University of Illinois (Chicago Circle) and Notre Dame Collaboration and Dr. P. Kenney and Dr. T. Groves, Private Communication.

8. Syracuse University and University of Rome
    Collaboration and Dr. T.E. Kalogeropoulos,
    Private Communication.

9. C. Whitehead, J.G. McEwen, R.J. Ott,
    D.K. Aitken, G. Bennett, R.E. Jennings,
    Rutherford Laboratory Preprint (1968).

10. Aachen-Birmingham-Bonn-Hamburg-London-
    Munchen Collaboration. Phys. Letters 10,
    240 (1964); Y.Y. Lee, B.P. Roe, D. Sinclair
    and J.C. Vander Velde, Phys. Rev. Letters 12,
    342 (1964); V. Hagopian and W. Selove, Phys.
    Rev. Letters 10, 533 (1963); Saclay-Orsay-
    Bologna Collaboration, Phys. Letters 19, 65
    (1965).

11. Ref. 1, page 130.

12. Dr. L. Gutay, Private Communication.

13. Dr. E. Flaminio, Private Communication.

14. J.K. Kim, Phys. Rev. Letters 19, 1079 (1967).

15. An exposure of 20 events/μb, for example, is
    a typical K$^-$p experiment. After correction
    for both visible K$^o_1$ decays one gets 20/9
    events/μb. Assuming S* production cross
    section of $\sim$5 μb in the K$^-$p interaction,
    one obtains about ten K$^o_1$K$^o_1$ events in the S*
    mass region.

16. V.E. Barnes, P.J. Dornan, G.R. Kalbfleisch,
    G. London, R. Palmer, R.R. Rau, N.P. Samios,
    I.O. Skillicorn, M. Goldberg, K. Jaeger,
    C.Y. Chang and J. Leitner, Phys. Rev.
    Letters 19, 964 (1967) and Dr. V.E. Barnes,
    Private Communication.

17. R. Ammar, R.E.P. Davis, C. Hwang, W. Kropac, J. Mott, B. Werner, S. Dagan, M. Derrick, F. Schweingruber, and J. Simpson, Phys. Rev. Letters 19, 1071 (1967) and Dr. R. Ammar and Dr. M. Derrick, Private Communication.

18. A. Astier, J. Cohen-Ganouna, M. Della Negra, B. Marechechal, L. Montanet, M. Thomas, M. Baubillier, J. Duboc, Phys. Letters 25B, 294 (1967).

19. W. Kienzle, B.C. Maglic, B. Levrat, F. Lefebvres, D. Freytag and H.R. Blieden, Phys. Letters 19, 438 (1965).

20. J. Alitti, J.P. Baton, B. Deler, M. Neveu-Rene, J. Crussard, J. Ginestet, A.H. Tran, R. Gessaroli, and A. Romano, Phys. Letters 15, 69 (1965).

21. G. Chikovani, M.N. Focacci, W. Kienzle, C. Lechanoine, B. Levrat, B. Maglic, M. Martin, P. Schübelin, L. Dubal, M. Fischer, P. Grieder, H.A. Neall and C. Nef, Phys. Letters 25B, 44 (1967); W. Kienzle in Proceedings of Informal Meeting on Experimental Meson Spectroscopy, Philadelphia, April 1968 (to be published).

22. D.J. Crennell, U. Karshon, K.W. Lai, J.M. Scarr and I.O. Skillicorn, to be published in Phys. Rev. Letters (June 3, 1968).

23. G.S. Abrams, B. Kehoe, R.G. Glasser, B. Sechi-Zorn and G. Wolsky, Phys. Rev. Letters 18, 620 (1967).

APPENDIX I

The Phase Shifts

The world compilation of δ_o^o by L. Gutay.

The references;

Purdue I; L.J. Gutay, P.B. Johnson, F.J. Loeffler, R. L. McIlwain, D.H. Miller, R.B. Willmann and P.L. Csonka, Phys. Rev. Letters 18, 142 (1967).

Purdue II; P.B. Johnson, L.J. Gutay, R.L. Eisner, P.R. Klein, R.E. Peters, R.J. Sahni, W.L. Yen, and G.W. Tautfest, Phys. Rev. 163, 1497 (1967).

Baton and Reignier; J.P. Baton and J. Reignier, Nuovo Cimento 36, 1149 (1965).

Notre Dame-Purdue-SLAC; P.B. Johnson, J.A. Poirier, J.H. Campbell, L.J. Gutay, Z.G.T. Guiragossian (to be published).

UCLA; E. Malamud and P.E. Schlein, Phys. Rev. Letters 19, 1056 (1967).

Wisconsin; W.D. Walker, J. Caroll, A. Garfinkel, and B.Y. Oh, Phys. Rev. Letters 18, 630 (1967).

Jones et al.; L.W. Jones, E. Bleuler, D.O. Caldwell, B.E. Elsner, D. Hartung, W.C. Middelkoop and B. Zackarov, Phys. Rev. 166, 1405 (1968).

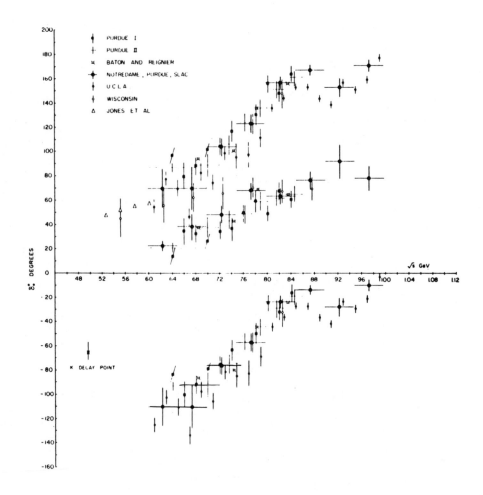

The Lengendre Polynomials

Source of information;   Notre Dame–Purdue–SLAC
collaboration.   Reference is given on the
previous page.

   Beam momentum;   3.6–4.16 GeV.

   Statistics;   8000 events of the final state
            $\pi^+\pi^-n$.   Over half of it Purdue
            data at 4.1 GeV/c.

Interpretation;

            The graph represents the
            coefficients of
            $$W(\theta) = A_o + \sum_{\ell=1}^{4} A_\ell P_\ell(\cos\theta)$$

            Note;   a.   Sharp rise of A_2/A_o
                    at $\sqrt{s} \sim 1$ Gev.

                    b. $A_1/A_o \sim 0$ at $\sqrt{s} \sim$
                    1 GeV.

                    c.   Dip in A_2/A_o at $\sqrt{s} \sim$
                    1.1 GeV.

                    d.   Dip in A_4/A_o at $\sqrt{s} \sim$
                    1.1 GeV.

   Remarks;   The above structure indicates a
            very rapid variation of δ_o^o.   Because
            there is some δ_o^2 (contributing
            positively to A_o) it is possible
            that $\delta_o^o(1\ \text{GeV}) \sim \begin{cases} 180^o \\ 0^o \end{cases}$ and then

passes through resonance with
$\Gamma < 100$ MeV, $M_{S*} \sim 1.1$ GeV.

LEGENDRE   COEFFICIENTS   FOR $t \leq .2 \, (GeV/c)^2$

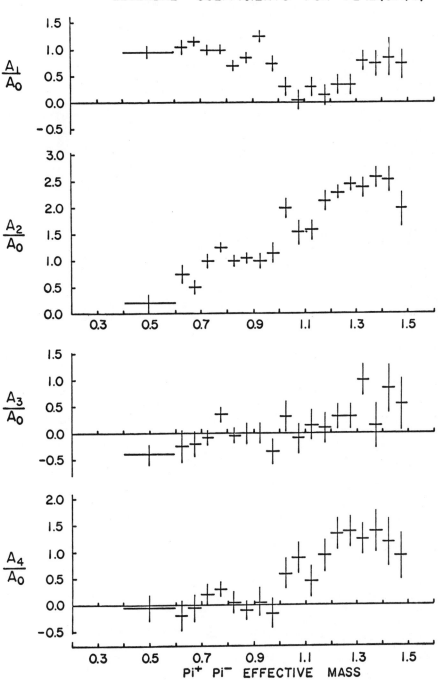

THE R-REGION AND OTHER

MULTIPION RESONANCES [*]

T. Ferbel
University of Rochester
Rochester, New York

In this note[1] I hope to discuss some new information which I have acquired from various people regarding the f^o, the B-meson and the resonances in the R-region. I will also make a few brief remarks concerning the A_1.

---

[1]This report is based entirely on a talk dealing with the f^o, B and the R-mesons which I gave at the Conference on Meson Spectroscopy in Philadelphia, Pennsylvania on April 27, 1968. In preparing for the Penn Conference I relied extensively on the references given in A. H. Rosenfeld et al, UCRL-8030(Jan. 1968 Rev.). Of particular use were the summary papers of G. Goldhaber at the 1966 Berkeley Conference and of I. Butterworth at the 1967 Heidelberg Conference.
[*]Research supported by U.S. A. E. C.

Observation of $f^o \rightarrow 4\pi$

There is a new result from the Illinois group[2] regarding the possible evidence for $f^o \rightarrow \pi^+\pi^+\pi^-\pi^-$. Figure 1 shows the effective mass distribution of $(4\pi)^o$ in the reaction $\pi^- p \rightarrow \pi^+\pi^+\pi^-\pi^- n$ at an incident momentum of 5 GeV/c. The authors have compared the observed $(4\pi)^o$ signal with data obtained by the Purdue Group[3] for $f^o \rightarrow \pi^+\pi^-$ decay; using the momentum transfer cut shown in Fig. 1 for both of the observed decay modes Illinois quotes a branching rate $(f^o \rightarrow \pi^+\pi^+\pi^-\pi^-)/(f^o \rightarrow$ All $2\pi)$ $\sim$ 1%. Illinois is presently studying whether this $(4\pi)^o$ mode contains a contribution from a $\rho^o \rho^o$ decay of the f^o.

B-meson.

The B-meson, since its discovery,[4] has been

---

[2] D. Mortara et al.,University of Illinois 5GeV/c π^-p 4-prongs (Private communication).

[3] C.G. Howard et al.,Purdue University 5GeV/c π^-p 2-prongs (Private communication).

[4] M. Abolins et al.,Phys. Rev.Letters 11,381(1963). La Jolla 3.5 GeV/c π^+p.

supported by some[5] slandered by many[6] and finally

vindicated[7,8]. There are several interesting new

results and some peculiar ones regarding the

properties of the B-meson. For one thing, it is

easier to observe the B-meson at higher energies-

no cuts on the data are required to see a signal

of reasonable size[9].

Figures 2, and 3 show some of the features

typically observed in studies of the reactions π^{+}-p →

π-$\pi^{+}\pi^{+}\pi^{-}\pi^{o}$p at energies in excess of ~ 5 GeV/c.

---

[5] π^{+}p interactions at 4 GeV/c (ABBBHLM) Aachen,
Berlin, Birmingham, Bonn, Hamburg, London, Munchen,
W. Aderholz et al.,Phys. Rev. 138 (1965).

[6] (a) G. Goldhaber et al.,Phys. Rev.Letters 15,118
(1965).
(b) Multipion Final States from π^{-}p Interactions
at 3.2 and 4.2 GeV/c. S.U.Chung, O.J.Dahl, J.
Kirz, D.H.Miller, UCRL 16881 Rev.(May 1967).
(c) T.Ferbel, Physics Letters 21,111 (1966).

[7] C.Baltay et al.,Phys. Rev. Letters 18, 93 (1967).

[8] G. Gidal et al.,π^{+}p 3-4 GeV/c UCRL-17984 (1967).
Also private communication from G. Gidal.

[9] As will be shown later (Figs.4 and 7) the B cross
section does not fall very rapidly with energy.
The background in the B region, on the other hand,
appears to decrease considerably as the incoming
pion momentum is raised.

The results are from the GHMS Collaboration[10],
and from SLAC[11] for the reaction $\pi^- p \to \pi^- \pi^+ \pi^- \pi^0 p$
at 11 GeV/c, and at 16 GeV/c. The authors show
the invariant mass of the $(4\pi)^-$ system for all
their events. Two signals are apparent in each
distribution, one at the B-meson (associated
largely with ω^0 events)and the other (to be discussed later) at $\sim$ 1700 MeV.

The fact that the B-signal seems to be getting
cleaner with energy implies that the cross section
does not decrease strongly with energy. In Fig.4
I have plotted the B-meson production cross section versus the incident π momentum. The cross
sections were estimated in most cases by examin-
ing the "raw" $(4\pi)^{\pm}$ mass spectrum; when only $\pi^{\pm}\omega^0$
mass plots were available the cross sections were

[10]Analysis of 3π and 4π systems with mass around
1.7 GeV/c^2 produced by $\pi^- p$ collisions at 11 GeV/c.
Genova,Hamburg,Milano,Saclay Collaboration(GHMS).
C.Caso,et al,Submitted to Nuovo Cimento(Dec.'67).
[11]J. Ballam et al., Washington Meeting of A.P.S.
(1968) and private communication.

corrected for the imposed cuts on the data. Whenever possible I consulted with the experimenters
on the deduced cross sections. The numbers were
therefore obtained in a reasonably consistent
way[12] so that the energy dependence can be believed. From the plot it appears that our prediction is borne out, namely that the B total
cross section falls rather slowly at high energies
(approximately as $\frac{1}{p}$ for $p > 4$ GeV/c).[13]

There appears to be at present a small but
possibly significant discrepancy between the
measurement of the position and width of the B

---

[12] Where cross sections were estimated from $\pi^{\pm} \omega^{o}$
mass spectra corrections were made for the
cuts. It was assumed that ω^{o} was essentially a
Gaussian. The B meson was assumed to have a simple
Breit-Wigner shape up to $\sim 2\Gamma$ from the peak value.

[13] Having been conditioned by remarks of D.R.O.
Morrison regarding the energy dependence of cross
sections in quasi-two-body reactions (see for example the 1966 lecture at Stony Brook) this result
is somewhat surprising and may imply that the
simple rules are not adequate for resonances having arbitrary spin-parity.

meson in high-energy $\pi^{\pm}p$ data[14] and the measure-

ments in $\bar{p}p$ annihilations at rest.[7] Table I summa-

rizes the situation.[15] The errors on the position

are rather conservative - they include estimates

of possible systematic effects due to background

Table I

Properties of B Meson

	M(Mev)	Γ (Mev)
$\bar{p}p$	1200 $\pm$ 20	100 $\pm$ 30
$\pi^{\pm}p$	1250 $\pm$ 20	150 $\pm$ 30

---

[14]For results at energies below 5 GeV/c see reference 8 and S.Goldhaber,UCRL-16295(1965). From
$\pi^{\pm}\omega^0$ mass plots the B parameters were found to be:
M~ 1220 MeV,Γ ~ 120 MeV. These results fall right
in between the two "discrepancies".

[15]Figure 7 shows the compiled data from which we
obtained the position and width of the B. The
quoted width was corrected for resolution (not
necessarily Gaussian) and for the extra broadening of the distribution due to the addition of
data from different experiments. These corrections are educated guesses. I estimate an overall
25$\pm$10 MeV broadening in the poorly constrained
$(4\pi)^{\pm}$ signals. Similar corrections were used for
the other final states.

subtraction. If this discrepancy is a real one[16] then it may be due to either the fact that there are two B-like objects, or more likely that interference of the B with the background reactions is particularly insidious.[17]

The Illinois Group presented at the recent Washington Meeting of the American Physical Society[17] their study of the spin-parity of the B based on a sample of about 200 B-mesons.[17] A moment analysis of the $\pi^- \omega^0$ decay indicates

---

[16]There were some new results reported at Heidelberg by the CERN-College de France collaboration. This group measured the same reaction as ref. 7 and obtained (according to UCRL-8030) M=1220 ± 20 MeV, Γ =150±20 MeV. I have not seen these results as yet (they are apparently not available for circulation), so that a final judgment has to be reserved for a future occasion.

[17]G. Ascoli, G. B. Crawley, D. W. Mortara, A. Shapiro. University of Illinois 5 GeV/c π^-p Preprint COO-1195-123(1968). These authors also point out thedifficulty in obtaining a reliable estimate for the position and width of the B due to the presence of overlapping background reactions. In their J^P determination the authors are a bit more bold and utilize a background subtraction technique which assumes that there are no strong interference effects with the background.

consistency with a $J^P = 1^+$ assignment, however the possibility of $J^P = 2^+$, 3^-, 4^+... cannot be excluded on experimental grounds alone.[17]

The R-region.

Now I will discuss what Art Rosenfeld refers to as that "badly tangled" region, the multipion mass spectrum between 1500 MeV and 1900 MeV. Figure 5 is meant to orient you. The results are from the missing-mass-spectrometer work at CERN[18], indicating the presence of four R peaks. Table II

Table II

Meson	Mass (MeV)	Width (MeV)	$d\sigma/dt$ at $t = 0.23 \text{GeV}^2$ (μb/GeV^2)
R_1	1630 ± 15	< 15	~ 8
R_2	1700 ± 15	< 15	~ 10
R_3	1750 ± 15	< 15	~ 14
R_4	1830 ± 15	< 15	~ 4

Parameters of Bumps in R-region from MM Spectrometer work at CERN.

[18]
a) L. Dubal et al., Nuclear Physics B3 (1967).
b) L. Dubal CERN NP Internal Report No.10. I wish to thank Dr. Dubal for mailing me his report and slides.

presents the reported properties of these objects[18].

What I will try to do is to point out what has

been learned about this fine structure from anal-

ysis of some recent bubble chamber data.

In order not to further confuse the present

experimental situation I have reviewed the avail-

able literature and have ignored, perhaps unjustly,

any results which I felt needed more confirma-

tion[19].

ρ (1700) $\rightarrow$ 4π

The first resonance I will discuss is a state

of even G-parity located at 1700 MeV. I have al-

ready commented on the presence of this bump in

Figs. 2 and 3. Figure 6 shows the results of the

---

[19] I have been particularly hard on data from $\bar{p}p$ annihilations-probably because my thesis was in this subject and I still recall the frustration of having 9 combinations per event! I do not think that it is necessary at this time to comment on $K_S K_S$ (1440), $\rho\rho$ (1410), nor on η (1600) $\rightarrow 4\pi$ (see UCRL-8030). W. Kernan (Iowa) has mentioned to me that his group has measured a larger sample of events but the η (1600) signal has definitely weakened.

Notre Dame Group.[20] There is here again the typi-

cal feature of an enhancement at the B mass and at

1700 MeV in the uncut $\pi^-\pi^+\pi^-\pi^o$ mass distribution.

The same figure also gives the $\pi^+\pi^-\pi^+\pi^-$ mass spec-

trum in the neutron channel. It is clear that the

B and the ρ (1700) are not produced as strongly,

if they are produced at all, in the neutral four-

pion state.[21]

In Table III I have noted down the observed

positions and widths of ρ (1700) as reported in

the literature.[10,20,22,23] The values given as

[20]N.N.Biswas et al Phys. Rev. 166, 1395 (1968)
and Notre Dame preprints. Also private communication from N. Cason.

[21]The $f^o \rightarrow 4\pi$ decay signal is too small to be observed here.

[22]Toronto-Wisconsin Collaboration 7 GeV/c π^-p.
Preprint by T. F. Johnston et al, "Properties of
the g Meson" (April 1968). Also private communi-
cations from J.D. Prentice and W. D. Walker.

[23]Columbia-Rochester-Rutgers-Yale Collaboration -
CRRY. C. Baltay et al Phys. Rev. Letters 20, 887
(1968). Data are from 7 GeV/c π^+p and 8.4 GeV/c
π^+p. Figures 9 and 18 are from unpublished data,
a more extensive report is being prepared.

Table III

Observed Positions and Widths $\rho(1700)$

Beam	Momentum	Group	Position	Width
7.0	π^-	Toronto-Wisconsin	1675±10	90±10
11.0	π^-	GHMS	1700	100
8.0	π^-	Notre Dame	1710±23	160±50
7.0π^+, 8.5π^+		CRRY	1720±15	100±35

Best Bets:

M = 1700 ± 20 MeV

Γ = 110 ± 25 MeV

"best bets" are obtained from the compiled data

shown in Fig. 7. The estimated error on the posi-

tion and width takes account of different possibil-

ities for background.[15] The compiled data in

Fig. 7 is in 50 MeV bins so that no statement can

be made about the presence or absence of narrow

resonances having $\Gamma \lesssim$ 50 MeV. However, I wish to

point out that all the separate experiments

(Table III) are in agreement with the "best bet"

resonance parameters obtained from the compiled data.[15]

Before proceeding to the decay modes of ρ (1700) I wish to make a clarifying remark regarding nomenclature. According to the convention suggested by Rosenfeld et al[24] new resonances with isotopic spin one can be labeled either as ρ or π depending on their G-parity. Mesons in the J^P series $0^-, 1^+, 2^-, \ldots$ have a subscript A, signifying "abnormal" quantum numbers, while mesons in the J^P series $0^+, 1^-, 2^+, \ldots$ have a subscript N associated with them, signifying "normal" quantum numbers. Thus the old fashioned π, ρ, A_1, B, and A_2 would be labeled respectively $\pi_A(140)$, $\rho_N(760)$, $\pi_A(1080)$, $\rho_A(1220)$, and $\pi_N(1310)$.

The Toronto-Wisconsin 7 GeV/c $\pi^- p$ collaboration[22] believes that the ρ (1700) is the same object as the g-meson (to be discussed later).

---

[24] And modified at the Penn Conference at the strong urgings of M. Gell-Mann.

Since the g decays into two pions this identifica-

tion would enable us to label the 1700 MeV state

$\rho_N(1700)$. It is my feeling that at present there

is not enough information available for a firm

statement, and because the mass of the two-pion

state appears to be about 50 MeV below the mass of

the four-pion state I assumed for the purpose of

this presentation that ρ (1700) and the g-meson

are not one and the same resonance. Table IV then

presents the various observed branching rates for

ρ (1700).

The decay of ρ (1700) $\rightarrow \pi \omega$ establishes the

isotopic spin to be I = 1. Although all experi-

ments observe some decay of the ρ (1700) into two

ρ -mesons (they observe more than 100% decay into

"any ρ"), none of the groups have enough data to

quote a reliable estimate for this mode. The

difficulty here lies in the fact the ρ (760) has

a very large width, and the errors due to back-

ground subtraction in studying the ρ (760) over-

lap bands are so large as to make any analysis

Table IV

$$\rho(1700) \quad \text{Decay}$$

$$\frac{\rho^{\pm}(1700) \to \pi^{\pm}\omega^{o} \to \pi^{-}\pi^{+}\pi^{+}\pi^{-}\pi^{o}}{\rho^{\pm}(1700) \to \pi^{-}\pi^{+}\pi^{+}\pi^{-}\pi^{o}} = 0.20 \pm 0.08$$

$$\frac{\rho^{\pm}(1700) \to (\pi A_{2})^{\pm} \to \pi^{-}\pi^{+}\pi^{+}\pi^{-}\pi^{o}}{\rho^{\pm}(1700) \to \pi^{-}\pi^{+}\pi^{+}\pi^{-}\pi^{o}} = 0.50 \pm 0.30$$

$$\rho^{\pm}(1700) \to \rho^{\pm}(760)\rho^{o}(760) \quad \text{Exists}$$

$$\frac{\rho^{\pm}(1700) \to \pi^{\pm}\varphi^{o} \to \pi^{\pm}K^{+}K^{-}}{\rho^{\pm}(1700) \to \pi^{-}\pi^{+}\pi^{+}\pi^{-}\pi^{o}} < 0.05$$

$$\frac{\rho^{\pm}(1700) \to \pi^{\pm}\pi^{o}}{\rho^{\pm}(1700) \to \pi^{-}\pi^{+}\pi^{+}\pi^{-}\pi^{o}} < 0.10$$

essentially meaningless at the present level of statistics.

There is a minor controversy regarding the decay of $\rho(1700)$ into πA_{2}. The Toronto-Wisconsin Collaboration and the Notre Dame Groups quote only upper limits for this decay mode. The CRRY Collaboration has the largest sample of data and I thought it might be useful to present their evidence for the πA_{2} decay of $\rho(1700)$.

Figure 8 shows the $\pi^+\pi^+\pi^-\pi^o$ mass spectrum for the CRRY data.[23] A clear signal is again apparent at ~ 1700 MeV. Three mass regions labeled A, B, and C on the figure are used to study the decay properties of the observed resonance, side bands A and C serving as control samples for the central resonant region B. Figure 9 shows the $\pi^+\pi^-\pi^o$ mass combinations for the events in regions C, B, and A (top, middle, bottom). It is clear that there is a considerable amount of ω^o events in the background regions, but there is an extra enhancement of ω^o and A_2^o events for the central band B. To find the branching rates all that is now required is to estimate from regions A and C the average number of background ω^o and A_2^o events expected in region B. Any excess ω^o or A_2^o events found in region B can then presumably be attributed to the fraction of the ρ (1700) signal in region B.

The $A_2^o\pi^+$ decay of ρ^+(1700) should be twice the value of the $A_2^+\pi^o$ decay mode in the observed reaction. The data are consistent with this rate. The technique used for background subtraction by the CRRY group assumes as usual, that the interference of ρ (1700) with the background is negligible, and that kinematic differences between events in the central region B and the outer regions A and C can be ignored.

Figure 10 shows a compilation of the $\pi^+\pi^+\pi^-\pi^-$ mass spectrum. As noted before, the ρ (1700) does not appear to be produced as strongly in the neutral state as in the charged mode. This fact has led to the speculation that ρ (1700) decays dominantly into two ρ (760) mesons (this would then rather simply explain the absence of the ρ(1700) in the neutral spectrum). The errors on the ρ (1700) branching rates are certainly large enough so that this possibility cannot be excluded.

As for other conclusions from Fig. 10, the only firm one is that it would be very worthwhile to get more events in this channel.

ρ (1650) $\rightarrow$ 2π

The g-meson was, I think, first observed by the European C-EP-O-M-S Collaboration.[25] It has since been seen in the charged and in the neutral two-pion state by several groups.[26,27,28,29,22,3]

In Fig. 11 I show the Toronto-Wisconsin results at 7 GeV/c π^-p.[22] Note that the signals in the neutral spectra are again not very impressive looking. The authors in studying the final states most relevant to the g-meson have tried to establish, in one experiment, a relationship between the 2π and the 4π signals. They conclude from

[25] CERN-Ecole Polytechnique,Orsay-Milan-Saclay Collaboration (C-EP-O-M-S); M. Goldberg et al., Phys. Letters 17, July 15, 1967.

[26] Saclay-Orsay-Bologna Collaboration (BOS), A. Forino et al.,Phys. Letts. 19, 65 (1965).

[27] Notre Dame-Pennsylvania; J. A. Poirier et al., Phys. Rev. 163, 1462 (1967).

[28] D.J. Crennel et al.,Phys. Rev.Letts. 18,323, (1967),BNL-CCNY π^-p GeV/c.

[29] Aachen-Berlin-CERN Collaboration (ABC); K. Bösebeck et al., Nuclear Physics B4 (1968).

their mass plots and from studies of J^P that the
4π and the 2π decays are different channels for a
unique g-meson. In principle, this is the best
way to resolve the question of whether we have
here one or two resonances. However, due to background problems and particularly due to the limit-
ations of statistics   I feel that the Toronto-
Wisconsin results are not to be considered as
definitive.[30] Furthermore, the interpretation
given in this talk, i.e., the professed existence
of two separate states ρ (1700) and ρ (1650) is
more in agreement with the rest of the world data.

If you notice I said that the two separate
states hypothesis is more in agreement with the
world data than the one g hypothesis, but I did
not specify the goodness of fit! The trouble is
that there are several skeletons in the g closet
(see Table V). Figure 12 shows one of these

---

[30] It is worth pointing out that the Toronto-
Wisconsin results were included in the world
data compilation.

skeletons; these are the latest results from BNL

on their 6 GeV/c $\pi^- p$ experiment.[31] They quote a

position for the g^o peak which lies 80 MeV above

their g^- peak, and 65 MeV higher than the g^o mass

as given by Toronto-Wisconsin.[32] I must remind

you that these two experiments have good statis-

tics so that the differences between them cannot

simply be ignored. To preserve my sanity I

assume that in the 6 GeV/c data strong interference

effects must be present which tend to widen the

g signals.

In trying to arrive at some average resonance

parameters for the g meson I examined, separately,

the $\pi^+\pi^-$ and the $\pi^{\pm}\pi^o$ mass spectra for the avail-

able data. Figure 13 shows the results of this

---

[31] Private communication from K. W. Lai.

[32] The widths for the g measured by the BNL group
are about a factor of two larger than those
measured by Toronto-Wisconsin. However, this
discrepancy may not be too severe because the
observed Γ is very sensitive to background
assumptions. (Private communication from K. W.
Lai).

compilation. The singly charged distribution
appears to have a more defined peak than the neutral spectrum, but the two are certainly not
different enough to worry about adding them together in order to minimize fluctuations. (The
backgrounds are somewhat different in the two
cases - partly due to the presence of the f^o in
the $\pi^+\pi^-$ distribution). The summed data are
shown in the same figure; the curve is for the
"best bets" parameters given in Table V, these
values were obtained assuming the indicated background. It is clear from Table V that the dispersion in position of ρ (1650) is not as great
as the dispersion in the observed widths. Also
it seems that the charged ρ(1650) is more re-
producable than the neutral object.

$\pi(1640) \rightarrow 3\pi$

Now I will turn to the easiest part of my
talk - the discussion of the $(3\pi)^\pm$ state at
1640 MeV. I believe that almost everyone will

Table V

Observed Positions and Width for ρ (1650)

Alias g-meson

Beam Momentum	Observed	Group	Position	Width
7.0 π^-	g^-	Trnto-Wisc.	1675±10	90±10
7.0 π^-	g^o	Trnto-Wisc.	1655±10	80±10
8.0 π^-	g^o	Nd-Penn	1680±20	225±60
4.5π^+(d)	g^o	BOS	1640	40
6.0π^+(d),8.0π^-	g^o	C-EP-O-M-S	1670±30	180±40
8.0 π^+	g^+	ABC	1630±25	120±50
6.0 π^-	g^-	BNL	1645±25	150-250
6.0 π^-	g^o	BNL	1720±20	150-200

Best Bets

M = 1650 ± 20 MeV

Γ = 120 ± 30 MeV

agree with what I have to say on this subject.
The $\pi(1640)$ is observed in the final state
$\pi^+ p \to \pi^- \pi^+ \pi^- p$ from 3.9 GeV/c[33] up to 20 GeV/c.[34]
Figure 14 shows the Harvard data at 20 GeV/c $\pi^- p$.
The wide peak in the A region and the enhancement
near $\sim$ 1640 MeV are again typical of the data at
high-energy.

The next figure gives the energy dependence
of the $\pi(1640)$ production cross section. It
appears to be quite constant and independent of
the beam momentum from 7 GeV/c to 20 GeV/c. Unlike the cross section for the B-meson, the results
in Fig. 15 do not show a pronounced peak near
threshold.

Table VI has a summary of the values observed
in individual experiments for the position and

[33] V. Stenger et al, University of Hawaii(Private
communication) 3.9 GeV/c $\pi^- p$.

[34] Harvard preprint, M. L. Ioffredo et al.,(April
1968) and private communication from A. Brenner.

Table VI

Observed Positions and Widths for $\pi(1640)$

Beam Momentum (GeV/c)		Group	Position (MeV)	Width (MeV)
4.7	π^-	Moscow	1630±30	~100
8.0	π^-	Notre Dame	1610±20	100±40
11.1	π^-	GHMS	1660	130
20.0	π^-	Harvard	1660±20	~130
7.0π^+,8.5π^+		CRRY	1630±10	70±40
8.0	π^+	ABC	1660±16	115±45

Best Bets:

$M = 1640 \pm 15$ MeV

$\Gamma = 90 \pm 25$ MeV

width of $\pi(1640)$.[10,20,23,29,34,35] Here the

scatter in the resonance parameters is not very

large. Figure 16 shows the compiled $\pi^{\pm}\pi^{+}\pi^{-}$ mass

spectrum, in which the $\pi(1640)$ stands out rather

clearly.[36]

All experiments agree that the $\pi(1640)^{\pm}$

decays often into $\pi^{\pm}f^{o}$ but not into $\pi^{\pm}\rho^{o}$. The

results of the CRRY Collaboration[23] in Figure 17

show the $\pi^{+}\pi^{+}\pi^{-}$ mass spectrum for all the events

in the final state $p\pi^{+}\pi^{+}\pi^{-}$. For studying the de-

cay properties of $\pi(1640)$ the region near the

$\pi(1640)$ peak in Fig. 8 is divided into three mass

intervals A, B, and C. The $\pi^{+}\pi^{-}$ decay mass dis-

tributions for the events in these regions are

---

[35]I. Vetlitsky et al,Phys. Letts.$\underline{21}$,579 (1966)
Moscow 4.7 GeV/c π^{-}p.

[36]The A_2 appears to sit on a narrow background
(or a broad peak),which I interpret to be the
"true" A_1. My estimate of the parameters for the
A_1 obtained after subtraction of a peripheral-
type background are: M = 1150 $\pm$ 50 MeV and
Γ = 250 $\pm$ 80 MeV.

given in Fig. 18. All the three regions show some ρ^o and some f^o structure in the $\pi^+\pi^-$ mass projections. After making the standard background subtractions the $\pi^+\rho^o$ decay mode is found to be consistent with zero, while a finite branching rate is deduced for the π^+f^o mode (inconsistent with zero with 90% confidence).[23]

Table VII summarizes the results for the decays of this I = 1 object.

Comment on Cross Sections

The ABC Collaboration[37] has measured the momentum transfer spectrum for the events in the $\pi(1640)$ mass region. They obtain an exponential fall off in $t'(t-t_{min})$ of the form $e^{At'}$ with $A = 5.5 \pm 0.6$ GeV^{-2}. The CRRY data show a somewhat steeper t-dependence having $A = 7 \pm 1$ GeV^{-2}, and after background subtraction (which is performed in a manner similar to that indicated

---

[37]Private communication from D. R. O. Morrison.

Table VII

$\pi(1640)$ Decay

$$\frac{\pi^{\pm}(1640) \longrightarrow \pi^{\pm}\rho^{0} \longrightarrow \pi^{\pm}\pi^{+}\pi^{-}}{\pi^{\pm}(1640) \xrightarrow[\text{all}]{} \pi^{\pm}\pi^{+}\pi^{-}} < 0.4$$

$$\frac{\pi^{\pm}(1640) \longrightarrow \pi^{\pm}f^{0} \longrightarrow \pi^{\pm}\pi^{+}\pi^{-}}{\pi^{\pm}(1640) \xrightarrow[\text{all}]{} \pi^{\pm}\pi^{+}\pi^{-}} = 0.4 \pm 0.2$$

$$\frac{\pi^{\pm}(1640) \longrightarrow \pi^{\pm}\eta^{0} \longrightarrow \pi^{\pm}\pi^{+}\pi^{-}\pi^{0}}{\pi^{\pm}(1640) \xrightarrow[\text{all}]{} \pi^{\pm}\pi^{+}\pi^{-}} < 0.02$$

$$\frac{\pi^{\pm}(1640) \longrightarrow \pi^{\pm}\pi^{+}\pi^{-}\pi^{+}\pi^{-}}{\pi^{\pm}(1640) \xrightarrow[\text{all}]{} \pi^{\pm}\pi^{+}\pi^{-}} < 0.1$$

earlier) we obtain a value for the slope in t of $A = 9 \pm 4$ GeV^{-2}. The slope in t which was observed for the $\rho(1700)$ was 6 ± 3 GeV^{-2}. The ρ (1650) is also produced peripherally,[22] so that the momentum transfer dependences for these resonances in the R-region are therefore not unusual.

The ρ (1700) cross section in the 11 GeV/c $\pi^{-}p \rightarrow p\pi^{-}\pi^{+}\pi^{-}\pi^{0}$ data[10] is about 60 ± 20 μb (again

it seems to have a rather weak energy dependence).
Although the charged $\rho(1650)$ production cross
section is not known very well it appears to be
$\sim 40\mu b$ near 8 GeV/c.

The point of the above remarks is that the
mesons in the R-region are produced rather co-
piously at high-energies and do not exhibit unusual t-dependence.

We have measured the value of $\frac{d\sigma}{dt}$ at t = 0.23
GeV^2 for $\pi(1640)$ production in the $\pi^+\pi^+\pi^-$ decay
mode and for $\rho(1700)$ production in the $\pi^+\pi^+\pi^-\pi^o$
channel. Our measured values are $\sim 70\mu b/GeV^2$ and
~ 100 $\mu b/GeV^2$ for the $\pi(1640)$ and the $\rho(1700)$
signals respectively. The MM spectrometer is
sensitive to all decays of these objects and
therefore the results for the cross sections from
our experiment are expected to be smaller than the
values obtained using the missing-mass technique.
The results in Table II indicate that this is not
the situation. In fact it appears that the MM
spectrometer cross section measurements are about

a factor of ten lower than expected on the basis of the above!

A possible explanation for this inconsistency and one which could also explain the narrow widths[38] given in Table II, is the following. I assume that the MM spectrometer indeed sees all the fine-structure in the R-region but because there are many closely spaced objects this experiment detects only the "tips" of the partially overlapping Breit-Wigner peaks. This, if true, would clearly yield smaller cross sections and narrower resonances than those observed in bubble chamber experiments.

I want to make one last remark regarding cross sections and the A_1. If the A_1 is interpreted as the broad resonance under the A_2 peak (see Figs. 14 and 16 for example) then the cross section for the $A_1^{\pm}$ production in $\pi^{\pm}p \rightarrow A_1^{\pm}p$ reactions at high energy is ~ 500 μb (corrected by

---

[38] I am here taking the attitude that the R-resonances have widths of ~ 100 MeV.

a factor of 2 for $A_1^{+} \to \pi^{o}\rho^{+}$ decay). The corrected cross section for $K^{+}p \to Q^{+}p$ where Q^{+} is the strangeness one analog of the A_1, is also $\sim 500\mu b$.[39] The fact that these two cross sections are the same within measurement error ($\sim 25\%$) may be either accidental or significant.[40]

Other Experiments on the R-Region

Up to now I have only referred to data obtained in studies of the $\pi^{\pm}p$ collisions. I now wish to spend a little time on data from other reactions.

Figure 19 shows a small ~ 100 MeV wide signal for a possible $\omega \pi\pi$ decay of $\pi(1640)$. This is as yet an unsubstantiated result in $K^{-}p \to \Lambda^{o}+2\pi^{+}+2\pi^{-}+\pi^{o}$

---

[39] See for example J. C. Berlinghieri et al. Phys. Rev. Letters 18, 1087 (1967).

[40] I wish to thank S. Okubo for pointing out to me that if the production mechanism in both instances is the same, i.e.,the exchange of an SU(3) singlet (such as the vacuum) and if the A_1 and Q belong to an SU(3) octet then the production cross sections should be the same for both.

at 4.2 GeV/c from Maryland,[41] and it is still not

clear whether this peak can be associated with

the $\pi(1640)$.[42] The signal is also observed in the

"uncut" $2\pi^+2\pi^-\pi^o$ mass spectrum.

Figure 20 is from the CERN Liverpool Collab-

oration[43] on $\bar{p}p$ annihilations at ~ 3 GeV/c. They

present evidence for two resonances in the $2\pi^+2\pi^-$

system at 1717 MeV(R_2?) and at 1830 MeV(R_4?) in

the reaction $\bar{p}p \rightarrow 3\pi^+ + 3\pi^-$. These possible reson-

ances could be I = 0 objects, in which case there

is no problem. However, if they turn out to have

I = 1 and are to be identified with the R-region

then their narrow widths will force a revaluation

of the $\pi^{\pm}p$ results. I feel that it is very

---

[41]Private communication from G. Yodh and G. Yost,
Also see for comparison Fig. 7 in J. Danysz et al,
Nuovo Cimento 51(Oct.1,1967).

[42]The observed object could have I = 0, see for
example reference 46.

[43]J. A. Danysz et al, Physics Letters 24B, 309
(1967).

important to confirm the $\bar{p}p$ results.[44]

There have been two experiments near 5 GeV/c on double pion production in π^+d interactions.[45,46] The BBFOS Collaboration saw some evidence for $\pi(1640)$ production. In their recent results[46] the BBFO Group claims that the observed $\pi(1640) \longrightarrow \pi^+\pi^-\pi^o$ decay proceeds through $\rho^o\pi^o$ and therefore cannot be an I = 1 resonance. The evidence they give to support their findings is not very complete. Their main argument appears to be that the $\pi^+\pi^-\pi^o$ signal persists on making a $\pi^o\rho^o$ selection and that the $\pi^+\pi^-$ decay mass spectrum in the 1640 $\pi^+\pi^-\pi^o$ mass region shows far more ρ^o than f^o. I think it is clear from Fig. 18

---

[44]Notice that in Fig. 20 there are 660 events and 9 combinations per event! W. Kernan of Iowa soon plans to have a comparable sample of events at 2.5GeV/c (private communication).

[45]Bologna,Bari,Firenze,Orsay,Saclay (BBFOS) Collaboration, A. Forino et al, Phys. Letts. 19,68 (1965). 4.5GeV/c π^+d. I thank W. Fickinger for a private communication of results from this experiment.

[46]Bari,Bologna,Firenze,Orsay(BBFO) Collaboration, N. Armenise et al, Physics Letters 26B,336 (1968). 5.1 GeV/c π^+d.

(CRRY data) that the mere presence of a large ρ^{o} signal is not proof of a ρ^{o} decay mode. It would be interesting to see what a background subtraction applied to the $\pi^{+}d$ data does to the $\pi^{o}\rho^{o}$ interpretation. We may have here an object which has nothing to do with $\pi(1640)$, but a more quantitative statement regarding the $\pi^{o}\rho^{o}$ vs the $\pi^{o}f^{o}$ mode should be made in any case.

Conclusions About R-Region

The only definite statements that I can make about the structure of the R-region are the following. There are at least three I = 1 objects $\pi(1640), \rho(1650)$ and $\rho(1700)$, all having widths ~ 100 MeV (see previous tables for best estimates). Any other statement would border on speculation and would have to be qualified in one way or another.

There have been attempts at J^{P} determinations[22,26,37] for the R-mesons, but the results are at best suggestive and require much more data than any one group has available.

In concluding I wish to stress that higher
statistics experiments are required for a clear
understanding of the charged R-region. But what
is really quite essential for disentangling these
mesons is more information on the neutral systems.
I think more people should look into π^+d experiments[47] near 7 GeV/c!

I wish to thank B. Maglic and the Organizing
Committee of the Penn Conference for giving me the
opportunity to discuss these data, and for pro-
viding the gracious atmosphere which made the
meeting a success. I also thank all the physicists
who were kind enough to answer my call for data
and who spent time with me in discussing their
results, Ihope that I have not offended any of
them with my presentation. Finally I thank my
colleagues P. Slattery and H. Yuta for a critical

---

[47] Not only to study two-body resonance production
in the $\pi^+n \rightarrow p\pi^+\pi^-\pi^0$ reaction but also in the high-
ly constrained $\pi^+n \rightarrow p\pi^+\pi^-$ and $\pi^+n \rightarrow p\pi^+\pi^+\pi^-\pi^-$ states.

reading of this manuscript.

Other useful References not mentioned

specifically in Text:

G. Brandenburg et al, Harvard Preprint (1968)

"A Study of Resonance Production in 7GeV/c π^+p Interactions", P. Slattery et al.,Nuovo Cimento 50(1967), Rochester-Yale Collaboration.

"R, S. and T Resonances Produced in 8 GeV/c π^-p Interactions", N. N. Biswas, et al, University of Notre Dame, Notre Dame, Indiana, 1967 Athens (Ohio) Conference.

"Meson Resonances in the Reaction $\pi^+ d \to pp\pi^+\pi^+\pi^-\pi^-\pi^o$ at 3.65 BeV/c" Anthony Fisher, et al, University of Michigan, Ann Arbor, Michigan.

W. J. Kernan et al., Phys. Rev. Letters 15, 802 (1965). $\bar{p}$p 2.5 GeV/c. Iowa.

J. Von Krogh et al., 6.7 GeV/c π^-p, Colorado Preprint.

"Study of π^+-p 4-Prong Interactions at 16 GeV/c" J. Ballam, et al, Stanford Linear Accelerator Center, August 1967.

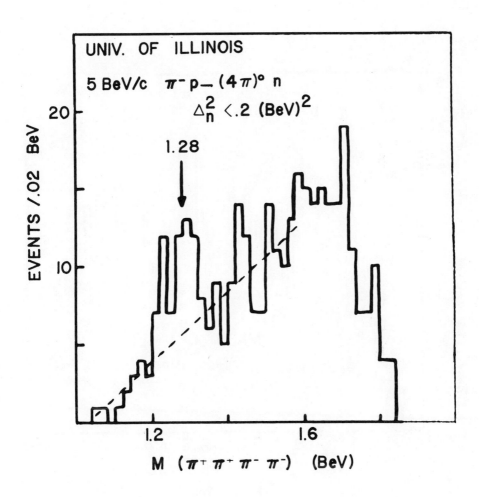

UNIV. OF ILLINOIS

5 BeV/c $\pi^- p \rightarrow (4\pi)^0$ n

$\Delta_n^2 < .2$ (BeV)^2

1.28

M ($\pi^+ \pi^+ \pi^- \pi^-$) (BeV)

EVENTS /.02 BeV

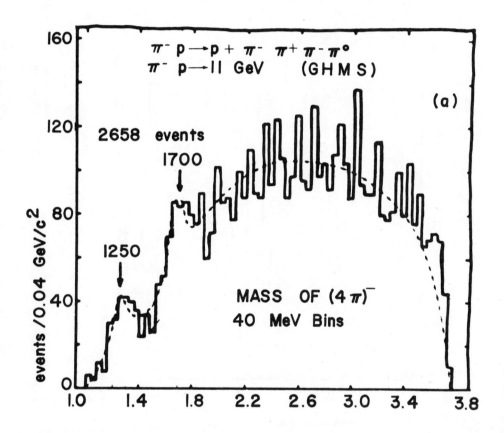

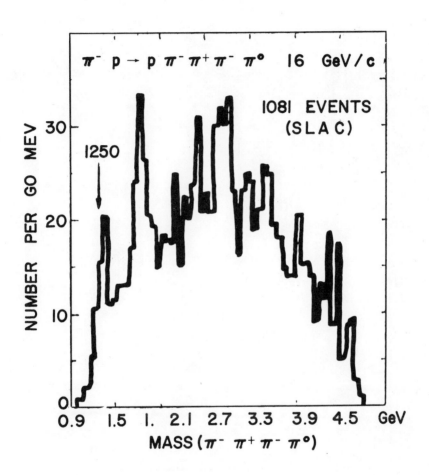

$\pi^-\ p \rightarrow p\ \pi^-\ \pi^+\ \pi^-\ \pi^o$ 16 GeV/c

1081 EVENTS
(S L A C)

1250

NUMBER PER 60 MEV

MASS$(\pi^-\ \pi^+\ \pi^-\ \pi^o)$

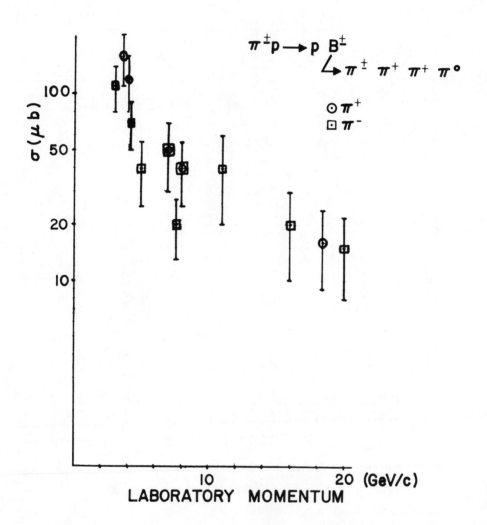

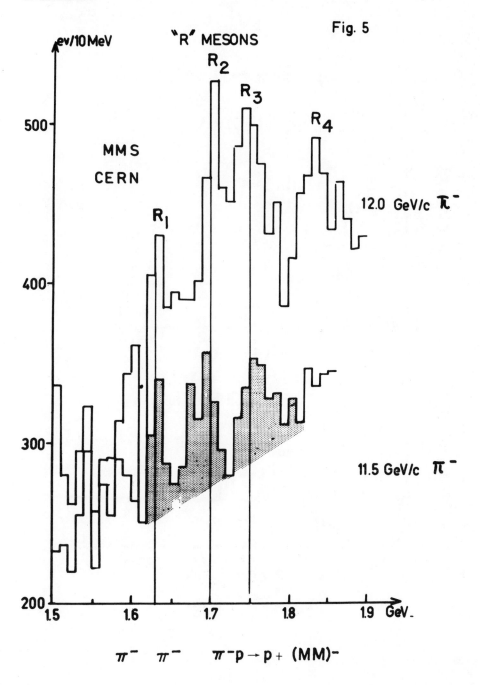

Fig. 5

"R" MESONS

$\pi^- \quad \pi^- \qquad \pi^- p \to p + (MM)^-$

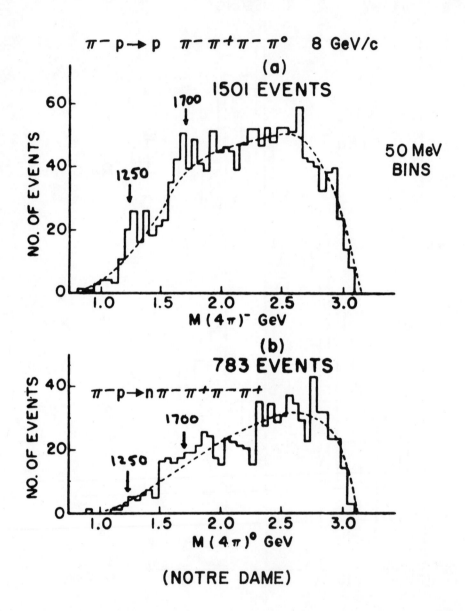

$\pi^- p \rightarrow p\ \pi^- \pi^+ \pi^- \pi^o$ 8 GeV/c

(NOTRE DAME)

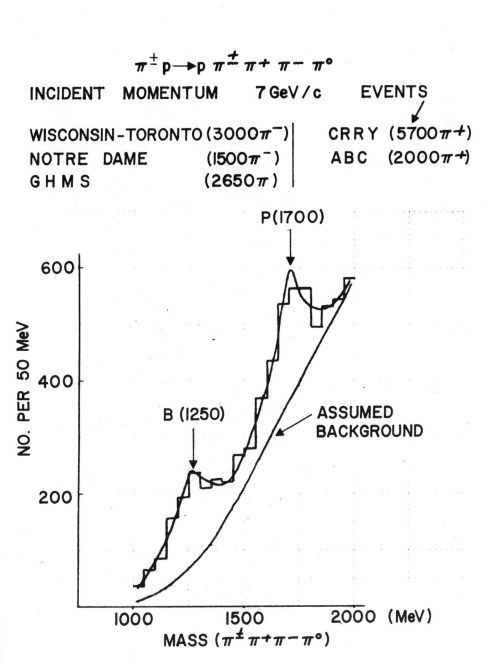

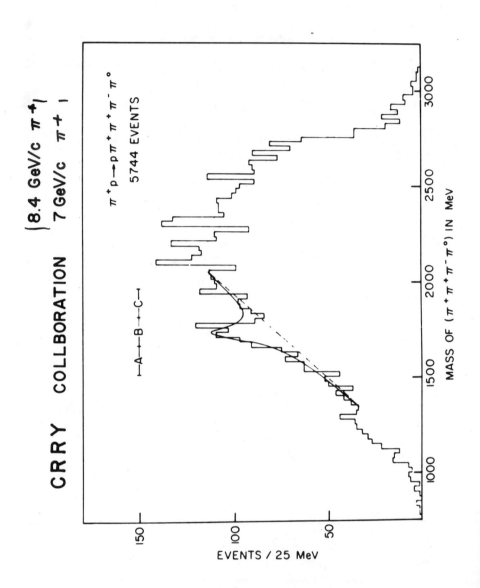

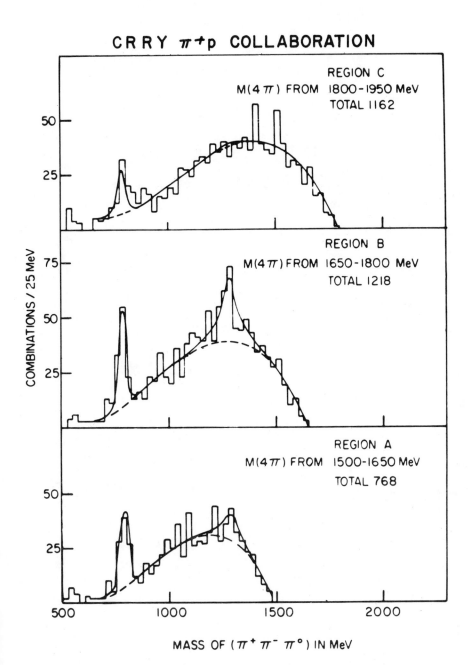

CRRY π^+p COLLABORATION

REGION C
M(4π) FROM 1800-1950 MeV
TOTAL 1162

REGION B
M(4π) FROM 1650-1800 MeV
TOTAL 1218

REGION A
M(4π) FROM 1500-1650 MeV
TOTAL 768

COMBINATIONS / 25 MeV

MASS OF (π^+ π^- π°) IN MeV

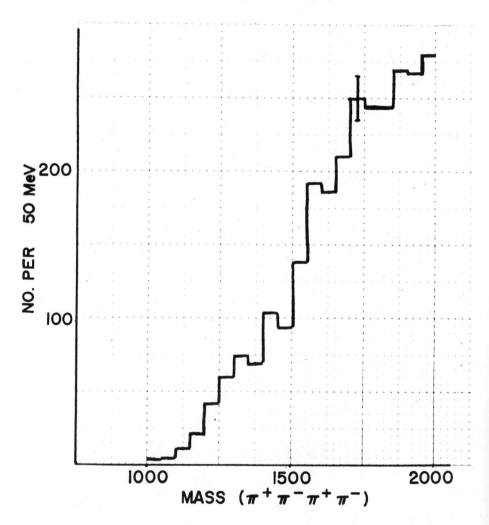

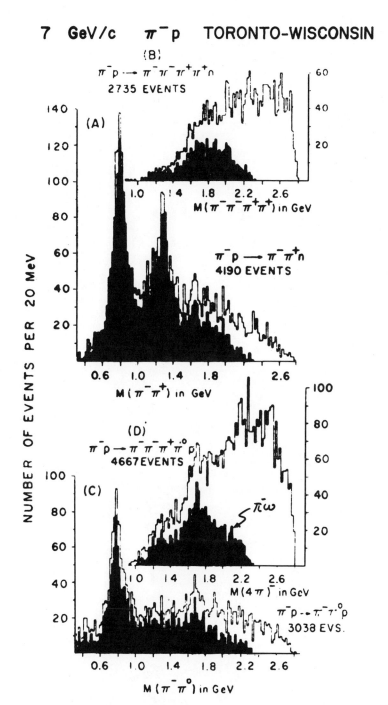

7 GeV/c $\pi^- p$ TORONTO-WISCONSIN

(B)
$\pi^- p \longrightarrow \pi^- \pi^- \pi^+ \pi^+ n$
2735 EVENTS

$M(\pi^- \pi^- \pi^+ \pi^+)$ in GeV

(A)

$\pi^- p \longrightarrow \pi^- \pi^+ n$
4190 EVENTS

$M(\pi^- \pi^+)$ in GeV

(D)
$\pi^- p \longrightarrow \pi^- \pi^- \pi^+ \pi^0 p$
4667 EVENTS

$\pi^- \omega$

$M(4\pi)^-$ in GeV

(C)

$\pi^- p \longrightarrow \pi^- \pi^0 p$
3038 EVS.

$M(\pi^- \pi^0)$ in GeV

NUMBER OF EVENTS PER 20 MeV

ALL DARK REGIONS HAVE $t_{pn} < 0.3$ GeV^2

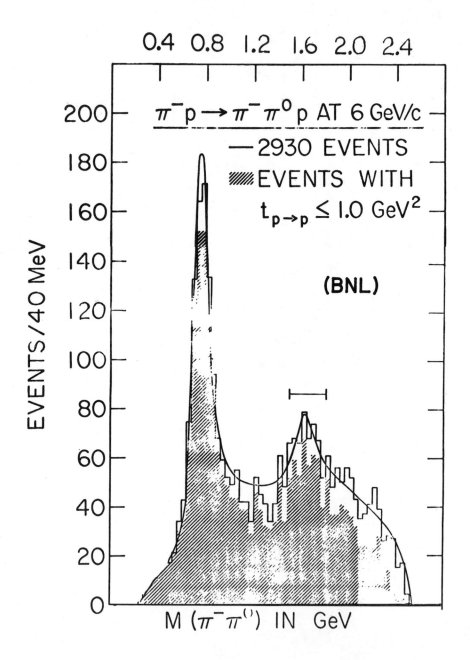

M ($\pi^-\pi^{()}$) IN GeV

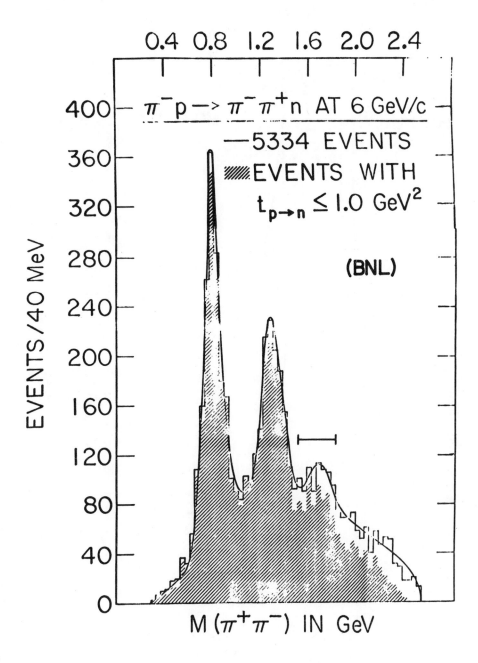

$\pi^- p \rightarrow \pi^- \pi^+ n$ AT 6 GeV/c

—5334 EVENTS

EVENTS WITH

$t_{p \rightarrow n} \leq 1.0$ GeV^2

(BNL)

M($\pi^+ \pi^-$) IN GeV

T. FERBEL

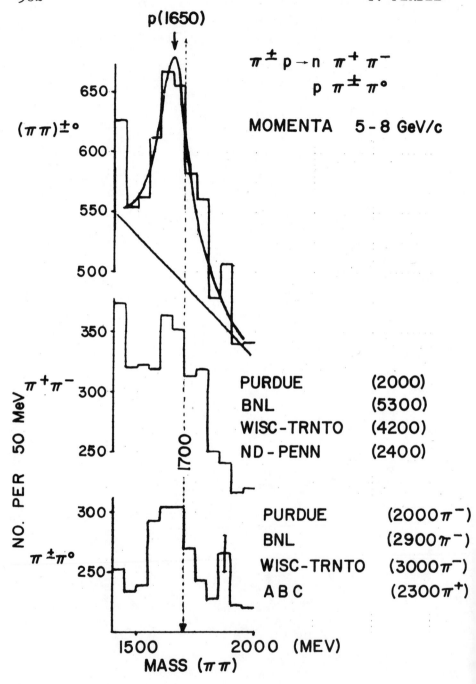

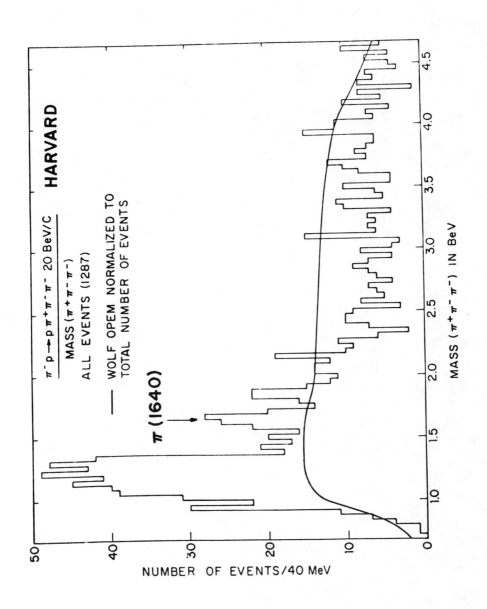

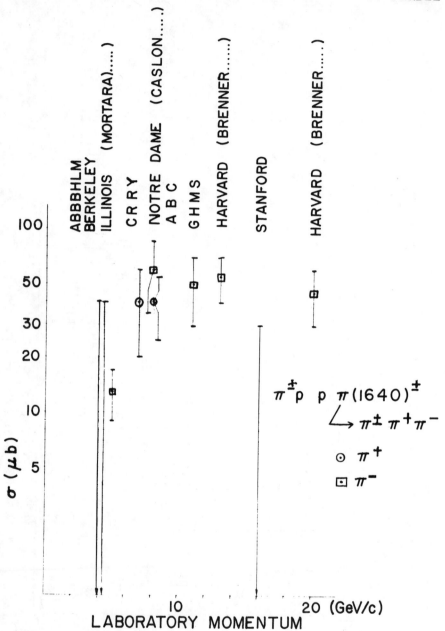

$\pi^- p \rightarrow p \pi^{\pm} \pi^+ \pi^-$

INCIDENT MOMENTUM $\geq$ 5 GeV/c

ILLINOIS	($7300\pi^-$)	CRRY	($6950\pi^+$)
NOTRE DAME	($2000\pi^-$)	A B C	($5800\pi^+$)
G H M S	($2800\pi^-$)		
HARVARD	($1850\pi^-$)	$\pi(1640)$	

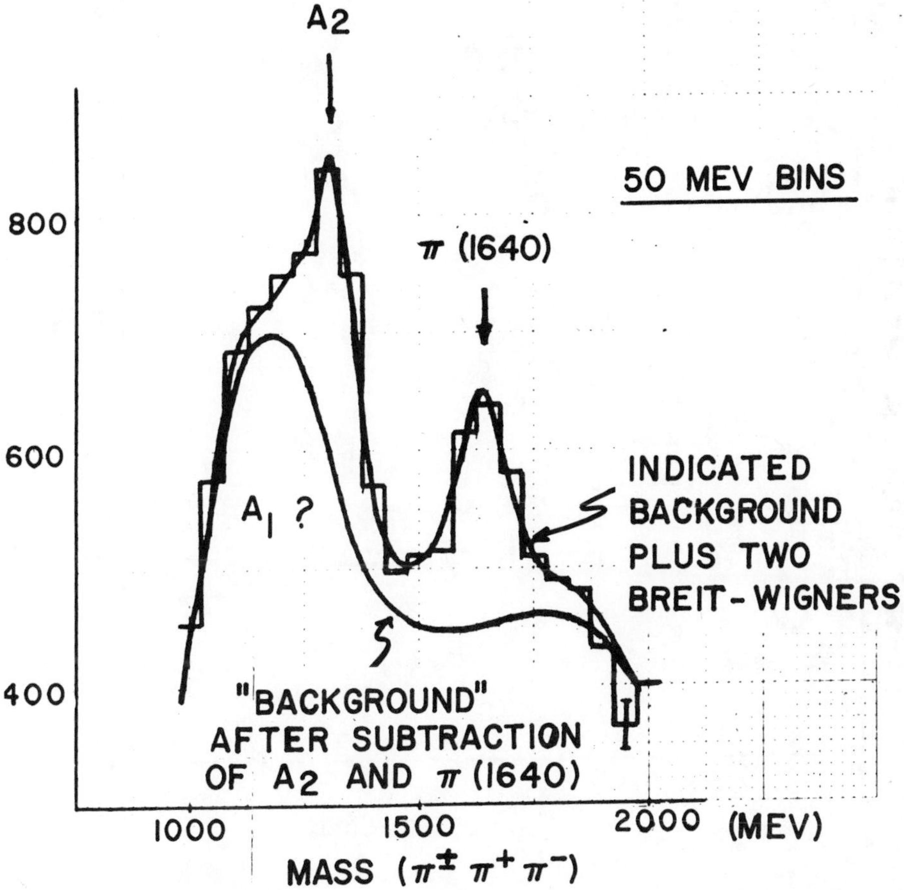
A2
50 MEV BINS
800
π (1640)
600
A1 ?
INDICATED BACKGROUND PLUS TWO BREIT-WIGNERS
400
"BACKGROUND" AFTER SUBTRACTION OF A2 AND π (1640)
1000
1500
2000 (MEV)
MASS (π± π+ π−)

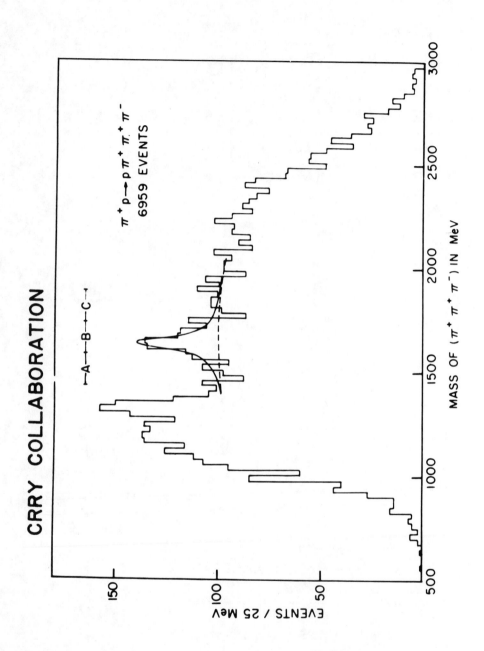

CRRY COLLABORATION

$\pi^+ p \rightarrow p \pi^+ \pi^+ \pi^-$
6959 EVENTS

EVENTS / 25 MeV

MASS OF $(\pi^+ \pi^+ \pi^-)$ IN MeV

CRRY COLLABORATION

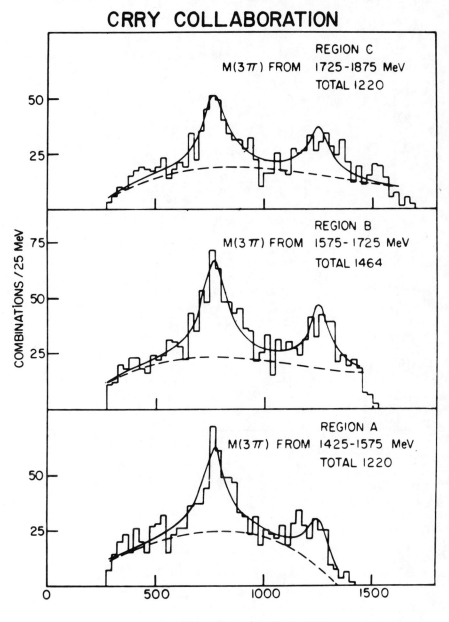

REGION C
M(3π) FROM 1725-1875 MeV
TOTAL 1220

REGION B
M(3π) FROM 1575-1725 MeV
TOTAL 1464

REGION A
M(3π) FROM 1425-1575 MeV
TOTAL 1220

COMBINATIONS / 25 MeV

MASS OF (π⁺π⁻) IN MeV

MARYLAND $K^-p \longrightarrow \Lambda^° \, \pi^+ \pi^+ \pi^- \pi^- \pi^°$

4.2 GeV/c

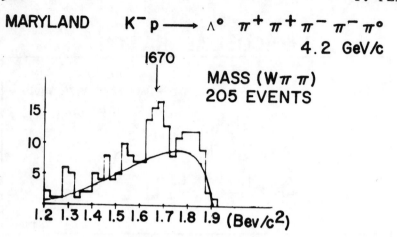

1670

MASS ($W \pi \pi$)
205 EVENTS

1.2 1.3 1.4 1.5 1.6 1.7 1.8 1.9 (Bev/c^2)

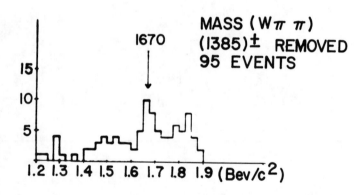

1670

MASS ($W \pi \pi$)
(1385)$^±$ REMOVED
95 EVENTS

1.2 1.3 1.4 1.5 1.6 1.7 1.8 1.9 (Bev/c^2)

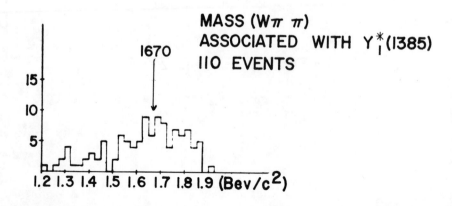

1670

MASS ($W \pi \pi$)
ASSOCIATED WITH Y_1^*(1385)
110 EVENTS

1.2 1.3 1.4 1.5 1.6 1.7 1.8 1.9 (Bev/c^2)

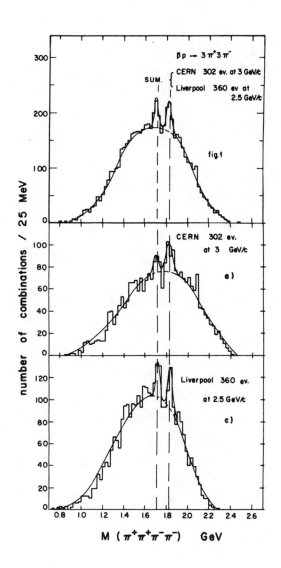

$\bar{p}p \rightarrow 3\pi^+ 3\pi^-$

CERN 302 ev. at 3 GeV/c

Liverpool 360 ev at 2.5 GeV/c

SUM.

fig.1

CERN 302 ev. at 3 GeV/c

a)

Liverpool 360 ev. at 2.5 GeV/c

c)

number of combinations / 25 MeV

M ($\pi^+\pi^+\pi^-\pi^-$) GeV

Non Strange Besons

D. Cline

University of Wisconsin

Accumulating evidence suggests that boson states with mass greater than $2M_N$ exist. It is likely that some of these states couple to the $N\bar{N}$ system and will, therefore, show up as direct channel resonances in this system. If these states couple strongly enough to be observed in $N\bar{N}$ scattering experiments a new technique will thus be available for the study of the boson spectrum (at least that fraction that couple sufficiently to the $N\bar{N}$ system). In this note we first review some of the evidence for bosons of mass $> 2M_N$ obtained from production experiments. We then discuss the present evidence concerning direct channel resonance

391

structure in the $\bar{p}p$ system. Since the evidence on the latter subject is evolving at a rapid rate our primary aim is to discuss the possible overall magnitude of the contribution of such boson states as well as the channels where these states might be most likely to be readily observed.

PRODUCTION EXPERIMENTS. Table 1 lists the boson states with $M > 2M_N$ that have been observed in various production reactions. Broadly speaking, the only statistically well established states are those observed by the missing mass spectrometer (MMS) technique. However, there is important information to be obtained from the less well established states observed in bubble chamber experiments since these experiments are likely to identify the dominant decay modes of the bosons. As a general rule it appears that the multiplicity of pions for the dominant decays increases rapidly with boson mass.

Figure 1 shows the MMS spectrum observed by

Foccaci, et al.[1] The S, T and U states are evident
on this plot. The MMS is not sensitive to the
G parities of these states and thus a direct
confirmation using other techniques must rely on
reproducing the charge ratios observed in the MMS
(see table 1). Fig. 2 shows the results of a more
recent run of the MMS with the data being analyzed
in Paris by Cotteron, et al.[2] In this spectrum the
S and T states appear to move from 1929 → 1945 MeV
and 2190 → 2145 MeV respectively. In addition there
now appears a new state at ~ 2 BeV. The S width
appears to be ~ 10 MeV in both experiments. Two
comments are in order (1) It is reassuring that the
MMS is able to observe both narrow (S) and broader
states (the state near 2 BeV has a width of
~ 40 MeV). (2) The mass shift of these states

---

[1]M. N. Foccaci, et al., Phys. Rev. Letters <u>17</u>, 890
(1966).

[2]Cotteron, et al., private communication from the
Paris group working with the MMS group at CERN.

between the two experiments is disturbing. However, since the data from the second experiment is
still preliminary, further analysis might allievate
the latter criticism.

Turning to other production experiments we
note that a number of states have been suggested
in recent p̄p and πp production experiments.
Table 1 lists some of these states. While any or
all of these states may actually survive, it is of
some interest to note two recent experiments which
used a novel experimental technique.

Figure 3 shows the $(6\pi)^{\pm}$ mass spectrum
collected by an Athens-Liverpool collaboration for
the reaction

$$pp \rightarrow (6\pi)^{\pm}\ \pi\bar{+}$$

at 2.5 BeV/c, where a $\pi^{+}\pi^{-}\pi^{\circ}$ combination in the 6π
state is required to be in the ω peak.[3]   In addition

---

[3]Clayton, et al., Athens-Liverpool collaboration
preprint (1967).

the remaining $(3\pi)^{\pm}$ events are required to have a mass between 1260 and 1320 MeV, in the A_2 mass region. The latter cut seems to be of significance since structure near 2150 and 2350 MeV is greatly enhanced compared to the control sample where the $(3\pi)^{\pm}$ mass is taken to lie in the mass band 1180-1240 MeV. If this structure turns out to be statistically significant, it suggests two important facts:

1. The large combinatorial background present in annihilation mulitpion final states can be substantially reduced by mass cuts.

2. The cascade process $\bar{p}p \rightarrow M + \pi$, where M is a high mass meson, may be an important contribution to $\overline{N}N$ annihilation process. Since the c.m. energy of the $\bar{p}p$ system is only 2600 in this experiment and the masses of one of these states is $\sim$ 2400, the Q value for the cascade process apparently does not have to be large.

Further search for these cascade processes is of

great interest for the study of high mass bosons
as well as for understanding of the dynamics of $\overline{N}N$
annihilation.

There is good reason to believe that the
missing mass spectrometer technique can be successfully applied to bubble chamber exposures with the
added advantage of identification of the G parity
of the states in favorable cases. Fig. 4 shows a
G = +1 spectrum by the Aachen-Berlin-CERN
collaboration using π^+p at 8 GeV/c.[4] For comparison
the bumps observed by the MMS are shown. A new
state at 2600 is suggested and there is a hint of
evidence for some of the states observed in the MMS.

FORMATION EXPERIMENTS. The tried and true technique
for searching for direct channel resonances in the
πN and K$^-$N system, namely high precision total cross
section measurements, has been applied to the $N\overline{N}$

---

[4]Morrison et al., reported in the CERN report 66-29
Vol. III.

system with some structure having been observed.

Fig. 5 shows the $\bar{p}p$ total cross sections down to the

lowest energies so far studied ($\sim$ 300 MeV/c) and

up to $\sim$ 3 BeV/c.[5] The only reliably established

structure is observed in the high precision exper-

iment of Abrams et al.[6] for momenta above 1 BeV/c.

The cross section measurements below 1 BeV/c,

while considerably less precise, do serve to

indicate an upper limit on the magnitude that

narrow boson states can contribute to the $\bar{N}N$ system.

It appears that the structure cannot be much larger

than 10% of the total cross section. There is some

hint of structure near 900 MeV/c which should be

further investigated by high precision cross

section measurements. Fig. 6 shows the topological

partial cross sections as a function of laboratory

momentum.[5,7] None of the channels show energy

----

[5]V. Amaldi et al., Nuovo Cimento <u>34</u>, 825 (1964)
V. Amaldi, et al., Nuovo Cimento <u>46</u>, 171 (1966).

[6]R. J. Abrams et al., Phys. Rev. Letters <u>18</u>, 1209
(1967)

[7]A. Cooper et al., private communication.

dependent structure greater than ~ 20% of the

individual cross section.

Figure 7 shows in detail the total

cross sections above 1 GeV/c measured by Abrams,

et al.[6] Structure is evident in the vicinity of

1.3 and 1.7 BeV/c. If this structure is attributed

to boson states the following parameters are

suggested

$$M = 2190 \pm 5, \; \Gamma = 85; \quad I = 1$$

$$M = 2345 \pm 10, \; \Gamma = 140; \quad I = 1$$

$$M = 2380 \pm 10, \; \Gamma = 140; \quad I = 0$$

Note that if these bumps represent meson states

either the widths of the states are inconsistent

with the width of the T and U states observed in

the MMS (see table 1) or several states contribute

to the total cross section structure. There is

little reason, however, to believe that all bumps

in total cross sections indicate the presence of

direct channel activity. The onset of new thres-

holds would also be expected to contribute to

fluctuations in total cross sections. In addition, coherent production processes on deuterium might cause structure. It is primarily a matter of the order of magnitude of the fluctuations. In the πN system the resonances couple strongly enough to cause the dominant structure in the total cross section with the non-resonant structure almost invisible. However, in the $\bar{N}N$ system the fluctuation observed above 1 GeV/c are on the order of 2% of the total cross section and might easily arise from the onset of new thresholds. Similar structure has been observed in NN and K^+N total cross sections. So far the structure observed in these processes has not been identified with direct channel resonances.

Recently a number of experiments have attempted to pin down the nature of these enhancements by looking directly for the channels causing the bumps. The most prominent enhancement is the one near 2190 in the I = 1 channel. Our group at Wisconsin has obtained a $\bar{p}d$ exposure in the ANL 30" MURA bubble chamber. The momenta of the

exposure are 1.23, 1.33, 1.45 and 1.65 BeV/c. We
have studied the 3 and 5 prong cross sections as
a function of energy. Our primary motivation for
studying the 3 prong excitation curve was to
verify whether the $\bar{p}p$ structure near 2190 was
associated with the T^-, which decays predominately
into three charged particles. Figure 8 shows the
topological cross section observed in the $\bar{p}d$
exposure as well as the I = 1 total cross section.
(The I = 1 cross section was obtained by Abrams,
et al.,[6] using the Glauber corrections.) The bump
in the I = 1 cross section appears to be ~ 5 mb,
no such bump is seen either in the 3 prong or
5 prong topological cross sections. <u>This suggests
that the T observed by the MMS and the $\bar{p}N$ total
cross section structure are not simply related</u>.
Parenthetically we note that there seems to be a
discrepancy between the I = 1 total cross section
as measured at BNL and our total cross section
measurement at 1.3 BeV/c which is obtained by taking
ratios of topological $\bar{p}p$ and $\bar{p}n$ cross sections and

correcting the $\bar{p}$n cross sections using the measured $\bar{p}$p cross section at this energy. The origin of this discrepancy may be due to the validity of the Glauber approximation at low energy or the magnitude of the real part of the forward amplitudes used by Abrams, et al., in unfolding the deuteron cross section. We observe rapid variation of one cross section in the vicinity of 1.3 GeV/c, namely for the process

$$\bar{p}n \rightarrow \bar{p}p \ \pi^-$$

while this alone seems incapable of explaining the bump (see Fig. 8). The process

$$\bar{p}n \rightarrow \bar{n}n\pi^-$$

may have the right size and energy dependence. The latter process is experimentally difficult to study reliably since it has two missing neutrals and, therefore, this conclusion must await further analysis. Fig. 9 shows the angular distribution of the $\bar{p}$ for the $\bar{p}p\pi^-$ final state as a function of center of mass energy. The reaction is very peripheral even at rather low energy suggesting that meson exchange is the dominate mechanism for this reaction even near threshold. It should be noted that Abrams et al.,[6] suggested that the total cross section structure appeared at the threshold for $\bar{\Delta}N$ and $\bar{N}(1450)N$, production. It is important to note that this explanation of the bumps as due of N^* thresholds can also account for the fact that the bump near 2190 is I = 1 ($\bar{\Delta}N$ is I = 1 or 2) whereas the bumps near 2360 are I = 1 and I = 1 ($\bar{N}(1450)N$ is I = 0 or 1).

An ANL group has also obtained bubble chamber film in the 1.3 BeV/c $\bar{p}p$ region. Again no single channel can be shown to give rise to the bump, but this group has suggested that the $\bar{N}N\pi$ excitation curve may explain only part of the bump with the remainder being possibly due to resonance formation.[8] Fig. 10 shows the basis for this conclusion. Unfortunately, all such speculation depends on the assumed background drawn under the bump. However, it seems likely that at least the bulk of the 2190

---

[8]A. Cooper et al., Phys. Rev. Letters <u>20</u>, 1059(1968).

bump does come from a threshold effect, with any
residual effects due to bosons being spread over
several topological channels of which they contribute
less than a percent or so and are, therefore,
extremely difficult to observe. There are probably
easier and more reliable ways to search for direct
channel states.

It seems likely that the best way to look
for direct channel resonances is to observe channels
with small background coming from other mechanisms.
Backward hemisphere $\bar{p}p$ and $\bar{p}n$ elastic scattering is
perhaps the best example, however, $\bar{p}p \rightarrow \pi\pi$, $\bar{K}K$, $\rightarrow 3\pi$
should also be reasonable channels to study. We
shall discuss here only two such channels, namely,
backward $\bar{p}p$ elastic scattering and $\bar{p}p \rightarrow \pi\pi$.

A number of recent measurements have been
carried out on backward $\bar{p}p$ elastic scattering. The
most promising results are obtained from a low energy
experiment carried out at Wisconsin. This experiment
uses film obtained at BNL using the 30" chamber
exposed to a $\bar{p}$ beam. The exposures cover the

momentum range of ~ 700 MeV/c to 200 MeV/c. In
this momentum range the c.m. energy resolution is
particularly good varying from ~ 3-7 MeV, allowing
a definitive search for narrow states in the S
region (the S would occur at ~ 450 MeV/c $\bar{p}$ momentum).
In addition, backward hemisphere elastic scattering
is relatively easy to detect on the scanning table
allowing for good statistics even though the backward cross sections are small. Fig. 11 shows the
backward hemisphere angular distributions in this
experiment.[9] A peak is evident near 180° with the
shape of the peak varying somewhat over the momentum
range of 300-600 MeV/c.

The existence of such a backward peak could
come from a variety of mechanisms. For example
many potential model calculations of elastic
scattering suggest a backward peak as does an
optical model fit to the low energy data. It is
unlikely that exchange mechanisms can account for

---

[9]J. English, et al., Wisconsin report (1968).

such a peak since the exchange of baryon number two

is required.   The backward peak can also come from

direct channel resonances, in which case rapid

energy variation of the backward cross section would

be expected.   Fig. 12 shows that the energy variation

of $d\sigma/d\Omega$ for various $\cos\theta$ cuts.   Two energy

fluctuations are evident: one at $\sim$ 300 MeV/c at

the mass of 1900 MeV and the other at $\sim$ 420 MeV/c

with a mass $\sim$ 1925 MeV.   The former fluctuation

occurs at $\cos\theta \sim 0$ and may perhaps partially arise

from the imposition of scanning table cuts.   At

present this 'bump' should probably not be taken

seriously.   The 180° fluctuation at 430 MeV/c is

suggestive of a direct channel effect.   The fact

that this bump only occurs near the backward

direction is evidence that a misestimate of the

flux is not the origin of this rapid energy

dependence.   The mass and width of this effect are

in approximate agreement with the S seen by the

MMS as shown in Table 1.

Turning to higher energies, the existence of

a backward peak in $\bar{p}p$ and $\bar{p}n$ elastic scattering

above 1 BeV/c is also firmly established. Fig. 13

shows some backward angular distributions obtained

at Wisconsin ($\bar{p}n$),[10] ANL ($\bar{p}p$ at 1.3)[8] and Michigan

($\bar{p}p$) at ~ 1.85 BeV/c)[11] all using the 30" MURA

chamber at the ZGS. Fig. 14 summarizes the measured

backward cross section between $\cos\theta$ = -.8 → -1.0 up

to 2.2 BeV/c. Except for a rapid energy dependence o

of the backward cross section ($\sim S^{-(7-12)}$) there is

little evidence of structure above 1 BeV/c. The

total cross section bumps, if interpreted as meson

states with the spins, expected from crude Regge

trajectory extrapolation would give elastic scatter-

ing cross sections of ~ 200 μb. It is interesting

to note that the $\bar{p}n$ backward hemisphere cross section

is somewhat larger than the $\bar{p}p$ in the range of

1.2-1.45 and at 1.65 the cross sections appear to

---

[10] J. Berryhill, et al., Wisconsin report (1968)

[11] J. Lys and C. T. Murphy, private communication.

be comparable. Fig. 15 shows the energy variation
of the $\bar{p}n/\bar{p}p$ ratio.[10] In summary, although no
5 std results can be quoted at present, the
possibility of direct channel structure in the backward cross section at a level easily measured by
counter experiments is not ruled out.

Finally we turn to $\bar{p}p \rightarrow \pi^+\pi^-$. This channel
should be an excellent place to look for high mass
states on the ρ trajectory as well as states on
lower G = +1 trajectories such as the ρ' etc.
Fig. 16-20 summarize the present state of knowledge
about this process. The cross section at low
energies is consistent with a 1/V fall (Fig. 16)[12]
deviating somewhat near 600 MeV/c. A Cal-Tech-BNL
counter experiment has measured the $\bar{p}p \rightarrow \pi\pi$ cross
section over a restricted angular range but with
very good statistics from 700-2400 MeV/c.[13] Fig. 17
shows the 90° cross section as a function of c.m.

---

[12]R. Terrell, et al., Wisconsin report (1968).

[13]J. Pine and A. Tollestrup, private communication.

energy. A broad maximum is evident near 2.1 BeV
with a width of > 400 MeV. The available angular
distributions are summarized in Fig. (18) and (19).
The angular distribution is seen to be forward
peaked (π^- in direction of $\bar{p}$) at low energy and
consistent with no forward backward asymmetry up
to ~ 2 BeV/c.[14] Fig. 19 shows the folded angular
distributions of the Cal Tech-BNL experiment.[13]
The folded angular distributions indicate that high
partial waves enter into this process above
700 MeV/c. Fig. (20) shows a compilation of all
total cross sections for pp → $\pi\pi$ from bubble chamber
measurements.[15] With a little imagination it is easy
to see that direct channel effects probably play
an important role in this process below 2 BeV/c.

　　Our present state of knowledge about the
boson spectrum below 2 M_N suggests (by extrapolation)
that many states should lie above 2 M_N. Thus it

---

[14] The data on this graph comes from reference 12,
and from A. Cooper (ANL) and T. Buhl (Wisconsin)
and C. T. Murphy (Michigan).

[15] Compliation supplied by C. T. Murphy.

will be of great interest to see which of the high
mass bosons couple strongly enough to $\bar{N}N$ to appear
as resonances. A number of states with $M > 2M_N$
have been suggested by production experiments and
there is fragmentary evidence that high mass boson
states contribute to $\bar{p}N$ interactions, at least
below 2 BeV/c. The next few years will undoubtedly
see a great deal of effort expended on this search.

I wish to thank A. Cooper, A. Tollestrup,
J. Pine, C. T. Murphy, and J. Lys for allowing me
to include their unpublished data in this report.
In addition I wish to thank Cotteron, et al., (and
B. Maglic) for permission to include the latest
MMS results. Also, I appreciate the use of data
obtained by students working with me at Wisconsin
and included here. Finally, I wish to acknowledge
the effort that U. Camerini and D. D. Reeder
have expended on the Wisconsin $\bar{p}N$ exposures.

Structure in the Antinucleon-Nucleon

Total Cross Sections in the Regions of

Energy above 2M

D. Michael

Brookhaven National Laboratory

It was felt that for the purpose of this conference it would be useful to discuss somewhat in more detail the structure seen in the antinucleon-nucleon total cross sections in the region of total c.m. energy above 2 GeV, and what relation this may or may not have to the formation of boson resonances in this region. The measurements were performed at the Brookhaven National Laboratory AGS by a group consisting of Abrams, Cool, Giacomelli, Kycia, Leontic, Li, and Michael, and the results have been in the literature for nearly a year.[1]

Antiproton total cross sections were measured with counters in a standard "good-geometry" transmission experiment, using a partially separated beam. The results for antiprotons on hydrogen are shown in Fig. 1. It was possible to obtain a statistical accuracy of

411

the order of one part in a thousand in a few hours of
running. Data was taken starting from the upper limit
of the beam, 3.30 GeV/c, and continuing down in laboratory momentum in steps of 0.05 GeV/c to 1.00 GeV/c.
At the end of the run, several points were repeated
and were found to reproduce within statistics. The point-
to-point statistical error is less than ±0.07 mb over
most of the range and is smaller than the size of most
dots plotted in Fig. 1. The points with the larger error
bars are from an earlier counter experiment at CERN.[2]
Of special interest for this conference is the energy
resolution of these measurements; there is a contribution
from only two sources: (1) the finite momentum acceptance,
±0.75%, of the incident beam, and (2) the uncertainty in
incident momentum caused by ionization loss as the
beam passed through the 93.4 cm liquid hydrogen target.
Expressed in terms of total c.m. energy, the upper
limit to the resolution was ±10 MeV, and remained nearly
constant over the range of these measurements. This
corresponds to about half the spacing between the points
in Fig. 1.

Two broad structures are seen on the rapidly
falling cross sections in Fig. 1: one at about 1.3 GeV/c,
and another near 1.8 GeV/c. If one tries to fit a smooth
curve without inflections to the data in this region, one
obtains an infinitesimal probability for the fit; hence, we
say that the size of the structure is large compared

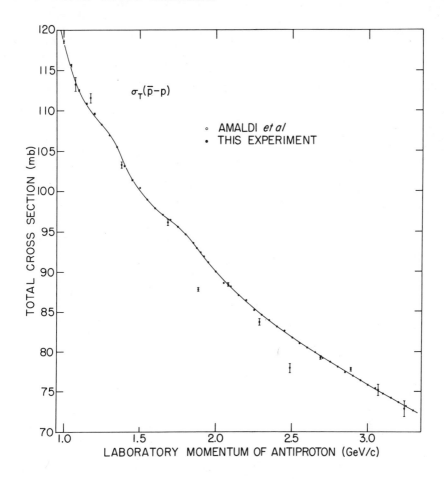

Figure 1. The total cross sections of antiprotons on protons. The point-to-point statistical uncertainty is less than 0.07 mb for momenta greater than 1.2 GeV/c. The systematic uncertainty in the absolute cross-section scale is of the order of 1%.

with the statistical uncertainty in the points. Note that near 1.9 GeV/c, in the region of the U, points were taken at 25 MeV/c intervals and no narrow structure was observed.

Since the antiproton-proton total cross section

consists of a mixture of half I=0 and half I=1 states, we
have taken data with a liquid deuterium target at the
same time as the hydrogen data in order to resolve which
of the isospin states is contributing to the structures.
The deuterium data, shown in Fig. 2, has about the same
statistical uncertainty as the hydrogen data. The two
structures appear in the same place in the deuterium
cross sections, but are broadened by the Fermi motion
in the deuteron. The antiproton-deuteron total cross
section consists of approximately one fourth I=0 and
three-fourths I=1 states. The total cross sections for

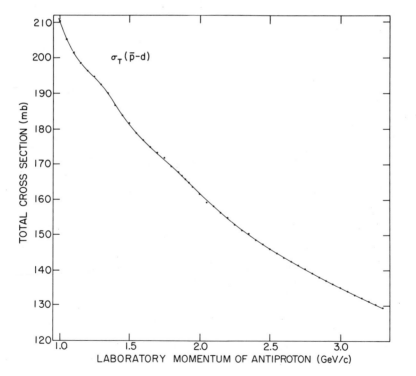

Figure 2.   The total cross sections of antiprotons on
            deuterons, from the same experiment.

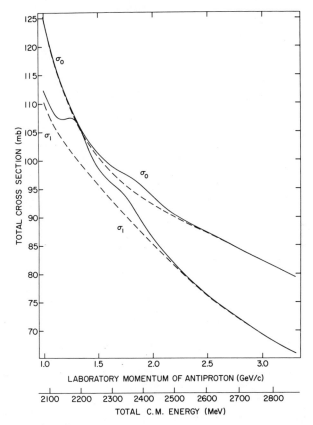

Figure 3.   The nucleon-antinucleon total cross section in
             the pure isotopic spin states σ_0 and σ_1,
             derived from the total cross sections shown
             in Figs. 1 and 2. The experimental resolution
             corresponds to ±10 MeV in the total c. m.
             energy. The dashed curves represent possible
             background curves under the assumption that
             the shape of each structure is given by a
             single Breit-Wigner resonance function. The
             results of a fit under this assumption yields
             the following values for the three structures:
             M = 2190 ± 10 MeV, Γ ≈ 85 MeV, and M
             = 2345 ± 10 MeV, Γ ≈ 140 MeV for the two
             in σ_1, and M = 2380 ± 10 MeV, Γ ≈ 140 MeV
             for the one in σ_0. Another possible interpre-
             tation is that the structures are the result of
             threshold effects.

the pure isospin states has been obtained from the data
of Figs. 1 and 2 by a procedure which takes into account
the effects of Fermi motion and screening in the
deuteron.[1] This procedure has been empirically verified
for pion total cross sections where one has an independent
means of obtaining the pure isospin cross sections, and
has been used in the past to determine the isospin of
higher mass Y^{*} resonances seen in K^{-} - nucleon total
cross sections.[3]

The total cross sections for the two pure isospin
states are shown in Fig. 3. The structure near 1.3 GeV/c
is seen to be present only in I=1, while the structure
near 1.8 GeV/c has a contribution from both states. We
have not attempted to put error bars on these curves
because the procedure of folding and unfolding Fermi
momentum complicates the propagation of the statistical
uncertainty. The statistical uncertainty in σ_{1}, however,
is roughly the same as for the hydrogen data, and the
uncertainty in σ_{0} is roughly four times as large; that
is, the statistical uncertainty in these curves is considerably smaller than the size of the structures.

There are two possible interpretations of these
structures: either they are the result of the formation
of boson resonances, or they are the result of the opening
of thresholds for rapidly rising inelastic processes.
Assuming the first possibility, we have attempted to fit
each structure with a single Breit-Wigner resonance

function (with constant width) plus a smooth background
curve, and have obtained good fits with the resonance
parameters listed in the caption to Fig. 3. The background
curves obtained with these fits are shown as the dashed
curves in Fig. 3. It can be seen from Fig. 3 that the
background curves are not severely constrained by the
data; hence, the values we obtain for the widths have a
rather large uncertainty. It is clear, however, that the
data are not compatible with (single) resonances with
widths as narrow as 10 MeV, although the masses appear
to be in the same region as the T and U seen in the
missing-mass experiment.[4] The more conservative
interpretation, of course, is to say that the structure
is the result of threshold effects. One possible mechanism
that has been proposed[1] is the production of Δ(1236)
and $\bar{\Delta}$(1236) in the region of 2190 MeV, and the production of N(1400) and $\bar{\text{N}}$(1400) in the region of 2350 MeV.
This would successfully explain the isospin combinations
of the structures, for instance; although it may be noted
that if a higher mass value (1470) is taken for the N(1400),
it would be perhaps too high to account for the structures.

In conclusion, we may say that the presence of
structure in the antinucleon-nucleon total cross sections
in the energy region of the T and U is established with
a high degree of statistical confidence, but that a unique
interpretation of this structure is not yet possible.
Whether or not this structure is related to the formation

of boson resonances must be determined in future
experiments.

REFERENCES

1. R. J. Abrams, R. L. Cool, G. Giacomelli, T. F.
    Kycia, B. A. Leontic, K. K. Li, and D. N.
    Michael, Phys. Rev. Letters 18, 1209 (1967).
2. V. Amaldi, Jr., T. Fazzini, G. Fidecaro, G.
    Ghesquiere, M. Legros, and H. Steiner, Nuovo
    Cimento 34, 825 (1964).
3. R. J. Abrams, R. L. Cool, G. Giacomelli, T. F.
    Kycia, B. A. Leontic, K. K. Li, and D. N.
    Michael, Phys. Rev. Letters 19, 678 (1967); R.
    L. Cool, G. Giacomelli, T. F. Kycia, B. A.
    Leontic, K. K. Li, A. Lundby, and J. Teiger,
    Phys. Rev. Letters 16, 1228 (1966), also Phys.
    Rev., to be published.
4. G. Chikovani, L. Dubal, M. N. Focacci, W.
    Kienzle, B. Levrat, B. C. Maglic, M. Martin,
    C. Nef, P. Schubelin, and J. Seguinot, Physics
    Letters 22, 233 (1966).

Some New Detector Systems[*]

S. J. Lindenbaum, Brookhaven National Laboratory,

Upton, New York

Introduction

The first part of my talk will be concerned with two
relatively new hodoscope detector systems recently used at
the Brookhaven National Laboratory AGS for single particle
detection and momentum measurement by a magnetic spectrometer
system with on-line computer determination of missing mass.

The first system (fig. 1) is a counter hodoscope
system[1] whereas the second (fig. 4) is a spark chamber
hodoscope (wire) system.[2]

The remainder of my talk will be concerned with a new
double V (vertex) magnetic spectrometer detector system
(figs. 6-7) which has been under development by my group[3,4]
for the past several years and is scheduled to be completed,
assembled, and tested at the AGS this coming fall and winter.
This system will be composed of two multi-particle detecting

[*]This work was performed under the auspices of the U.S.
Atomic Energy Commission.

419

magnetic spectrometer arms on line to a computer and will be
suitable for detecting and automatically measuring the
momentum of the charged decay particles from double vertex
events such as, to cite a few examples:

$$\pi^- + p \rightarrow K^o \quad + \quad (\Lambda^o \quad \text{or} \quad \Sigma^o) \tag{1}$$
$$ \rightarrow (\pi^+ + \pi^-) \quad \rightarrow (p + \pi^- \text{ or } \gamma + p + \pi^-)$$

$$\pi^- + p \rightarrow Y(\text{or } Y^*) + K^o \tag{2}$$

$$\pi^+ + p \rightarrow N^{*++} + \begin{pmatrix} f^o \\ \rho^o \end{pmatrix} \tag{3a}$$

$$\rightarrow p \begin{pmatrix} A_1 \\ A_2 \\ B \end{pmatrix} \tag{3b}$$

$$K^+ + p \rightarrow K^o + N^{*++} \qquad \text{or} \tag{4a}$$

$$\rightarrow K^* + p \tag{4b}$$

$$K^- + p \rightarrow Y^{*+} + \pi^- \tag{5a}$$

$$\rightarrow \Lambda + \emptyset \tag{5b}$$

$$\rightarrow \Lambda + \omega \quad \text{etc.} \tag{5c}$$

and similar types of new reactions.

Single Arm Counter Hodoscope Magnetic Spectrometer System With On-Line Computer

This system[1] is shown in figs. 1a-1b. It represents
the third generation of an original system first used in the
fall of 1962 in the first on-line computer counter experiments
performed.[5] It was primarily developed for measuring small

angle elastic scattering with ultra high precision and high
data rates in order to determine the real part of the
nuclear scattering amplitude by observing Coulomb-nuclear
interference.[1] The system has about 500 counter hodoscopes
arranged in $> 10^{12}$ counter combinations so that average
overall (system plus beam, etc.) momentum resolutions of 0.4%
and average overall angular resolutions of $< \frac{1}{2}$ milliradian
are attained.

Beam particle identification is performed by a
Cerenkov counter system in the incident momentum analyzed
beam. Hodoscopes HO1 and HO2 were used to measure the
location and the angle of the particle incident on the 2'
long hydrogen target to ± 0.15 mrad. The vertical elements
of H2 and the horizontal elements of H4 measure the outgoing
angle. The vertical elements of H4 were used to measure
the deflection of the scattered particle in the magnet and
hence allow a determination of its momentum. Hodoscopes HO1
and HO2 consisted of $\frac{1}{8}''$ wide counter elements. The first 48
elements of hodoscope H2 consisted of $\frac{1}{8}''$ wide counter elements
in order to obtain very high resolution in the small angle
region. The last 80 elements of H1 consisted of $\frac{1}{4}''$ wide
counters. After passing through H2 the scattered particles
passed through three 30 D 72 analysis magnets ($\sim$ 100 milli-
radians deflection for the beam particle momentum). The
µ-counters were used to detect and reject muons and when
pions were selected by the Cerenkov counter system the muon
contamination was kept to below 0.25%. The hodoscope H1 was
used in conjunction with HO1, HO2, and H2 to determine the
location along the beam path of the point of scatter in order
to reject events where the interaction occurred outside the
hydrogen target. In order to reduce accidentals, events in

which more than one incident hodoscope counter per screen was
struck, were vetoed electronically. The net accidental
corrections were small (< 1%). A fast (five nanosecond)
coincidence between HO1, HO2, the Cerenkov counters, the beam
determining scintillators, and three anti-counters outside
the beam was used to identify the incident particle. A
further 20 nanosecond coincidence between H2 and H4 determined that the particle had scattered into a selected fiducial
region. When such a coincidence signal was received, 144
fast gates were opened for 20 nanoseconds to identify which
of the counters had been struck. This information was then
transferred to a digital data handler[6] which had a buffer
memory of 4096 words of 72 bits each, and 15 μsec later the
system was ready to receive another event. Up to 2,000 such
events were recorded each pulse (∿ 3 million/hour). At the
end of the AGS pulse the data in the buffer was transferred
to the PDP-6 computer for on-line data analysis and in
parallel onto magnetic tape for a permanent record. The
computer and digital data handling devices are provided and
maintained by the Brookhaven On-Line Data Facility group
under the direction of the author. This computer equipment
is used partly in rotation and partly in time sharing by as
many as ten research groups including about five outside
university user groups.*

---

* For example, the recent check of CP violation by the
   Steinberger (Columbia) group was done using the PDP-6 computer on-line simultaneously with a BNL-Carnegie Tech group's
   spark chamber hodoscope magnetic spectrometer measurements
   utilizing the time sharing feature of the computer.

   The on-line computer program continuously evaluated a
portion of the data (at least 10%), calculated the scattering
angle and momentum of each particle, and constructed momentum
spectra for each of 30 scattering angle bins of width 0.4 to
1 mr. Counter performance and the magnetic fields of the
beam transport, and the momentum measuring magnets, etc. were
monitored by the computer. The empty target backgrounds were
generally $\sim$ 10% except at the small angles. Fig. 2 shows a
typical momentum spectra for the reaction

$$\pi^- + p \rightarrow \pi^- + \text{missing mass} \tag{6}$$

plotted versus the missing mass and exhibits several peaks
corresponding to the well known nucleon isobars. In addition
there is the large and wide peak at a mass of 1.4 BeV
previously observed only in p-p interactions. Using this
apparatus we have observed this 1.4 BeV mass peak in p-p and
$\pi^\pm$-p interactions from 10 to 26 BeV/c in the range of four
momentum transfer $0.01 < |t| < 0.2$ $(\text{BeV/c})^2$ implying the con-
clusion that it is a bona fide isobar. Typical inelastic
momentum spectra are shown in fig. 3.

   The apparatus was only used to measure missing mass in
the following reactions which we observed as a by product to
an elastic scattering investigation:

$$\pi^\pm + p \rightarrow \pi^\pm + \text{missing mass} \tag{7}$$

$$p + p \rightarrow p + \text{missing mass} \tag{8}$$

However, this apparatus could also be used in other missing
mass reactions such as:

$$\pi^{\pm} + p \rightarrow p + \text{missing mass} \qquad\qquad (9)$$

$$K^{\pm} + p \rightarrow p + \text{missing mass} \qquad\qquad (10)$$

$$\rightarrow K^{\pm} + \text{missing mass}$$

and others. For some of the general applications illustrated above, a Cerenkov counter system would be placed behind H4 to allow identification of the detected particle.

Single Arm Spark Chamber (Wire) Hodoscope Magnetic Spectrometer System

Another system used recently by Anderson et al[2] at BNL is shown in fig. 4a. It is essentially similar to the above described system in general features, except that spark chamber hodoscopes have been used instead of counter hodoscopes. The overall system characteristics are shown in fig. 4b. The outgoing particle is identified by Cerenkov counters. The momentum and angular resolution are comparable with the previous system. It was used, however, with a larger angular acceptance by a factor $\sim 1.5 - 2$. The resolution time is 1 μsec compared to 20 nanoseconds for the counter hodoscope system and the maximum event rate is 120/pulse instead of 2,000 per pulse of the counter hodoscope system.[†] However, one should note that the spark chamber system was primarily used for observing backward elastic scattered and recoiling particles. Hence the average event rate capability was not a limitation. One should also note that spark chamber

---

[†] This limit was imposed by the data handling and detection system and could in principle be operated at 20,000 to 100,000/pulse.

hodoscopes are usually much cheaper than counter hodoscopes of similar size. Fig. 5 shows the results obtained in the reaction $\pi^- + p \rightarrow p + B^*$ showing the well-known peaks of the ρ, the A_2, and the R at a mass squared about 0.5, 1.6, and 2.9 $(BeV)^2$ respectively. These missing mass reactions were originally studied by Maglic and co-workers[8,9] at CERN employing a variety of specially developed missing mass spectrometers.

The Double Vee Magnetic Spectrometer System

As mentioned in the introduction, this system has been under development for some time. It was first conceived in the latter part of 1963 and an illustrative sketch of an early proposed version which was described in the 1964 Dubna Conference Proceedings is shown in fig. 6. Some illustrative reactions that can be studied with this apparatus have been given on page 2, eqs. (1-5).

Fig. 7 shows a schematic of the basic arrangement that will be utilized at the AGS this fall.

The incident charged particle beam (coming from the left) has its momentum measured to a few tenths of a percent by a counter hodoscope system (not shown) before and after deflecting magnets. A series of Cerenkov counters (not shown) in this incident beam identify the incident particle, which is then allowed to pass through a 2' liquid hydrogen target, and double vertex and other inelastic interactions occur.

A scintillation counter hodoscope trigger system (not shown) with associated logic is used in coincidence with the incident beam equipment to select a wide variety of events of interest and trigger on them and provide identifying tags.

The following are some of the various triggers to be used:

(a) K^o or other long lived neutral going through the forward leg decaying into 2 charged particles after leaving the H2 target.

(b) Two charged particles passing through the forward leg.

(c) One or more charged particles going through the wide angle leg.

(d) A particular electronically identified particle passing through the forward magnets.

(e) One or two charged particles passing through the forward leg accompanied by one or two charged particles being detected in wide angle leg.

The Spark Chamber Hodoscopes. The spark chamber hodoscopes shown are each constructed of a pair of hodoscope (wire) planes with parallel wires separated by a 1/2" spacer inserted between their epoxy frames and covered by mylar sheets and filled with nelium with a small amount of alcohol. There are three types of wire planes, x, y, and w. The x planes have two sets of vertical wires (out of page) and determine the x co-ordinate. The y planes have two sets of horizontal wires and the w planes have two sets of parallel wires running diagonally. An x, y, w set of hodoscope planes therefore can uniquely locate each of a reasonable number of incident charged particles with a negligible number of ambiguities and in general each spark chamber hodoscope shown is composed of such a set. However, for various reasons we have in many cases introduced a number of redundant wire planes. The 5 mil Be-Cu wires are spaced 20-32 to the inch. Magnostrictive

readout is employed and the resolution has been measured to be
about 0.3 mm.

        The last chamber shown behind the 120" wide by 36"
deep magnet is designed with x plane hodoscopes of 23'.   In
order to have the capability of producing such large chambers
economically a new production method was developed. Fig. 8
shows this production method. This method for obtaining large
wire hodoscope planes and the readout system, etc. were
primarily developed by S. Ozaki and E. Platner. An epoxy
glass (NEMA 11) frame is constructed to outline the desired
sensitive area. The apparatus can accommodate up to 23' of
sensitive area in either direction. This limitation is due to
the limited size of the high bay assembly area in the Physics
building. The epoxy glass frame is then mounted so that it can
be spun at 10-20 rpm around a vertical axis at its center, the
upper part of which is shown in the photograph. The end of
the axis is just below the center of the lower part of the
frame. The cam followers shown along the lower edge of the
frame are used as casters and ride on ground steel beds to set
the wire spacing which can be varied from 0.020" upwards and
the location accuracy is about two mils. The wire spacings
which are used are in the range 20-50 per inch and 5 mil Be-Cu
wire is used. The wire feed at the left is driven by a lead
screw along the vertical slide. The tension on the wire is
controlled to better than 5% by a long vacuum column shown
on the left, to the right of the operator. This apparatus
typically winds 1-2 feet of chamber per hour and a 23' long
sensitive region frame can be wound in less than a day.
A rubber strip allows for thermal expansion, etc. The wire
is held by the rubber and epoxy glue to the frame and is cut
away from one side. Two such frames are assembled with
the wires parallel and facing each other but separated by a

spacer which contains two 0-ring seals. A vacuum is created between the seals to keep the chambers together. The outside of both frames is covered with two mil thick mylar and the chamber is filled with neon-helium gas and quenched with alcohol. Tests of the chambers have shown that the readout resolution is ± 0.3 mm or better.

In the arrangement shown, with a 40 mc clocking frequency, the angular resolution due to the incident measuring uncertainty is ~ 0.1 mr. Hence the multiple scattering controls angular resolution. Each leg of the apparatus has $< \frac{1}{100}$ radiation length so that multiple scattering in the hydrogen target is the real limit for charged particles traversing the target. For ~ 10 BeV/c particles the angular resolution in the forward leg is a few tenths of a mr. The multiple scattering due to traversing the H2 target is still a fraction of a mr. for 10 BeV/c particles. In the wide angle leg the multiple scattering due to the spectrometer is about 4 mr. for $t \approx 0.25$ $(BeV/c)^2$ and about 2 mr. for $t \approx 1$ $(BeV/c)^2$.

The forward leg has a momentum resolution $\frac{\Delta p}{p}$ of about 0.2% at 10 BeV/c and the wide or recoil leg has a momentum resolution for protons ~ 1.5% at p = 1 BeV/c. Upon a suitable trigger logic signal a voltage pulse (7-8 k.v. about 150 nanoseconds wide) is applied to the chambers and then the chambers are read out. There is enough readout scaler capacity to handle 7 sparks/chamber but an average of 4 is expected. The data handler memory capacity of 4096 words of 108 bits each will on the average then allow 50 trigger selected events/AGS pulse to be recorded.

The Data Handling Arrangement. This arrangement is shown in fig. 9. The digital data handlers and on-line computer are those previously described for the BNL On-Line Data Facility.

An on-line computer program will sample $\sim$ 10% of the data and will compute final results to any degree of completeness desired. The bulk of the data will probably finally be reduced off-line at the BNL CDC 6600 computer. The computer programming methods and organization have been primarily done by W. A. Love. The apparatus is expected to handle $\sim 10^5$ incident charged particles per AGS pulse. The solid angle is severely limited by the use of presently available magnets, but is still such that typically an average of two orders of magnitude increase in rate over bubble chamber experiments for typical pion induced reactions will occur.[*]

Therefore, the considerably higher data rates and resolutions attained should allow interesting new results to be obtained with this apparatus. It has been proposed by the author for the past several years that special magnets be purchased which would allow even more solid angle and resolution, and it was proposed that a MKII version of this apparatus be constructed as a large user facility for the various potential university users as well as BNL users. This facility would have its own experimental staff and operate in analogy to the BNL hydrogen bubble chamber facilities. Unfortunately, lack of funds and manpower have not yet allowed implementation of this proposal.

---

[*] At low $|t|$ generally only the proton from the decay baryon (say Λ or Σ, for example) will enter the wide leg magnet for the typical rates given. The pion direction will generally be detected.

REFERENCES

1. K. J. Foley, R. S. Jones, S. J. Lindenbaum, W. A. Love,
    S. Ozaki, E. D. Platner, C. A. Quarles, and E. H. Willen,
    Phys. Rev. Letters 19, 193 (1967); Phys. Rev. Letters 19,
    397 (1967).

2. E. W. Anderson, E. J. Bleser, H. P. Bleiden, G. B. Collins,
    D. Garelick, J. Menes, F. Turkot, D. Birnbaum,
    R. M. Edelstein, N. C. Hien, T. J. McMahon, and J.F. Mucci,
    Charged Boson Production and Elastic Scattering Near 180°
    in $\overline{\pi}$ Proton Interactions at 8 BeV/c, Proceedings of the
    Heidelberg Conference on Elementary Particles, Heidelberg,
    Germany, September, 1967.

3a. K. J. Foley, R. S. Jones, S. J. Lindenbaum, W. A. Love,
    S. Ozaki, E. Platner, C. A. Quarles, and E. Willen,
    Proceedings of the XII International Conference on High
    Energy Physics, Dubna, 1964 (Atomizdat., Moscow, 1966),
    p. 418.

3b. S. J. Lindenbaum, Ann. Rev. of Nuclear Science 16, 619
    (1966).

4. The present version of the system is being developed by
    D. Cheng, K. J. Foley, S. J. Lindenbaum, W. A. Love,
    S. Ozaki, E. Platner, A. Saulys, and E. Willen.

5. K. J. Foley, S. J. Lindenbaum, W. A. Love, S. Ozaki,
    J. J. Russell, and L. C. L. Yuan, Phys. Rev. Letters 10,
    376,543 (1963); 11, 425,503 (1963); Nuc. Inst. and
    Methods 30, 45 (1964).

6. K. J. Foley, R. S. Gilmore, R. S. Jones, S. J. Lindenbaum,
    W. A. Love, R. Yamada, and L. C. L. Yuan, Proceedings of
    the XII International Conference on High Energy Physics,
    Dubna, 1964 (Atomizdat., Moscow, 1966), p. 418.

REFERENCES

7. S. J. Lindenbaum, Ann. Rev. Nuc. Science <u>16</u>, 619 (1966).
8. M. N. Focacci, W. Kienzle, B. Levrat, B. C. Maglic, and M. Martin, Phys. Rev. Letters <u>17</u>, 890 (1966).
9. W. Kienzle (See paper this conference).

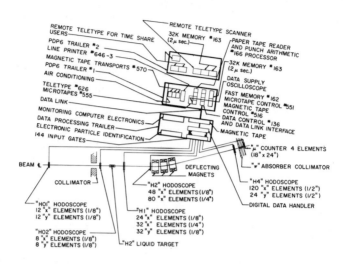

Figure 1(a)   A simplified sketch of the counter hodoscope
and the associated on-line computer system for
studying small angle scattering, utilizing a
high resolution, high data rate capacity
magnetic spectrometer. Hodoscopes H01 and H02
measure the location and direction of the
particle before scattering in the hydrogen
target. Hodoscopes H1 and H2 determine its
location and direction after scattering and
reject events not coming from the target.
Hodoscope H4 after the magnets then determines
its momentum. The digital data handling
equipment is in the 40' x 10' trailer near the
hodoscopes. The on-line PDP-6 computer system
is contained in the other 40' x 10' trailers.
The apparatus is about 400' long.

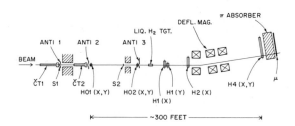

	NUMBER OF ELEMENTS		DIMENSIONS (inches)		
	X	Y	WIDTH	LENGTH	THICKNESS
HO1	12	12	0.123	1.5	0.125
HO2	10	10	0.123	1.25	0.0625
H1	24	32	0.126	4.0	0.125
	36		0.262	4.0	0.125
H2	48		0.127	6.0	0.3
	80		0.266	6.0	0.3
H4	120		0.504	12.0	0.5
		24	0.500	60.0	0.5

Figure 1(b)   A detailed diagram of the actual experimental
               arrangement. The system had a momentum
               resolution ~ 0.4% and an angular resolution of
               ~ 0.4 mrad.

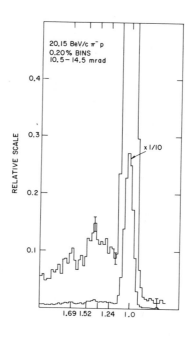

Figure 2:   Examples of the elastic peak with the inelastic
              background blown up a factor of ten. The usual
              peak at 1.4 BeV which previously was observed
              only in p-p is clearly prominent in $\pi^{\pm}$-p
              interactions throughout the s and t range
              covered by this experiment, thus strongly imply-
              ing that it is a bona fide isobar.

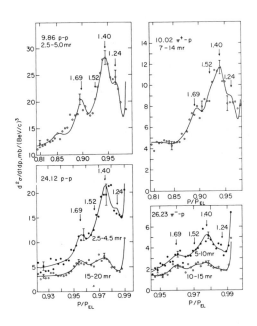

Figure 3:   Typical inelastic momentum spectra, $\frac{d^2\sigma}{dpdt}$, plotted versus the ratio of particle momentum to that of elastically scattered particles at the same angle. The arrows show the expected locations of the isobars. The solid lines are least squares fits described in the text.

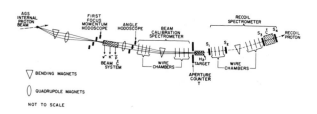

Figure 4(a): The experimental arrangement for measuring
              missing mass with a wire chamber hodoscope
              system.

Overall System Characteristics

$\Delta p/p$ (FWHM)	0.7% (55 MeV/c) at 8 GeV/c
	0.6% (100 MeV/c) at 16 GeV/c
$\Delta\theta$	0.5 mrad
Angular aperture	40 mrad
Momentum acceptance	30%
Dead time	2 msec
Resolving time	~1 μsec
Maximum event rate	~120/pulse
Average event rate	~ 40/pulse

Figure 4(b): Characteristics of the apparatus.

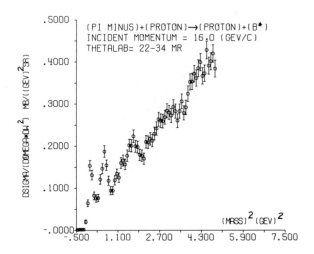

Figure 5:   The missing mass spectrum for $\pi^- + p \rightarrow p + B^*$
             showing well-known peaks of ρ, A_2, and R.

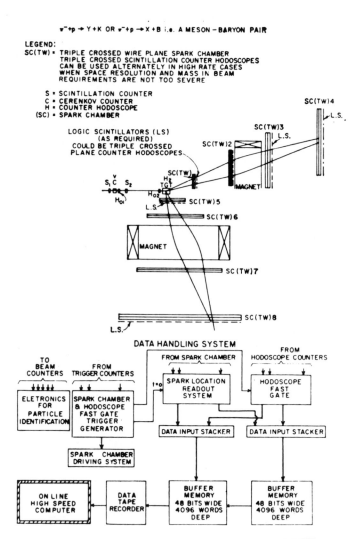

Figure 6:   An earlier schematic representation of a
                 Double V(ertex) Magnetic Spectrometer using
                 combinations of counter hodoscopes (especially
                 useful for trigger logic), digitized spark
                 chamber hodoscopes, and on-line computer system.
                 This spectrometer is being developed by the
                 author's group for detection of associated
                 production and many other classes of double
                 vertex events.

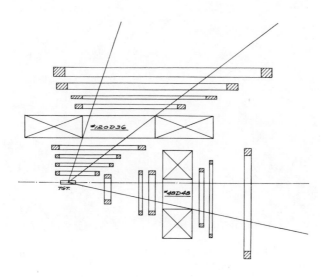

Figure 7:   The basic spark chamber hodoscope arrangement
              for the presently being developed double
              V(ertex) Magnetic Spectrometer system.
              Generally each chamber indicated contains an
              x, y, w set with various additional redundancies
              for various reasons. Trigger logic hodoscopes
              (not shown) behind the last chambers and
              elsewhere are employed for trigger logic. The
              wide angle magnet is 120" wide while the forward
              leg magnet is 4' wide.

Figure 8:   This figure shows the wire spark chamber hodo-
              scope winder built in the high bay area of the
              Physics building. It can wind up to 24' by 24'
              with wire spacing adjusted to any desired
              distance from 0.020" and up. The wire chamber
              frame rotates about its vertical axis while it is
              positioned on ground steel beds. The wire feed
              point is driven by a lead screw along the
              vertical slide. The tension on the wire is
              controlled utilizing a long vacuum column to
              better than 5%.

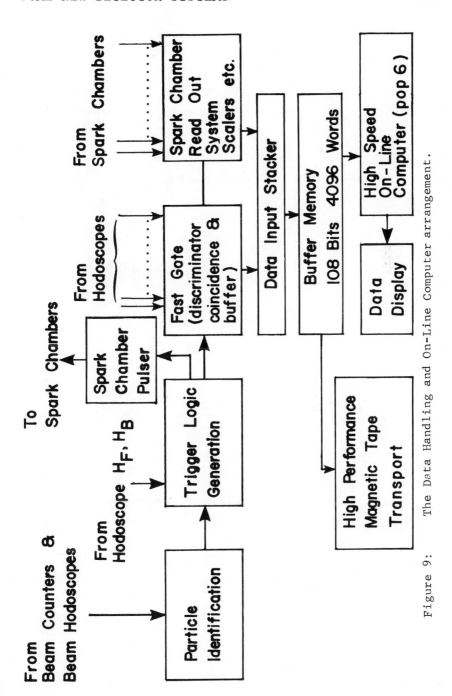

Figure 9:   The Data Handling and On-Line Computer arrangement.

TOTAL ABSORPTION DETECTORS FOR HIGH ENERGY PHYSICS*

Robert Hofstadter

Department of Physics and High Energy Physics Laboratory

Stanford University, Stanford, California

The guiding element in the approach of this paper is the belief that sharp spectral lines will become a natural and even a dominant aspect of elementary particle physics of the future. The domain of high energy gamma ray spectrometry has unfortunately not been pursued because satisfactory detectors with high energy resolution and high capture efficiency have not been developed. Similarly the "spectroscopy" of strong interaction particle physics is only in its infancy because detection instruments have not been adequately developed. This conference marks a beginning in the special branch of meson spectroscopy but, it is to be noted, only through the use of instruments of limited resolving ability.

The recent development at the High Energy Physics Laboratory of Stanford University of major improvements in gamma ray, electron and positron spectrometry[1,2] open up a

---

*
Work supported in part by the U.S. Office of Naval Research, Contract [Nonr 225(67)] and by a grant of the Research Laboratory of the General Motors Corporation.

completely new field of gamma ray spectroscopy in GeV and
multi-GeV (1 - 1000 GeV) physics. The further proposal of
total absorption nuclear cascade ("tanc") detectors for
neutral and charged particles promises to open up a new field
of spectroscopy in the highest energy regions of elementary
particle physics.

The detectors described above are intended eventually
to have the following properties for both neutral and charged
particles:

1)   100% detection efficiency
2)   high speed counting and timing ability
3)   good energy resolution
4)   application to virtually all types of particles
5)   discrimination between particle types
6)   large dynamic range
7)   virtually no limit to the highest energy detect-
      able
8)   reasonably large solid angles of acceptance.

Other desirable features, such as e.g., the determination of directionality, may be obtained by adding
counter hodoscope devices as auxiliaries to the techniques
already developed. To meet the very desirable features
listed above three principal developments have been made.
Each will be illustrated below.

The first development has been made with PbF$_2$
Cerenkov counters[1]. Crystals of diameter 5.0 in. and length
5-1/4 in. have been coupled to a 9.0 in. 60 AVP photomulti-
plier and placed in a monoenergetic positron beam at SLAC.
The energy of the beam could be varied between 2.0 and
12 GeV. The resulting pulse height distributions are shown
in Fig. 1. Figure 2 shows the results obtained for the

energy resolution behavior of the equipment (curve B) with
the 9.0 in. phototube. The linearity of the crystal
response as a function of energy is quite good except for a
slight droop at the highest energies. The non-linearity is
probably connected with leakage of gamma rays from the sides
and end of the crystal. Curve C shows the behavior expected
theoretically[1]. Work now in progress with a 6.0 in. PbF_2
crystal should remove the slight non-linearity at the highest
energies. Such counters will find their main applications
in the detection of gamma rays, electrons and positrons
where speed and small size of the detecting element are of
prime importance.

The second development[2] was made to achieve improved
energy resolution. In this case a 20 in. (51 cm) thickness
of NaI(Tl) crystal was used as a scintillator. The diameter of each of the crystal slabs was 9-3/8 in. (23.8 cm).
Figure 3 shows the details of the NaI(Tl) counter arrangement. With this detector the response to 10 GeV/c electrons
is shown in Fig. 4. The electron peak near channel 150 has
a width of 2.3% (FWHM). The apparent peak near channel 240
is fictitious and is caused by amplifier saturation occurring
when two electrons hit the crystal during the same accelerator pulse. Part of the width of the electron peak is instru-
mental and represents momentum spread (~ 1.0%) in the
original electron beam. The true energy resolution of the
NaI(Tl) crystal spectrometer is probably in the neighborhood
of 1.0% (FWHM). The 20 in. NaI(Tl) stack shows nearly
perfect linearity of response as a function of energy up to
13 GeV as shown in Fig. 5.

Figure 6 shows the behavior of the same NaI(Tl) crystal assembly when exposed to 10 GeV/c positive particles

(positrons and pions). The sharp positron peak is in the
same position as the 10 GeV/c electron peak of Fig. 4.
Gamma rays of 10 GeV/c are expected to provide the same
response. In other words, gamma ray spectrometry in high
energy physics is now possible! The detectors described
above already exhibit the properties 1) - 8) listed above
with the exception of property 4).

The third development[3] concerns the tanc counter,
which is based on absorption of the energy released by the
interaction of strongly interacting particles in nuclear
cascades. This detector uses a homogeneous mass of scintillation crystal material large enough to absorb the entire
energy of an incident strongly interacting particle, whether
charged or uncharged. The thickness of the detector should
be as large as is necessary for the most penetrating particle
to be studied at the highest energy to be used. For many
purposes 60 in. - 75 in. of NaI(Tl) would appear to be
adequate but these figures can easily be increased. This
length is equivalent to six mean free paths for protons or
neutrons. A mean diameter of the crystal stack should be on
the order of 10 in. or 11 in. Some details concerning the
expected energy absorption (~ 98%) are given in Ref. 3.
Tests are now under way to examine the operation of a block
of NaI(Tl) crystals 61 in. in length and of average diameter 11 in.

Preliminary tests of a small (in the sense of tanc
counters) block of NaI(Tl) crystals 20 in. long are also
shown in Fig. 6. The pulse distribution corresponding to
10 GeV/c positive pions is labeled "pions". In this case
the crystal length is equivalent to only 1.3 mean free
paths for pions of 10 GeV/c. Nevertheless, a rudimentary

"peak" has already started to form. With the expected
addition of 40 in. or 55 in. of NaI(Tl) to the "small"
20 in. stack, it is anticipated that a major narrowing of
the pion peak will take place. Such blocks of crystals have
just become available at the High Energy Physics Laboratory
at Stanford University. It is also expected that the pion
peak will shift to higher energies and will lie close to the
positron peak, perhaps near channel 128. Preparations for
tests of this predicted behavior are now in progress.

       Tanc counters should be suitable for particles of
·even the highest energies (>> 100 GeV) as well as particles
of "low" energies (0.1 GeV - 100 GeV). The tanc counter
differs in principle from the idea of the "calorimeter"[4,5]
since the tanc counter provides total absorption and regis-
tration of all ionizing particles or photons, whereas the
calorimeter method employs a sampling technique in which a
very large fraction of the energy lost by the incident particle is not absorbed in the active scintillating material.
Tanc counters are not able to stop neutrinos or high energy
muons but have as much potential stopping power as any other
type of detector devised up to the present time.

       Further extension of the tanc counter method to
Cerenkov materials, semiconductor materials, and crystal
conduction counters is discussed in Ref. 3.

ACKNOWLEDGMENT

       I wish to thank my colleagues Drs. E. Dally, E. B. Hughes,
W. A. Lakin and J. J. Murray for many illuminating discussions.

REFERENCES

1.   E. B. Dally and R. Hofstadter, "A Lead Fluoride
        Cerenkov Shower Counter", High Energy Physics Labor-
        atory, Stanford University, Stanford, California,
        HEPL 550, February 1968; to be published in the
        Proceedings of the 11th Scintillation and Semiconductor
        Counter Symposium, Washington, D.C., Feb. 28, 1968.

2.   W. A. Lakin, E. B. Hughes and R. Hofstadter, "A NaI(Tl)
        Spectrometer for γ-Rays in the GeV Range", High Energy
        Physics Laboratory, Stanford University, Stanford,
        Calif., HEPL 551, April 1968.

3.   R. Hofstadter, "Total Absorption Nuclear Cascade
        Detectors for High Energy Physics", High Energy Physics
        Laboratory, Stanford University, Stanford, Calif.,
        HEPL 556, April 1968. To be published in Nuclear
        Instruments and Methods.

4.   N. L. Grigorov, V. S. Murzin and I. D. Rapaport,
        JETP 7, 348 (1958).

5.   P. V. Ramana Murthy, B. V. Sreekanta, A. Subramanian
        and S. D. Verma, Nucl. Inst. and Methods 23, 245 (1963).

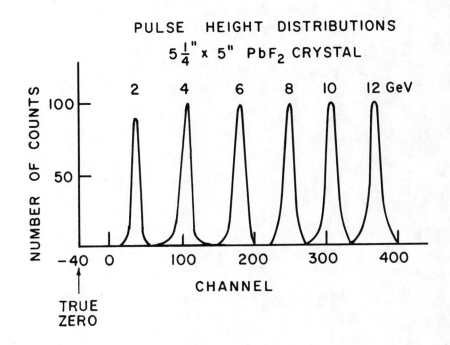

Fig. 1   Pulse height distributions in a PbF_2 detector.

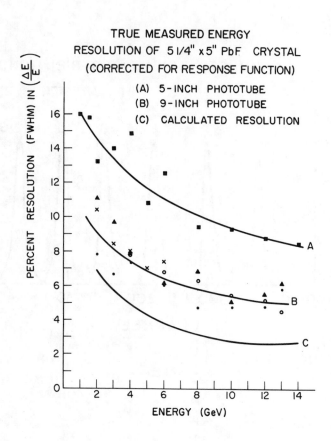

Fig. 2   True energy resolution observed with a 5-1/4 in.
          × 5 in. PbF$_2$ crystal (Curve B). Curve C shows
          the best possible energy resolution expected
          theoretically for this size of crystal.

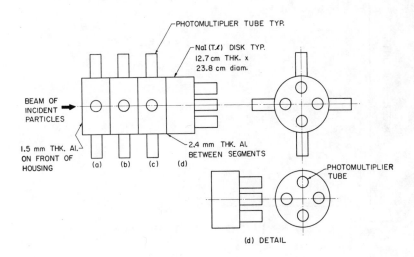

Fig. 3   A schematic representation of a NaI(Tl) spectrometer used in the work of Refs. 2 and 3.

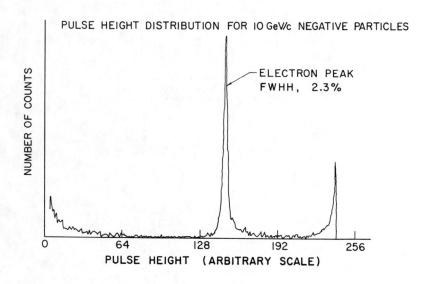

Fig. 4   Pulse height distribution for the counter of Fig. 3
          for electrons of 10 GeV/c.

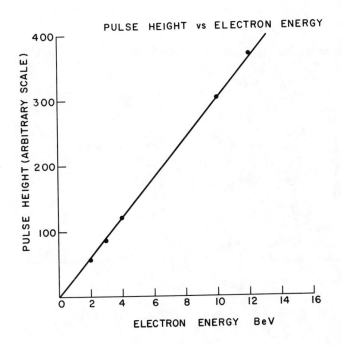

Fig. 5   Linearity of response of the   NaI(Tl)   detector.

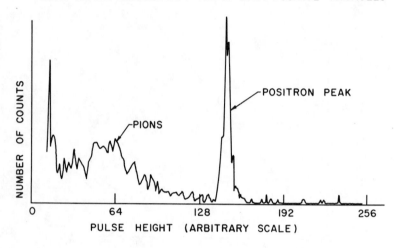

PULSE HEIGHT DISTRIBUTION FOR IO GeV/c POSITIVE PARTICLES

Fig. 6   Pulse height distribution obtained with the NaI(Tl)
counter of Fig. 3 in a beam of 10 GeV/c positrons
and positive pions. The positron peak is sharp and
the pion "peak" is broad and rudimentary. Only a
portion of the pion energy is absorbed in this
"small" tanc counter. A Landau straggling peak for
pions lies near the unlabelled peak at the far left
but is only partially shown. The data represent
unpublished work of E. B. Hughes, W. L. Lakin and
R. Hofstadter.

ARE THERE ANY FAR-OUT MESONS OR BARYONS?

Arthur H. Rosenfeld

Department of Physics and Lawrence Radiation Laboratory,
University of California, Berkeley, California

To save the time of readers who might look here for positive evidence, let me immediately state my answer to the question in the title: There is no evidence for any "far-out" mesons. I will show that the number of claims published corresponds reasonably well to the number of statistical fluctuations that one would expect. If far-out mesons are being produced, their cross sections are down to the 10-μb level. Some evidence for complicated <u>baryon</u> supermultiplets <u>has</u> been seen in K^+p and K^+n interactions. Even though this <u>is</u> mainly a paper on mesons, I will discuss this and warn that the evidence is still in some doubt.

In this paper I shall discuss the following:

VI.   Explaining Peaks vs. Explaining them Away.

Page 26

I.   PROPERTIES OF FAR-OUT MESONS

If mesons are "formed" out of quark-antiquark pairs then they can belong only to the 8 and 1 representations of SU(3), and can never be found more than one step from "home", i.e. the origin of weight space, as shown in Fig. 1.

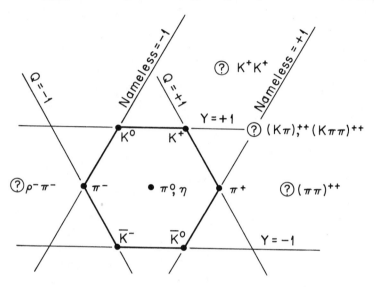

XBL686-2743

Fig. 1.   The familiar octet bounded by $|Y| = 1$, $|Q| = 1$ (and a third set of nameless lines along which V-spin happens to be constant).   We shall discuss the ?'s outside the **hexagon**.   The labels π, η, and K are, of course, just examples.   We could have chosen ρ, ϕ, K^*, $\cdots$ instead.

This means that they must lie on (or within) the walls of a hexagonal citadel bounded by $|Y| = 1$, $|Q| = 1$, and a third pair of lines of constant V spin.

Great interest than attaches to evidence for any meson with $|Y|$ or $|Q| \geqslant 2$.[1]   These candidates have been called "exotic."[2]   I mildly prefer "far-out" because it combines the slangy connotation of the unusual with the idea that these mesons would be far-out in weight space.

The search for far-out particles has been discussed recently by G. Goldhaber.[2] This makes my job easier, and I want first simply to copy an idea.

II. ABSENCE OF INDIRECT EVIDENCE, i.e. ABSENCE OF EXCHANGE OF VIRTUAL FAR-OUT MESONS

As is well known, two-body reactions in the BeV region lead in general to both forward (meson exchange) and backward (baryon exchange) peaks, unless the exchange of a virtual far-out resonance is required, in which case the corresponding peak disappears. In his Hawaii lectures[2] Goldhaber introduces some nice figures supplied by Barger to illustrate this point. Barger chose four reactions listed in Table I, and reproduced here in Fig. 2. Note that the forward peaks, if allowed, run 300 $\mu b/sr$, the backward ones run 5 to 10 $\mu b/sr$. Hence the suppression is particularly dramatic for the forward (meson-exchange) peaks. Where a far-out meson would be needed, the "peak" is 1 $\mu b/sr$ or less, i.e., suppressed by a factor of 300.

III. EXPECT SEVERAL 4σ FLUCTUATIONS PER YEAR

Before we go on to survey far-out mass spectra where bumps have been reported in $(K\pi\pi)_{3/2}$, $(\pi\rho)^{--}$, ... we should first decide what threshold of significance to demand in 1968. I want to show you that although experimentalists should probably note 3σ effects, theoreticians and phenomenologists would do better to wait till the effect reaches $> 4\sigma$. (Note that doubling the counts on a real 3σ peak should increase its significance to $3\sqrt{2}\sigma \sim 4.25\sigma$, so I am not suggesting an impossibly long wait.)

In appendices to our January 1967 compilation of particle properties,[3] we presented a collection of histograms in which we tried to kill the kappa and H mesons. We wounded both but killed neither, and ourselves learned something of the statistical problems that arise when each year bubble chamber physicists numbering nearly a thousand (if you include graduate students) hunt through tenthousand mass distributions in search of striking features, either real or statistical fluctuations.

A. TOTAL FLUCTUATIONS EXPECTED (ALL CHANNELS, ALL MASSES). The number of "potential resonances"

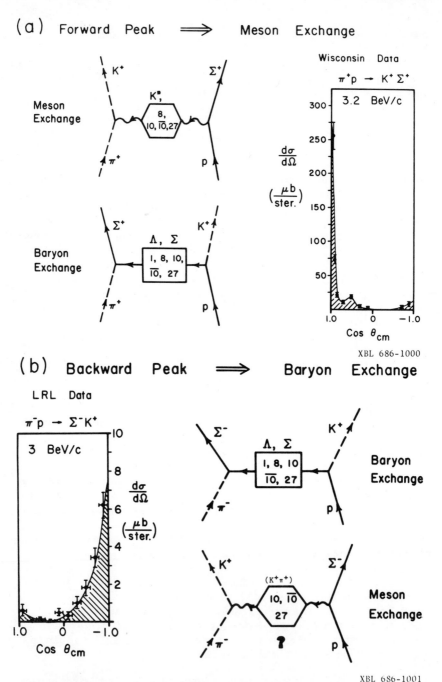

Fig. 2. Barger's summary of forward and backward
peaks arising from exchange of virtual particles.

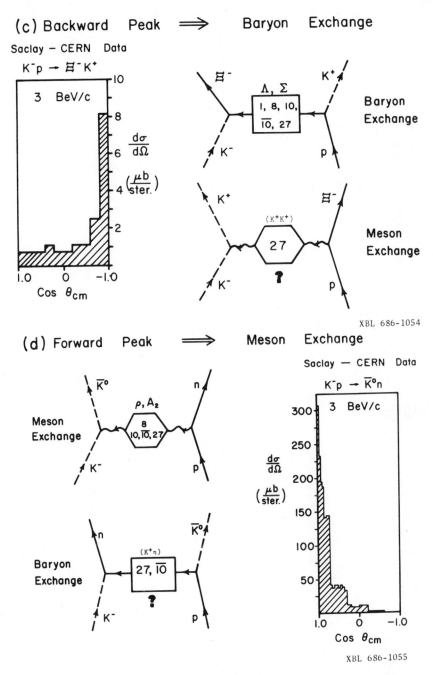

Fig. 2 (continued). The reactions are listed in Table I.

Table I.

Reactions shown in Fig. 2, which shows forward and backward peaks. 2b and 2c show backward peaks only; 2d shows a forward peak only.

		Q and Y carried by exchanged						
		Meson			Baryon			Peaks
Fig.	Reaction	Y	Q	Example	Y	Q	Example	expected
2a	$\pi^+ p \to K^+ \Sigma^+$	1	0	K^*	0	0	Λ	both
2b	$\pi^- p \to K^+ \Sigma^-$	1	2	far-out	0	0	Λ	backward
2c	$K^- p \to K^+ \Xi^-$	2	2	far-out	0	0	Λ	backward
2d	$K^- p \to K^0 n$	0	1	ρ	2	1	far-out	forward

scanned by physicists each year is the product of the following:

Number h of histograms plotted.   (I show in 1 below that
        this is on the order of 15,000 i. e. h ~ 15,000.
Number f/h of possible deceptive fluctuations in each
        histogram.   (I show in 2 below f/h ⩾ 10.)
The product h × b/h is then > 150,000. But a 4σ upwards
fluctuation should happen once every 32,000 potential bumps,
and therefore once every few months! Let me now justify
these numbers.

1. Number h of histograms plotted each year. E. C.
Fowler, R. J. Plano, and I run an annual survey of bubble-
chamber data processing, and Table II gives some recent
data. It shows that about 1.4 million events were completely measured in the United States in the year ending August
1967. If we make a wild guess of another 50% measured
elsewhere, we find about 2 million measurements mainly of
events with four outgoing prongs.

        If such a 4-prong event gives a 4-constraint fit (no
missing particles) there are 10 mass combinations to calculate (six 2-body + four 3-body). But if it gives a 1c fit
(missing neutral) or a 0c "fit" (more than one missing neutral) then the number of mass combinations of five 4-vec-
tors shoots to 25 (10 + 10 + 5). In this discussion I shall
assume that half the 4-prongs require a missing neutral, so
that on the average there are 17 mass combinations per e-
vent.

        This reasoning on multiplicities, extended to all com-
binations of all outgoing particles and to all countries, leads
to an estimate of 35 million mass combinations calculated
per year.

        How many histograms are plotted from these 35
million combinations? A glance through the journals shows
that a typical mass histogram has about 2,500 entries, so
the number we were looking for, h, is then 15,000 histograms per year. (Our annual survey also tells us that the
U. S. measurement rate tends to double every two years,
so things will get worse.)

2. Number f/h of bumps/histogram. Our typical 2,500-
entry histogram seems to average 40 bins. This means
that therein a physicist could observe 40 different fluctua-

Table II.

Hydrogen bubble chamber events measured in U. S. in year ending August 1967 (excluding about 300,000 image-plane-digitizer measurements made to study Σ leptonic decay).

Outgoing prongs	Outgoing particles	Number of mass combinations	Events measured (thousands)	Mass combinations (millions)
2	2 or 3	1 3 } avge = 2	500	1
4	4 or 5	10 25 } avge = 17	1200	21
6	6 or 7	56 119 } avge = 88	70	6
Total U. S. :			~1,700	~28
Assume 20% were remeasurements:			~1,400	~23
×1.5 (?) to include other countries:			~2	~35

Divide by 2500 events/histogram; yields 15,000 histograms.

tions one bin wide, 39 two bins wide, 38 three bins
wide, ••• . This arithmetic is made worse by the fact that
when a physicist sees "something": he then tries to enhance it by making t-cuts, looking both inside and outside
N^* bands, selecting on ρ bands, etc. Fortunately however, the arithmetic seems to be made far better by the ex-
ercise of considerable judgement and restraint. Thus most
physicists are properly skeptical of fluctuations which are
only one bin wide, particularly if their resolution is comparable with one bin. Thus most physicists look for some
other supporting evidence of a resonance -- some change in
some angular distribution for instance. This fortunate imposition of good judgement is unfortunate only in that it
makes it impossible for me to make a good estimate of the
desired fraction f/h.

My colleague Gerry Lynch has instead tried to
study this problem "experimentally" using a "Las Vegas"
computer program called Game. Game is played as follows. You wait until an unsuspecting "friend" comes to
show you his latest 4σ peak. You draw a smooth curve
through his data (based on the hypothesis that the peak is
just a fluctuation), and punch this smooth curve as one of
the inputs for game. The other input is his actual data. If
you then call for 100 Las Vegas histograms, Game will generate them, with the actual data reproduced for comparison
at some random page. You and your friend then go around
the halls, asking physicists to pick out the most surprising
histogram in the printout. Often it is one of the 100 phoneys,
rather than the real "4σ" peak. Figure 3 shows two Game
histograms, each one being one of the more interesting
ones in a run of 100. The smooth curves drawn through
them are of course absurd; they are supposed to be the
background estimates of the inexperienced experimenter.
But they do illustrate that a 2σ or 3σ fluctuation can easily
be amplified to "4σ" or "5σ"; all it takes is a little enthusi-
asm.

In summary of all the discussion above, I conclude
that each of our 150,000 annual histograms is capable of
generating somewhere between 10 and 100 deceptive upward
fluctuations; to be conservative, I used the number 10 for
the number f/h.

Then, to repeat my warning at the beginning of this
section; we are now generating at least 100,000 potential
bumps per year, and should expect several 4σ and hundreds

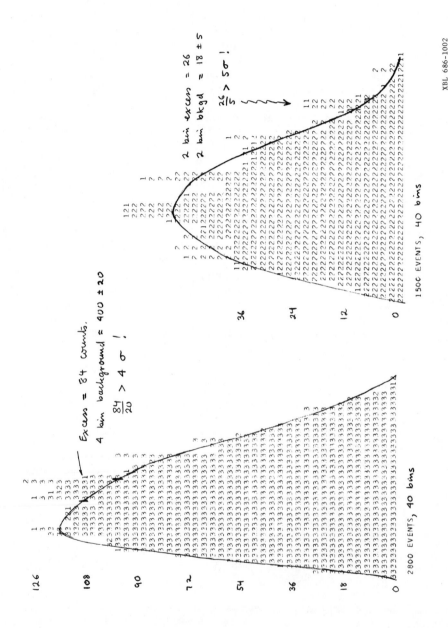

Fig. 3. Two "Las Vegas" histograms generated by G. Lynch's program GAME.

of 3σ fluctuations. What are the implications ? To the
theoretician or phenomenologist the moral is simple; wait
for nearly 5σ effects. For the experimental group who have
just spent a year of their time and perhaps a million dollars,
the problem is harder. I suggest that they should go ahead
and publish their tantalizing bump (or at least circulate it as
a report.) But they should realize that any bump less than
about 5σ constitutes only a call for a repeat of the experiment. If they, or somebody else, can double the number of
counts, the number of standard deviations should increase by
$\sqrt{2}$, and that will confirm the original effect.

In connection with this point, Paul Murphy pointed
out at the conference most experimentalists look at their
data by the time that half the events are measured anyway.
Murphy suggested that they publish their data as two independent experiments, so that one could confirm or deny the
other. After some thought I conclude that splitting the data
does no good. On the other hand, as I have just said; if
you have a 4σ effect on half your data, it had better increase to $4\sqrt{2}\sigma$ by the time it is all processed; otherwise
the effect is fading away.

B. FLUCTUATIONS EXPECTED IN ANY SINGLE BIN:
e.g. THE KAPPA. Here it is easier to estimate the number
of potential kappa peaks scanned each year. About 1/4 of
all events measured seem to have ≥ 3-body final states with
at least one K and one π. There are probably two Kπ
combinations in these events. Table II tells us that we are
producing about a million Kπ mass combinations per year.
As before, we gather them into histograms containing about
2500 Kπ combinations, so we generate about 400 histograms
annually. Each of these contains only one bin at the kappa
mass, so each year we scan 400 potential kappas and
should expect about one 3σ effect. It is my impression that
this agrees with the rate of new claims for the kappa.

Let me also summarize the past history of the kappa. When it first appeared it was more convincing than
many other resonances that have since weathered the tests
of time. But the kappa has not been satisfactorily corrob-
orated and by now we had best assume that it was a spurious
fluctuation. I copy the thoughts from our 1967 study. [3] So
far there have been five impressive bumps, and a number
of smaller ones. But every time an experiment has been
run to confirm a kappa claim, it has failed. At the same
time (if it is a large statistics experiment) the second ex-

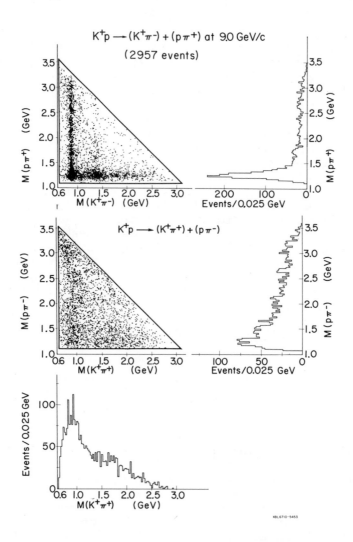

Fig. 4. (a) $(K\pi\pi)^{++}$ (and other) spectra from 9-GeV/c $Kp\pi^+\pi^-$. The path length in this typical experiment corresponds to ~ 5 events/μb. This figure should serve as a warning: It shows that there are no significant bumps with cross sections corresponding to more than ~ 10 μb in either K^+p or $p\pi^-$ [with the exception of $\Delta^0(1236)$]. But notice that in the $p\pi^-$ state, which can be better studied in the s channel, we now know there are about a dozen resonances! (Figure from Ref. 12.)

periment often reports the kappa in a different channel.
The result is that the kappa's existence currently depends
entirely on three uncorroborated "sightings." This strikes
me as similar to the problem with flying saucers; they
keep appearing, but always in different places, and can
never be reproduced. It seems to me that we are going to
have to learn not to be fooled by frequent large fluctuations.

IV. ABSENCE OF DIRECT EVIDENCE FROM MASS SPECTRA

I will now survey briefly the four far-out spectra
noted in Fig. 1, and along the way make some complaints
about the partisan way that claims are presented, and call
for less-biased, more-helpful reporting.

A. $(\pi\pi)^{\pm\pm}$ AND $(K\pi)^{++}$. To my surprise I find among these
simple spectra no suggestion of the production of any resonances with cross sections greater than 10μb. For an example, see Fig. 4a.

I think there is a need for a high-statistics spec-
trometer study of the reaction $\pi^+ p \rightarrow n \, X^{++}$, in the same
way that Maglic group at CERN pioneered studies of
$\pi^- p \rightarrow p \, X^-$.

B. $\rho^- \pi^-$ (1320, $\Gamma = 150$). This peak was reported a year
ago by Vanderhagen et al. [3a] in the reaction
5 GeV/c $\pi^- d \rightarrow pp\pi^- \pi^0 \pi^-$. Figure 4b gives their $\rho^- \pi^-$ spectrum. They report a 4σ bump (it looks more like 3σ to me)
of 39 events above background, corresponding to a 15-μb
signal. As I discussed in Sec. III, the only conclusion I can
draw is that the experiment should be repeated. A lower-
energy experiment (2.26 GeV/c) has recently been reported
by Benvenuti et al. at the 1968 Spring Meeting of the APS in
Washington, D. C. [3b] They have about the same number of
events as reported by Vanderhagen et al. but their spectrum ends at 1300 MeV, so they have nothing to say about
the Vanderhagen bump. They point out $(\rho\pi)^{--}$ bumps at 970
and 1180 MeV, but I feel that the valley between these peaks
is merely another 2σ fluctuation, enhanced slightly by enthusiastic ρ selection. (It is well known that selection of
ρ's from a 3π spectrum peaks up this spectrum at 1000 and
1300 MeV. This was first pointed out by Benson et al. [10]
and has recently been very clearly demonstrated by Fung
et al. [11])

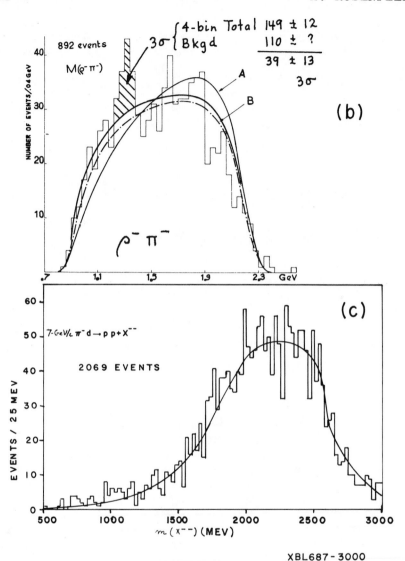

XBL687-3000

Fig. 4. (b) Peak in $\rho^-\pi^-$ from 5-GeV/c $\pi^-d \to pp\pi^-\pi^0\pi^-\Sigma$.
Curve A is phase-space normalized to all events. Curve B
is 80% phase space, 20% Deck effect, and is normalized
outside the $\rho^-\pi^-$ peak. (From Vanderhagen et al., Ref.3a.)
(c). Mass spectrum for doubly charged meson system X^{--}
produced in the reaction $\pi^-p \to ppX^{--}$. Any bump present
corresponds to < 8 μb. (From Katz et al., Ref. 3b.)

C. OTHER DOUBLY CHARGED SPECTRA. These spectra
show nothing above 10μb. As an example, I reproduce in
Fig. 4c the spectrum shown by Katz et al. (Rochester) at
the 1968 spring meeting of the APS in Washington, D. C.[3b]

D. $(K\pi\pi)_{3/2}$ (1270) AND $(K\pi\pi)^{++}$ (1120).

1. $(K\pi\pi)_{3/2}$ (1270, Γ = 60). There have been two sets of
claims for this resonance. It was originally seen by Böck
et al. (CERN) in 3- to 4-GeV/c $\bar{p}p$ reactions, but not seen
by Baltay et al. (Yale, BNL) at 3.7 GeV/c. In my rapporteur's talk at the September 1965 Oxford conference[4] I
combined the latest CERN spectrum (their original 182 e-
vents had by then risen to 257) with the Yale distribution,
and found the sum rather unimpressive.

    In addition there was short-lived evidence for a
bump in the $K^+\pi$ spectrum from 3.0 GeV/c $K^+p \rightarrow \Delta K^*\pi$. In
this 1966 Berkeley rapporteur's talk,[5] Goldhaber announced
that this too has washed out.

    What may seem new is a second paper by French
et al. (CERN, Birmingham).[6] This is the original group
that published as Böck et al. This paper presents a
(another?) $K^*\pi$ peak from 3- to 4-GeV/c $\bar{p}p$. It does not
warn of any conflicting data -- it mentions neither my
Oxford talk nor Goldhaber's Berkeley talk. But don't be
confused, the events are just the same ones that they gave
me to include in Fig. 62 of my Oxford talk.

2. $(K\pi\pi)^{++}$ (1170). Here we come to a set of five independent claims, which might tend to suggest to the reader that
there is really a resonance, but I doubt it. The early
claims are summarized in Fig. 5, which is page 52 of my
Oxford talk.[4] It shows the original evidence of Wangler
et al. (Wisconsin),[7] which is certainly striking, and some
possible corroboration by Miller et al. (Purdue).[7] However
it also shows the spectra of Hardy et al.[7] (LRL), which fail
to confirm the bump. The lower right-hand curve is the
sum of the data available in 1965. At that time there was
no suggestion that the I spin might be unusual.

    Next, Bishop et al. (Wisconsin)[7] discovered some-
thing of a bump in $(K\pi\pi)^{++}$ produced by 3.5-GeV/c K^+p reactions. And now there is a preprint by Goshaw et al.[6]
(Wisconsin)[7] which seems to be the data of Bishop et al. increased by 5/3. Figure 6 is the relevant page of their pre-

Figure 51

Wangler et al. (Wisconsin)
3.0 GeV/c π^-, 164 events

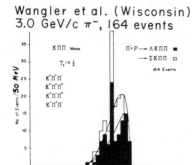

Invariant mass histogram of the K$\pi\pi$ system produced with Λ's and Σ's. The upper solid curve is phase space and the lower solid curve is phase space modified for a Y_1^*. The Λ events are shaded and the Σ events are unshaded.

Figure 53

Miller et al. (Purdue)
2.7 GeV/c π^-
242 events

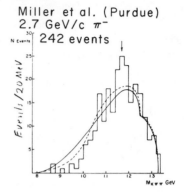

K$\pi\pi$ mass spectrum for 242 events of the type YK$\pi\pi$.

Figure 52

Hardy et al. (LRL)

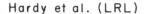

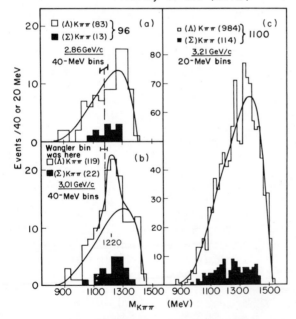

Figure 54

Sum of all

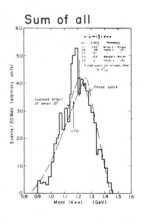

Figures 51, 52, 53, 54. Kπ spectra giving evidence for and against a bump at 1170 MeV; Fig. 51 from Wangler et al. (Ref. 41), Fig. 52 from Hardy et al. (Ref. 42), Fig. 53 from Miller et al. (Ref. 43), Fig. 54 is the sum.

XBL 686-1005

Fig. 5. $(K\pi\pi)^{++}(1170)$. First reaction: $\pi^- p$. (From Rosenfeld's Oxford review, Ref. 4.)

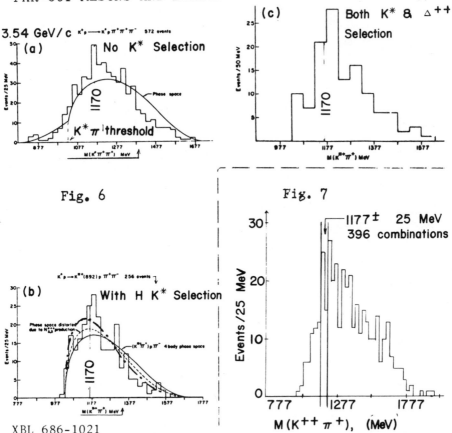

XBL 686-1021

Fig. 6. Possible evidence for a $K^{*+}\pi^+$ bump in 3.54-GeV/c $K^+p \to K^0p\, \pi^+\pi^+\pi^-$, from Goshaw et al.[7] The solid curve in (b) is phase space for $K^*p\pi\pi$ production; the dashed curve is further modified to take into account Δ^{++} production. I have even further modified the dotted curve in two ways to give the dot-dash curve: (1) 4-body phase space (assuming K^* production) can be thought of as 5-body phase space (assuming $K\pi$ production) multiplied by a δ-function, $\delta(m^2(K\pi) - 893^2)$. But of course the $K\pi\pi$ Dalitz plot is really ly covered by two bands of finite width. The correction (area covered by finite bands)/(area covered by δ-function) peaks the spectrum towards low $K^*\pi$ mass. See Refs. 10 and 11. (2) There is a preference for small momentum transfer to the $K^*\pi$ system, which further peaks its spectrum towards low mass. See for example Appendix II of Ref. 4.

Fig. 7. 396 $K^{*+}\pi^+$ combinations produced by 4.6-GeV/c $K^+p \to K^0p\, \pi^+\pi^+\pi^-$. These events are selected in exactly the same way as the 266 events of Goshaw et al., Fig. 6(b).

print. Their peak still does not seem striking to me. Accordingly I present Fig. 7, which shows a comparable number of events at slightly higher energy - 4.6 GeV/c K$^+$. This figure was prepared by Chumin Fu of the Goldhaber-Trilling group (LRL), using exactly the selections, bin sizes, etc. of Goshaw et al. It neither confirms nor denies the $(K\pi\pi)^{++}$ bump.

One other comment on the paper of Goshaw et al. They suggest that the resonance may be a manifestation of the "triangle singularity" suggested by Month et al. During the period 1964 through 1966, it was widely believed that at certain energies, in analogy to classical rescattering, there might be a quantum-mechanical singularity, and we might see a resonance. In 1967, Christoph Schmid showed that this could not be so,[8] and I think all the other theoretical exponents of the triangle singularity now agree that although rescattering can rearrange events within the Dalitz plot, it cannot enhance the whole plot.

The final claim on $(K\pi\pi)^{++}$ (1170) is by Barnham et al. (Birmingham, Glasgow, Oxford).[7] They have 10-GeV/c K$^+$ events, and find a bump at 1170 MeV, but not in the channel where Goshaw et al. have their bump. I must say this begins to remind me of the kappa, which always shows up in a new reaction and never reproduces itself.

Having just spent an evening sorting out all these conflicting claims, I would like to express mild irritation at the way they tend to be written up. The style is too frequently "The bump of interest was discovered by X et al. (Ref. 1) and confirmed by Y et al. (Ref. 2) although higher-energy reactions do not show the effect." (No reference to relevant experiments which fail to support the bump even though three rapporteurs have recently discussed and buried it.) Frequently too, the statement is missing that the data in Fig. X is not all new, but merely supercedes their earlier publication, based on half the events. I feel that, in general, authors could be much more helpful to the poor confused reader.

E. K^+K^+ AND $(KK\pi)^{++}$. This is not a channel in which one could dismiss a 3σ peak as a fluctuation, since so far the total number of mass combinations reported is only about 1000. However there are no noteworthy peaks at all.

Figure 8 is taken from Goldhaber's 1966 Berkeley rapporteur talk.[5] It shows that an original CERN KK bump[7]

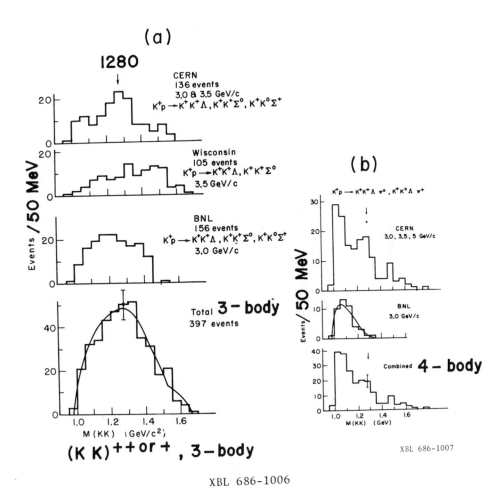

XBL 686-1006

Fig. 8. Summary of KK(1280) Y = + 2 bump from G. Gold-haber's 1966 Berkeley review talk, Ref. 5.

(made mainly with 3 GeV/c K^+) has now washed out. Since
then Ferbel[9] has looked at 400 events of the form 13-GeV/c
$K^+p \rightarrow \Lambda X^{++}$ and reports no bump larger than 8 μb. Also
Alexander et al. have amassed 600 such events at 9 GeV/c.
Their data are in Fig. 9; they cover the X^{++} mass range
up to 3 GeV, and still show nothing interesting.

SUMMARY OF MESONS

Strongly interacting mesons certainly interact in
states with far-out quantum numbers. For example, at the
conference, Schlein pointed out that his $K^+\pi^-$ and $K^0\pi^0$
phase shifts are quite different, so that he needs an I = 3/2
amplitude. But there is no evidence so far that the forces
are strong enough to produce resonances.

V. A SWITCH TO BARYONS. STATUS OF THE FAR-OUT $Z_0(1865)$ AND $Z_1(1900)$[*]

So far we have considered evidence for far-out
mesons and found little; this is consistent with the fact that
no such mesons are listed on our wallet sheets.[7]   However,
the baryon table of the wallet set does list a possible far-
out[*] candidate, $Z_0(1865)$, accompanied by a warning "resonance ··· not established." Even in a talk on mesons it
does not seem right to ignore this possible evidence for
complicated quark structures -- if I were really convinced
that there exist far-out baryon resonances of five quarks
($qqq\,\bar{q}q$), I would not be so surprised at the discovery of far-
out meson resonances of four quarks ($\bar{q}q\,\bar{q}q$).

The evidence for Y = +2 baryons was reviewed by J.
Meyer at the 1967 Heidelberg Conference,[13] so here I shall
merely repeat the warnings of some of my friends[18] as to
the experimental difficulties with $Z_0(1865)$ and some difficulties in interpreting $Z_1(1900)$.

$Z_0(1865)$. Cool et al.[14] and Bugg et al.[15] have accurately
measured the total cross sections $\sigma(K^+d)$ and $\sigma(K^+p)$, both
of which have peaks at 1.2 GeV/c (1900 MeV). The K^+p peak
is the candidate for the resonance called $Z_1(1900)$, which is
discussed below. The difference between $\sigma(K^+d)$ and $\sigma(K^+p)$
peaks allows us (in principle) to extract a large I = 0 peak,

[*]The baryons with which we are now familiar fit into SU3
singlets, octets, and decuplets, and can be considered as
being made of three quarks. "Far-out" baryons would then
be members of any other supermultiplets.

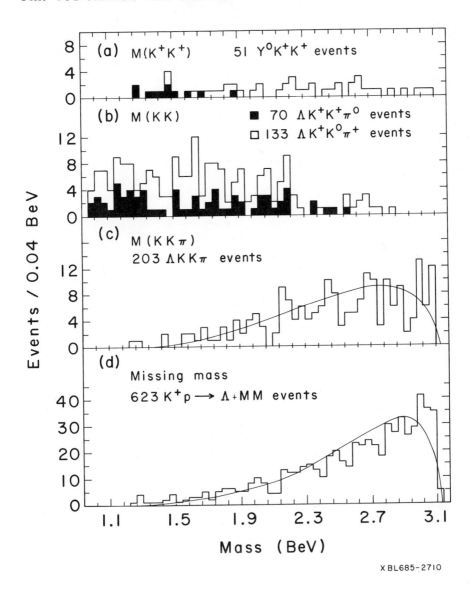

Fig. 9. Spectrum of Y = 2, Q = 2 events from 9-GeV/c K⁺p. (From Alexander, Firestone, and Goldhaber, Ref. 9a.)

$Z_0(1865)$. But I now want to point out a recent experiment by Carter et al. [16] which tests this extraction procedure and shows that, as currently carried out, it leads to discrepancies of _several_ millibarns at at least one momentum.

The experiment of Carter et al. [16] is to precisely measure $\sigma(\pi^+d)$, $\sigma(\pi^+p)$, and $\sigma(\pi^-p)$, the latter of course by charge symmetry being equal to $\sigma(\pi^+n)$. One then expects

$$\sigma(\pi^\pm d) = "\sigma(\pi^+p)" + "\sigma(\pi^-p)" - \sigma_{GW}(\text{shading}), \qquad (1)$$

where the quotation marks mean that each $\sigma(\pi N)$ has been averaged over its internal momentum in the deuteron, and σ_{GW} is the Glauber-Wilkin[17] correction for the mutual shadowing of nucleons in deuterium. Naturally we expect σ_{GW} to be positive. But look at Fig. 10 from Carter et al. [16] The solid lines A and B are $\sigma(\pi^-d)$ and $\sigma(\pi^+d)$; they should agree except for small Coulomb effects (and they do). Let us just consider their average. The bumpy dashed line is $\sigma(\pi^+p) + \sigma(\pi^-p)$, and the smoother dotted line labeled $"\sigma(\pi^+p)" + "\sigma(\pi^-p)"$ has been averaged over the Hulthén distribution for the internal momentum in the deuteron. It can easily be seen that, although the averaged curve has been somewhat smoothed, it has not been smoothed enough. Thus one would expect the difference between the dotted line and the average πd line to be nearly constant, reflecting a mutual shielding which changes only very slowly with energy. Instead this difference, which averages a reasonable value of 1 to 2 mb, rises to ~ 3 mb at 1.4 GeV/c and goes negative at 800 MeV/c. So something seems to be wrong with the current folding procedures tested in Eq. (1); it may be that the right prescription calls for averaging over an effective internal momentum distribution which is wider that that given by the simple impulse approximation.

We can now return to the 6-mb peak called $Z_0(1865)$, which is extracted from the difference between K^+d and K^+p cross sections; I want to make two contradictory comments. 1) Uncertainties in the folding are amplified in the subtraction:

a) After one inserts the right Clebsch-Gordan factors, the $I = 0$ cross section σ_0 turns out to be

$$"\sigma_0" = 2\sigma(K^+d) - 3"\sigma(K^+p)" - 2\sigma_{GW}, \qquad (2)$$

so we see that the uncertainties in folding are multiplied threefold, and the shading uncertainties are doubled.

b) Then one still has to <u>unfold</u> "σ_0" , and there is no unique prescription for so doing, so that errors are further magnified.

2) Despite these warnings, it is going to be difficult to make the I = 0 peak go away, unless the data change slightly. I should point out that the peak depends mainly on the Brookhaven data of Cool et al., [14] and are not really very quantitatively confirmed by the Rutherford data of Bugg et al. [15] [Just to get some idea of the maximum uncertainty possible, I have tried making the nonsense unfolded subtraction $\sigma_0 = 2\sigma(K^+d) - 3\sigma(K^+p)$. In the case of the BNL data one is left with a broad 1-mb peak, but for the RHEL data little is left.]

In conclusion on $Z_0(1865)$, it is clear that more experimental work and more thought about Eq. (2) is needed before we can wholeheartedly accept this bump.

$Z_1(1900)$. Here there is no question of extraction; one can see a bump directly in the K^+p s-channel, as shown in Fig. 10, which is taken from Bland et al. [19] Figure 11 not only shows the peak originally discovered[14] in $\sigma(K^+p)$, but also shows that it can be associated with a sudden rise in the inelastic cross section, particularly of $K^0\Delta^{++}$. To decide whether we have a K^+p resonance, we need partial-wave analysis, either of the elastic channel, or of the $K\Delta$ channel. Meyer[13] summarizes the status of the elastic partial-wave analyses, and concludes that the data are still inadequate to uncover a resonance. (Fortunately a K^+p elastic scattering experiment with a polarized target is scheduled to run soon at Argonne National Laboratory; this should remove some bothersome ambiguities).

But a partial-wave analysis of the $K\Delta$ channel has recently been completed by Roger Bland[20] of the Goldhaber-Trilling bubble chamber group at Lawrence Radiation Laboratory. Figure 12 is from Bland's thesis, and gives his Argand diagrams. Be warned that the errors on this plot have to be interpreted cautiously since for an inelastic channel there is no readily available reference phase. Hence, in the analysis leading to Fig. 12 it was necessary to assume a constant phase for the M1' amplitude (higher partial waves predicted by the Stodolsky-Sakurai ρ-exchange model). We see that only P_3 (the notation is L_{2J+1}) looks much like a resonant circle, and even here there is trouble with the velocity along the circle. In momentum the 1900-MeV peak centers not far from 1160 MeV/c, and the data points plotted

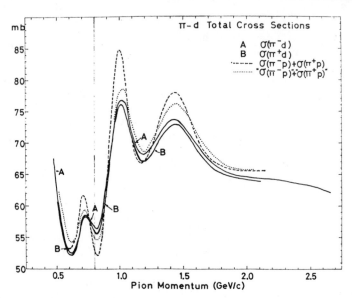

Fig. 10.   Comparison of total cross sections for pions on
deuterium and on nucleons, from Carter et al. Ref. 16.

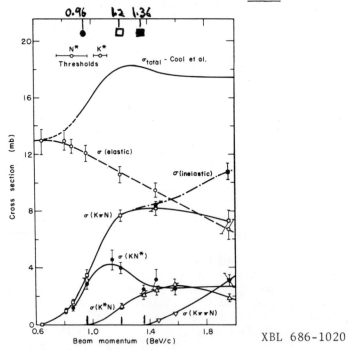

XBL 686-1020

Fig. 11.   Total and partial K$^+$p cross sections, from Ref. 19.

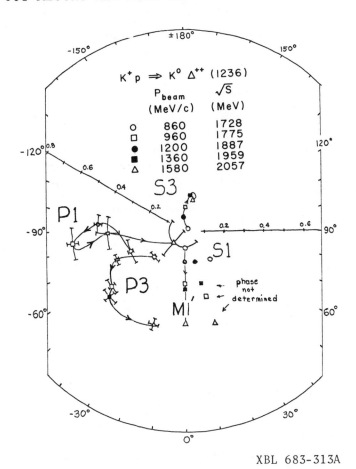

XBL 683-313A

Fig. 12. Argand plot of the partial-wave amplitudes for
$K^+p \to K^0\Delta^{++}$(1236). Phases are measured relative to the
M1' amplitude (see text) which is <u>assumed</u> to be constant in
phase. The points at 1580 MeV/c <u>are from</u> Vic Seeger
(Goldhaber-Trilling Group, Lawrence Radiation Laboratory).
From Ref. 20.

at 960 MeV/c and 1360 MeV/c fall about $\Gamma/2$ on either side.
At the top of Fig. 11, I have drawn circles and squares at
the relevant momenta . Thus one would expect a resonant
amplitude to be changing faster with energy at 1160 MeV/c
than on either side. Instead it is almost stationary. I conclude that we cannot yet decide if there is a Z_1(1900, $3/2^+$)
resonance. Bland's P_3 solution indeed looks more like a
resonance than most of those labeled "probable" by
Lovelace[21] on his Argand plots for πp elastic scattering.

But there should be a difference in acceptance criteria for ordinary vs far-out resonances, simply because we expect the former, and not necessarily the latter.

SUMMARY OF BARYONS

To summarize my discussion of Z_0 and Z_1 resonances, I will say that we have never put $Z_1(1900)$ on our list of baryons, and we are now not sure if we should have included $Z_0(1865)$. Thus for far-out resonances, the situation is the same for baryons as it was for mesons; there are certainly appreciable forces between particles like K^+ and p (which taken together have far-out quantum numbers), but it has not yet been established that these forces are strong enough to produce resonances.

VI. "EXPLAINING" PEAKS vs "EXPLAINING THEM AWAY"

Before I leave the question of how to interpret the peak in $\sigma(K^+p)$ at $K\Delta$ threshold, I want to express one general piece of understanding that has slowly dawned on me.

In the last section, I said:
"There is a peak, but no partial waves resonate, so we explain away the $Z_1(1900)$ bump as a threshold effect."
But if P_3 had followed a slightly more suggestive counterclockwise circle, I would have said:
"There is a peak, which motivates us to study the partial waves in this region, and sure enough the threshold channel resonates, so we classify the peak as $Z_1(1900, 3/2^+)$."
Note that the presence or absence of the nearby threshold is irrelevant to the final interpretation, which depends only on the shape of the Argand plots.

I emphasize this point because experimentalists before claiming a resonance always try to explain it away. And so they should if their bump is just the kinematic reflection of some other resonances. But I just showed that nearby threshold effects cannot necessarily explain away a bump. The same applies to t-channel and other complicated effects (Deck effect, etc.). After all, we all believe that resonances (in the s-channel) are the result of forces (in the t-channel), and theorists may even be starting to be able to calculate s-channel output from t-channel input. Right now, there is no way to foretell whether an effect in some other channel will explain a resonance, or explain it away.

I know of only two ways to identify a resonance. The first is to find a bump so clear and narrow that we recognize it without having really to understand it. The second is to see if it seems to correspond to a pole in the partial-wave amplitude. If there is a pole, this amplitude (for two-bodies in, two out) when plotted on an Argand diagram, will follow a characteristic counter-clockwise "circle." Even with knowledge of the partial waves, it may still turn out to be very hard to decide in many cases -- if recognizable resonant circles show up simultaneously in several channels, the decision is simple, but we will seldom be so lucky.

ACKNOWLEDGMENTS

I want to thank Gideon Alexander, Angela Barbaro-Galtieri, Chumin Fu, Gerson Goldhaber, Bernard French, Gerald Lynch, Paul Söding, and William D. Walker for helpful comments.

This work was done under the auspices of the U. S. Atomic Energy Commission.

FOOTNOTES AND REFERENCES

1. $|Y|$ or $|Q| \geqslant 2$ is merely a concise mnemonic. Actually of course I mean to include any meson, even with $|Q| \leqslant 1$, if there is evidence that its Ispin I is $\geqslant 3/2$.

2. G. Goldhaber, in Proceedings of the Second Hawaii Topical Conference in Particle Physics (1967) (University of Hawaii Press, Honolulu, 1968), p. 256.

3. A. H. Rosenfeld, A. Barbaro-Galtieri, W. J. Podolsky, L. R. Price, P. Söding, C. G. Wohl, M. Roos, and W. J. Willis, Rev. Mod. Phys. 39, I (1967). See Appendix I by G. R. Lynch, A. Rittenberg, A. H. Rosenfeld, and P. Söding, and Appendix II by T. Ferbel et al.

3a. R. Vanderhagen, J. Huc, P. Fleury, J. Duboc, R. George, M. Goldberg, B. Makowski, N. Armenise, B. Ghidini, V. Picciarelli, A. Romano, A. Forino, R. Gessaroli, G. Quareni, and A. Quareni-Vignudelli, Phys. Letters 24B, 493 (1967).

3b. Bull. Am. Phys. Soc. 13, 611 (1968). See the following abstracts: W. Katz, T. Ferbel, P. Slattery, T. Yamanouchi, and H. Yuta, Abstract DI3. A. Benvenuti, E. Marquit, and J. C. Vander Velde, Abstract DI2.

4. A. H. Rosenfeld, in Oxford International Conference on
    Elementary Particles, September 1965, Supplement
    (Rutherford High Energy Laboratory, Chilton,
    England, 1966), p. 5
5. G. Goldhaber, in Proceedings of the XIIIth International
    Conference on High-Energy Physics (University of
    California Press, Berkeley, 1967).
6. B. R. French, J. B. Kinson, R. Rigopoulos, V. Simak,
    F. McDonald, G. Petmezas, and L. Riddiford,
    Nuovo Cimento 52A, 438 (1967).
7. For these references see either A. H. Rosenfeld, N.
    Barash-Schmidt, A. Barbaro-Galtieri, L. R. Price,
    P. Söding, and C. G. Wohl, Rev. Mod. Phys. 40, 1,
    (1968), or Oxford International Conference on Ele-
    mentary Particles (Ref. 4).
8. C. Schmid, Phys. Rev. 154, 1363 (1967).
9. H. Yuta, J. C. Berlinghieri, M. S. Farber, T. Ferbel,
    B. Forman, A. C. Melissionos, and T. Yamanouchi,
    "Multiple Vee Events in K^+p Interactions at 13 GeV/c",
    University of Rochester preprint, 1968.
9a. G. Alexander, A. Firestone, and G. Goldhaber,
    UCRL-18236, May 20, 1968, submitted to Phys.
    Letters.
10. G. Benson, L. Lovell, E. Marquit, B. Roe, D. Sinclair,
    and J. Vander Velde, Phys. Rev. Letters 16, 1177
    (1966).
11. S. Y. Fung, W. Jackson, R. T. Pu, D. Brown, and G.
    Gidal, "Evidence for the Kinematic Origin of the H
    Enhancement", University of California Riverside
    preprint, UCR-34P107-64. Phys. Rev. Letters 21,
    50 (1968).
12. See chapter by Gerson and Sulamith Goldhaber, in
    Advances in High-Energy Physics, R. E. Marshak and
    R. Cool, Eds. (John Wiley - Interscience, to be pub-
    lished, 1968.
13. J. Meyer, in Proceedings of the 1967 Heidelberg Inter-
    national Conference on Elementary Particles, (North-
    Holland Publishing Co., Amsterdam, 1968), p. 117.
14. R. L. Cool, G. Giacomelli, T. F. Kycia, B. A. Leontic,
    K. K. Li, A. Lundby, and J. Teiger, Phys. Rev.
    Letters 17, 102 (1966); R. J. Abrams, R. L. Cool,
    G. Giacomelli, T. F. Kycia, B. A. Leontic, K. K.
    Li, and D. N. Michael, Phys. Rev. Letters 19, 259
    (1967).
15. D. V. Bugg, R. S. Gilmore, K. M. Knight, D. C. Salter,
    G. H. Stafford, E. J. N. Wilson, J. D. Davies,
    J. D. Dowell, P. M. Hattersley, R. J.

Homer, A. W. O'Dell, A. A. Carter, R. J. Tapper, and K. F. Riley, Phys. Rev. 168, 1466 (1968).

16. A. A. Carter, K. F. Riley, R. J. Tapper, D. V. Bugg, R. S. Gilmore, K. M. Knight, D. C. Salter, G. H. Stafford, E. J. N. Wilson, J. D. Davies, J. D. Dowell, P. M. Hattersley, R. J. Homer, and A. W. O'Dell, Phys. Rev. 168, 1457 (1968).

17. R. Glauber, Phys. Rev. 100, 242 (1955); C. Wilkin, Phys. Rev. Letters 17, 561 (1966).

18. I want to thank my colleagues Gideon Alexander, Gerson Goldhaber, and Gerald Lynch for interesting me in these problems with deuterium.

19. R. W. Bland, M. G. Bowler, J. L. Brown, G. Goldhaber, S. Goldhaber, V. H. Seeger, and G. H. Trilling, Phys. Rev. Letters 18, 1077 (1967).

20. R. W. Bland, "Single Pion Production in the K^+p Channel from 860 to 1360 MeV/c," Thesis, UCRL-18131, March 11, 1968 (unpublished).

21. C. Lovelace, in Proceedings of the 1967 Heidelberg International Conference on Elementary Particles (North-Holland Publishing Co., Amsterdam, 1968); see p. 79.

Meson Classification in the Quark Model

GEORGE ZWEIG[*]

California Institute of Technology, Pasadena, California

The ace or quark model, as it was originally conceived, stated that the low-lying meson states were to be
classified according to the energy levels of a three-
dimensional harmonic oscillator.[1] These mesons were to have
the same mass spectrum and quantum numbers as a harmonically
bound quark-antiquark pair. Although this hypothesis was far
removed from the usual assumptions made in strong interaction
physics, it still provided a useful classification scheme for
the existing mesons. The current status of this classification system will now be examined.

The energy levels of a three-dimensional harmonic
oscillator are shown in Fig. 1. The angular momentum L of
the levels is plotted against the "energy" quantum number
"n". Empirically, it is the $(mass)^2$ which is proportional
to n. Both rotational and vibrational excitations are present. Associated with each of the (n, L) levels is another

---

[1] G. Zweig, An SU_3 Model for Strong Interaction Symmetry and
its Breaking, CERN Reports No. 8182/Th 401, January 1964;
No. 8419/Th 412, February 1964 (unpublished).

[*] Alfred P. Sloan Foundation Research Fellow.

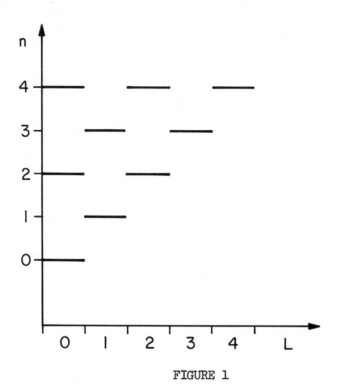

FIGURE 1

angular momentum quantum number "S" which takes on both the
values 0 and 1. It corresponds to the total spin of $\overline{A}A$
(antiquark-quark). The total angular momentum of the system,
i.e., the spin of the meson, is given by J where $J = |L+S|$,
. . . or, $|L-S|$. Finally, for each (n, L, S, J) there are nine
possible states of $\overline{A}A$, i.e., $\overline{A}_i A_j$, $i,j = 1,2,3$ with
$A_1 = n_o$, $A_2 = p_o$, $A_3 = \lambda_o .^{1)}$ A meson could now be labeled
by $(n, L, S, J, \overline{A}_i A_j)$. In the crudest approximation the mass of
the meson depends only on n. In reality, the mass also
depends on a variety of perturbations. This is exemplified
in Fig. 2 where we have given a possible classification of
the existing mesons. The perturbations we include are, from
left to right in Fig. 2: [see Figure Captions at end of
paper]

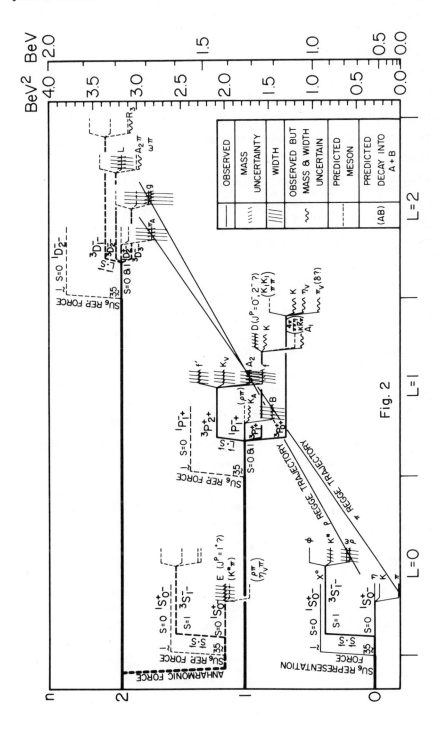

Fig. 2

(1) An anharmonic term in the $\overline{A}A$ potential which splits
$(n = 2, L = 0)$ from $(n = 2, L = 2)$. The evidence for this
type of interaction is very weak and comes from the $J^P = 0^-$
assignment for the E meson. If 0^- is correct for the E,
then we view it as the first vibrational state of the η (or
possibly X^o).

(2) A force which varies from one SU_6 representation to the
next.[2,3] It is responsible for the bulk of the X^o, η mass
splitting.

(3) A SU_6 symmetry breaking $\vec{S} \cdot \vec{S}$ interaction which splits
the π and ρ masses.

(4) An $\vec{L} \cdot \vec{S}$ term which, for example, is present in the
$L = 1$ states and accounts for the $^3P_2$, $^1P_1$, $^3P_1$, $^3P_0$
splitting.

(5) The λ_o, n_o (strange, nonstrange) mass difference which
splits the K, π masses and is responsible for the bulk of
the ω-ϕ type mixing.

The mass relations we might expect are:

(1) With increasing $(\text{mass})^2$, parities of resonances should
alternate. This general feature appears to be correct up to
~ 3 BeV^2.

(2) Within any octet or nonet, the $(\text{mass})^2$ difference
between the $I = 1/2$ and $I = 1$ objects should be approxi-

[2] G. Zweig, lectures at the International School of Physics
"Ettore Majorana", Erice, Italy (1964), ed. A. Zichichi.
For later versions of the quark model, with additional
references, see R. H. Dalitz, rapporteur's talk, Proceedings
of the 13th International Conference on High Energy Physics,
Berkeley, California (1966).

[3] B. Sakita, Phys. Rev. 136, B1756 (1964); F. Gürsey and
L. Radicati, Phys. Rev. Letters 13, 173 (1964).

mately the same and equal to $K-\pi = (0.25 - 0.02)$ BeV^2 =
0.23 BeV^2. (This number is a measure of the λ_o, n_o mass
split.) As may be seen from Fig. 2, this rule appears to be
well-satisfied.

(3) $\vec{L} \cdot \vec{S}$ coupling for the $L = 1$ states gives an equal
(mass)^2 spacing rule,

$$^3P_2 - {}^1P_1 = {}^1P_1 - {}^3P_1 = {}^3P_1 - {}^3P_0 \quad , \quad (1)$$

which crudely describes the data (Fig. 2). This indicates
that the $\vec{S} \cdot \vec{S}$ term is small for $L = 1$. $\vec{L} \cdot \vec{S}$ for
$L = 2$ yields

$$^3D_1 - {}^3D_2 = 2\,({}^3D_2 - {}^1D_2) = {}^1D_2 - {}^3D_3 \quad . \quad (2)$$

If $\vec{S} \cdot \vec{S}$ splitting is present for $L = 2$, only the triplet
states are related;

$$^3D_1 - {}^3D_2 = \frac{2}{3}\,({}^3D_2 - {}^3D_3) \quad .$$

There is insufficient data to discuss the detailed applica-
bility of the model for $L = 2$.

(4) In analogy with the vector mesons, all nonet states
should have strong ω-ϕ type mixing and satisfy, in order of
expected precision:

$$(a) \quad (\phi-\rho)(\omega-\rho) = \frac{4}{3}\,(K^*-\rho)(\phi+\omega-2K^*) \quad .^{[1,2]} \quad (4)$$

Note that the particle symbol stands for the (mass)^2 of that
particle. If the octet-singlet splitting is small compared
to the λ_o, n_o mass splitting (as it is with the 1^- and 2^+
mesons),

$$(b) \quad (\omega-\rho)/2 \ll \phi - \omega \quad , \quad (5)$$

in which case (4) reduces to

$$(\omega-\rho)/2 \;\approx\; \phi + \rho - 2K^* \qquad\qquad . \qquad (6)$$

In the limit where the octet and singlet are degenerate, the
two sides of (6) decouple and become equal to zero, i.e.,

$$(c)\quad \omega \approx \rho \qquad\qquad\qquad ,$$
$$K^* \approx (\phi+\rho)/2 \qquad\qquad . \qquad (7)$$

The 1^- and 2^+ nonets satisfy relation (4) to the
accuracy with which the masses are known. Taking
$\sqrt{\phi} = 1019.3 \pm 0.6$, $\sqrt{K^*} = 892.7 \pm 0.5$, $\sqrt{\omega} = 783.3 \pm 0.7$,
we find

$$\sqrt{\rho} \;=\; 758 \pm 1.5 \text{ MeV} \qquad\qquad ,$$

as compared with the electron-positron colliding beam experimental value[4] of

$$\sqrt{\rho} \;=\; 764 \pm 11 \text{ MeV} \qquad\qquad .$$

Also,

$$\sqrt{A_2} \;=\; 1297 \pm 10 \text{ MeV} \qquad\qquad ,$$

using $\sqrt{f'} = 1514 \pm 5$, $\sqrt{K_V} = 1418.6 \pm 3.2$, $\sqrt{f} = 1263 \pm 10$.
Because (5) is satisfied for both these nonets, (6) is
essentially equivalent to (4). Equations (7) are not
strictly valid, but do form reasonable approximations.

In using (4), it is helpful to solve for either ρ,
K^*, ϕ, or ω in terms of parameters which are expected to be
small:

[4] V.L. Auslander, G.I. Budker, Ju. N. Pestov, V.A. Sidorov,
A.N. Skrinsky, and A.G. Khabakhpashev, Physics Letters 25B,
433 (1967).

$$\rho = \omega + \frac{(\phi - \omega)}{2} [1 - 2\alpha - \sqrt{1 - 2\alpha^2}]$$

$$= \omega - (\phi - \omega) \alpha [1 - \frac{\alpha}{2} - \frac{\alpha^3}{4} + 0(\alpha^5)] \qquad ,$$

$$\alpha = \frac{2}{3} \frac{(\phi + \omega - 2K^*)}{(\phi - \omega)} \qquad ;$$

(4)

or $$K^* = \rho + \frac{(\phi - \rho)}{4} [1 + \beta + \sqrt{1 - 4\beta + \beta^2}]$$

$$= \rho + \frac{(\phi - \rho)}{2} [1 - \frac{\beta}{2} - \frac{3}{4} \beta^2 + 0(\beta^3)] \qquad ,$$

$$\beta = \frac{\omega - \rho}{\phi - \rho} \qquad ;$$

(4)

or $$\phi = 2K^* - \rho + (\phi - \rho) \frac{\beta}{2(1 - \gamma)} \qquad ,$$

$$\beta = \frac{\omega - \rho}{\phi - \rho} \qquad , \qquad \gamma = \frac{3}{4} \frac{(\omega - \rho)}{(K^* - \rho)} \qquad ;$$

(4)

or $$\omega = \rho + (K^* - \rho) \frac{\delta}{1 + \frac{3}{4} \delta} \qquad ,$$

$$\delta = 2 \frac{(\phi + \rho - 2K^*)}{K^* - \rho} \qquad .$$

(4)

Another measure of the strength of ω-ϕ type mixing and the validity of Eqs. (7) is given by the degree of suppression of the decay of the ϕ-like object into mesons containing non-strange quarks[1] (e.g., the decay of the vector meson ϕ into $\rho\pi$ is proportional to the (mass)^2 difference ω-ρ and therefore strongly suppressed:

$$\Gamma(\phi \to \rho\pi) = 162 \text{ MeV} \left[\frac{(\omega - \rho)}{\sqrt{2} (\phi - \omega)} \right]^2 \approx 0.4 \text{ MeV} \quad ;$$

the experimental partial width is   3.6 MeV x 12% $\approx$ 0.4 MeV.
Similarly, the approximate equality of ω, ρ masses leads to
the well-established suppression of $\emptyset$ production in πN reactions). In this context it is interesting to note that
experimentally

$$\frac{\Gamma(f' \to \pi\pi)}{\Gamma(f' \to K\overline{K})} < \frac{1}{5} \qquad ,$$

even though phase space strongly favors the $\pi\pi$ mode. Also,
the f' has never been produced in πN reactions.

(5) All states where there is little octet-singlet mixing
satisfy the Gell-Mann - Okubo relation

$$K - \pi = 3 (\eta - K) \qquad . \qquad (8)$$

If we apply this to the L = 0 pseudoscalar mesons, there
is a definite discrepancy present. Even if we pick the
charge states of K and π to give the best agreement,

$$K^+ - \pi^+ = 3 (\eta - K^+) \qquad ,$$

$$0.225 \text{ BeV}^2 = 0.171 \pm 0.002 \text{ BeV}^2 \qquad , \qquad (9)$$

where the largest uncertainty lies in the η mass. The disagreement is usually attributed to the existence of a pseudoscalar meson whose mass is then computed via Eq. (4):

$$\eta' = \pi + 4(K-\pi) \left[1 + 2 \ \frac{(\eta-K)}{(K-\pi) - 3(\eta-K)} \right] \qquad . \qquad (4)$$

While a ninth pseudoscalar meson (X^0) does exist, we should
not expect to determine its mass from the observed discrepancy (9) since second order SU_3 breaking corrections are
expected to contribute corrections of this same order. Even
the relatively small breaking of SU_3 by electromagnetism
introduces uncertainties of the order of several hundred MeV

in η'. The quark model is not able to determine masses of SU_6 singlets with useful precision.

(6) Nonet representations (strong ω-ϕ type mixing) should show up for all quark spin triplet states (S = 1). The mass relations (4) through (7) are then applicable. The quark spin singlet representations (S = 0) are expected to have very weak octet-singlet mixing and will have a $(mass)^2$ difference structure much like the pseudoscalar mesons.

Note, however, that the ω-ϕ type mixing in the $^3P_1$ states appears to be qualitatively different from what was observed in the $^3S_1$ and $^3P_2$ configurations, i.e.,

(a) $K \neq (D + A_1)/2$, unlike $K^* \approx (\phi + \rho)/2$

and $K_V \approx (f' + A_2)/2$;   (7)

(b) $D \to \pi_V(1016) + \pi$, unlike $\phi \not\to \rho\pi$

and $f' \not\to \pi\pi$;

(c)   D is strongly produced in πN reactions
(ϕ and f' are not)   .

This anomalous behavior may be due to a misclassification of states. For example, the experimental evidence for the $J^P = 1^+$ assignment of the D is quite weak. If a strong $I^G \; J^P = 1^- \; 0^+$ $K\bar{K}$ interaction (π_V) is introduced into the spin-parity analysis of the D, then $J^P = 0^-, 2^-, \ldots$ also fits the data.[5] If we accept this latter possibility

[5] D.H. Miller, S.U. Chung, O.I. Dahl, R.I. Hess, L.M. Hardy, J. Kirz, and W. Koellner, Phys. Rev. Letters 14, 1074 (1965); Ch. D'Andlau, A. Astier, M. Della Negra, L. Dobrzynski, S. Wojcicki, J. Barlow, T. Jacobsen, L. Montanet, L. Tallone, M. Thomas, A-M. Adamson, M. Baubillier, J. Duboc, M. Goldberg, E. Levy, D.N. Edwards, and J.E.A. Lys, Physics Letters 17, 347 (1965).

and remove the D from the $^3P_1$ nonet then, from Eq. (7), the ϕ-like member of this nonet would be located at ~ 1400 MeV. It should decay primarily into $\pi_V(1016) + \pi$ (and $K^*\bar{K}$ if its mass is sufficiently high to put it above threshold). This object might be the E meson, although present experimental evidence favors a $J^P = 0^-$ assignment for the E.[6]

If the quark spin singlet states have little mixing, then definite branching ratio predictions may be made. For example, the η member of $^1P_1$ should decay primarily into $\rho\pi$ with a partial width of 140 MeV[1] ($\Gamma(B \rightarrow \omega\pi) = 130$ MeV is assumed). This η (at approximately 1330 MeV) has not been experimentally identified but could have been confused with the neutral A_2. If, on the other hand, the $^1P_1$ states formed a nonet with the same ω-ϕ type mixing as is observed for $^3S_1$ and $^3P_2$, then we would expect the existence of two $I = 0$ objects, one at roughly the B mass decaying into $\rho\pi$ with a width of 415 MeV,[1] the other at a mass of approximately 1400. This latter resonance would decay into $K^*\bar{K}$ and $\bar{K}^*K$ if its mass is sufficiently high to put it above threshold for this reaction. Its decay into $\rho\pi$ and $\omega\eta$ would then be weak (in analogy with the suppression of $\phi \rightarrow \rho\pi$).

In summary, we ask and comment on the following questions:

(1) Do we need a harmonic oscillator potential or, more generally, the quantum number n; that is, are there radial vibrations?

The only candidates for vibrational states are the E and D. Their J^P assignments are not well-determined. For

[6] G. Goldhaber, rapporteur's talk, <u>Proceedings of the 13th International Conference on High Energy Physics,</u> Berkeley, California (1966).

the E, $J^P = 0^-$ or 1^+. If 0^- is correct, then the E may be
the first vibrational state of the η. Its SU_3 partners are
then expected to form an octet (Fig. 2) with the I = 1
member lying at ~ 1310 MeV and decaying into $\eta_V(1070)\pi$
or $\rho\pi$. The I = 1/2 object would be at ~ 1390 MeV and decay
into K(1100)π or $K^*\pi$ (the K(1100) is the SU_3 partner of
π_V and η_V; it has been reported in a Kπ phase shift analysis[7]). Since these vibrational states would be formed by
"Pomeranchon exchange" their production cross section would
be constant with energy and their momentum transfer distributions would be sharply peaked.

(2) Do all quark spin singlet (S = 0) objects fall into
octets plus singlets with a (mass)^2 structure similar to the
pseudoscalar mesons (very little ω-ϕ mixing)? Do the triplet
states (S = 1) always form nonets with a (mass)^2 structure
like the vector mesons (large ω-ϕ mixing)?

The $^3P_2$ states do resemble the vector mesons. The
$^3P_1$ states do not follow this pattern, but the D may be mis-
classified (its J^P could be 0^-, 2^-, . . .). If the E is 1^+
and replaces the D, then the (mass)^2 differences of the $^3P_1$
states would mirror the vector mesons. If the E is 0^-, then
another state decaying into $\pi_V\pi$ or $K \overset{*}{\overline{K}}$ with a mass
approximately that of the E is expected to replace the D.
Finally, the $^1P_1$ states should form an octet, with the
η-like member decaying into $\rho\pi$ at ~ 1330 MeV.

(3) How does the $\vec{S} \cdot \vec{S}$ interaction vary with (n, L)?

For (n = 0, L = 0) it is large, but it is absent for
(n = 1, L = 1). Does this mean that it is non-zero only for

---

[7]E. Malamud and P. Schlein, paper presented at the Philadelphia Meson Conference, April 1968.

L = 0, or will it vary smoothly with L to reappear with
opposite sign for $(n = 2, L = 2)$?

(4) How does the $\vec{L} \cdot \vec{S}$ interaction vary with (n, L)?

Although the J^P assignments for the resonances in
the 1650 → 1750 MeV region are uncertain, their close spacing
indicates that the $\vec{L} \cdot \vec{S}$ term is smaller for $(n = 2, L = 2)$
than for $(n = 1, L = 1)$.

ACKNOWLEDGMENTS

The author has enjoyed helpful conversations with
Professor G. Goldhaber and Professor A. Rosenfeld.

FIGURE CAPTIONS

Fig. 1: Energy level diagram of a three-dimensional
harmonic oscillator.

Fig. 2: The meson $(\text{mass})^2$ spectrum. Whenever possible, the
notation and data is that of Rosenfeld's table. The
origins of the splittings are indicated by comments
written in the near vertical direction. If no
origin is given, then the splitting arises from the
λ_o, n_o mass difference. Note the use of the symbol
$^{2S+1}L_{J^P}^C$ where C is the charge conjugation of the
neutral, zero strangeness members of the octet,
singlet, or nonet. $\underline{35}$ and $\underline{1}$ refer to the SU_6
classification of levels. The $n = 2$ levels are
quite uncertain and have been included only to give
a qualitative indication of what might be expected
in the higher meson mass region.

MESONIC RESONANCE STATES

R. H. Dalitz

Department of Theoretical Physics

Oxford University, England.

1.   MESON NONETS IN THE QUARK MODEL

We shall discuss our knowledge about meson states in terms of the non-relativistic quark model[1-10]. With this model, we can imagine the meson systems as being like tiny diatomic molecules, consisting of a massive quark and antiquark tightly bound together. We consider only the simplest quark model[11], where the quarks q_i form a single triplet (p, n,), with the following quantum numbers:

Quark state	Charge (Q)	Isospin (I_3)	Baryon No. (B)	Hypercharge (Y)
$q_1 = p$	$+\dfrac{2}{3}e$	$+\dfrac{1}{2}$	$+\dfrac{1}{3}$	$+\dfrac{1}{3}$
$q_2 = n$	$-\dfrac{1}{3}e$	$-\dfrac{1}{2}$	$+\dfrac{1}{3}$	$+\dfrac{1}{3}$
$q_3 = \lambda$	$-\dfrac{1}{3}e$	0	$+\dfrac{1}{3}$	$-\dfrac{2}{3}$

In this quasi-molecular system, the internal motion of the quarks can be non-relativistic, owing to their great mass; in general, the condition for this is

$$\hbar/a \ll Mc, \tag{1.1}$$

where a denotes the range of the potential and M denotes the quark mass. With the lower limit $Mc^2 > 5\,GeV$, which we know from the failure to produce quarks in accelerator experiments[13], this inequality (1.1) is quite well satisfied for reasonable potential ranges, of order $a \approx 10^{-14}$ cm; we shall discuss the parameters appropriate to the physical situation later in this Section. We may expect this quasi-molecular system to be subject to the same kind of excitations, corresponding to both rotational and vibrational (radial) motions, as those well-known for the low-lying states of molecules.

For a given state of rotational (L) and vibrational (n) excitation and total Pauli spin S, specified by the notation $(n^{(2S + 1)}L_J)$, there are nine states of the type $\bar{q}_i - q_j$. With SU(3) - invariant interactions, these would generally separate into two unitary multiplets, an octet $\{8\}$ and a unitary singlet $\{1\}$. This would account at once for the fact that no mesonic state has been established with quantum numbers not compatible with its membership in some octet or singlet representation. There has been considerable search for anomalous mesonic states, especially in the systems K^+K^+, $\pi^+\pi^+$ (and $\pi^-\pi^-$) which would be characteristic of a $\{27\}$ representation, and in the systems $K^+\pi^+$, $K^{*+}\pi^+$ and $K^{*+}\rho^+$, which would be characteristic of a $\{27\}$ or $\{10 + \overline{10}\}$ representation, up to mass value about 2000 MeV. With SU(3) - breaking interactions, the (I = 0, Y = 0) octet state can become strongly mixed with the singlet state, especially if the mass separation between the singlet and octet states is less than or comparable with the magnitude of the SU(3) mass splittings (typically of the order 100–400 MeV). In this situation, we prefer to describe the system of states as a meson nonet.

For the configuration $(n^{(2S + 1)}L_J)$, the parity is given by

$$P = - (-1)^L, \tag{1.2}$$

and the charge configuration parity C for the neutral $Y = 0$
states by

$$C = (-1)^{L + S}. \tag{1.3}$$

For a $Y = 0$ substate with isospin I, the G-parity is then

$$G = C(-1)^I. \tag{1.4}$$

The ground state configuration naturally corresponds to zero
angular momentum, $L = 0$, and no radial excitation, thus $n = 1$.
The model therefore leads to the expectation of two low-lying
nonets, corresponding to the 1^1S_0 and 1^3S_1 configurations.
This is in accord with the observation that there are just two
nonets with mean mass below 1000 MeV, the pseudoscalar
nonet (π, K, $\overline{K}$, η, η') and the vector nonet (ρ, K*, $\overline{K}$*, ω, $\emptyset$),
and that these states have quantum numbers in agreement with
the expressions (1.2), (1.3) and (1.4).

Each nonet has one $I = 1$ isospin sub-multiplet. These
$I = 1$ states can be studied very directly by observations on the
reactions

$$\pi^\pm + p \longrightarrow p + M^\pm, \tag{1.5}$$

where the mesonic state $M^\pm$ generally decays to some final
system of mesons. The CERN "Missing Mass Spectrometer",
which makes momentum measurements only for the recoil
proton, has been used by Kienzle et al.[14] and Focacci et al.[15]
to study the mass spectrum for the states M^- with especially
large statistics. The "missing mass" distribution thus found
for the states M^- produced in this reaction shows a series of

striking peaks[15], the first two peaks corresponding to the first

two peaks corresponding to the $L = 0$ states π and ρ, the next

to $A_2(1300)$, then with further peaks, the R-cluster (about 1700

MeV), S(1929), T(2195) and U(2385), at higher mass values.

Focacci et al.[15] pointed out that if (mass)^2 for the ρ, A_2, R, S, T,

and U mesons were plotted against their order N in this sequence

$N = 1, 2, 3, \ldots$, as in Fig. 1, then this plot is approximately

linear. The presumption is that this line represents the Regge

trajectory for the ρ meson, so that the number N actually

specifies the total spin of the corresponding mesonic state.

About this possibility we can make the following remarks:

(i) The ρ and A_2 are known to have spin-parities

(1-) and (2+), respectively; at least one R-state is known[16]

to have spin-parity (3-), as required by the identification

of N with J. Spin values have not yet been determined for

the higher states.

(ii) With the quark model, the ρ and A_2 trajectories

are expected to be essentially coincident. In general, the

trajectories for even and for odd spin would be separated,

as a result of the presence of exchange forces. However,

exchange forces could arise here only from the exchange of

the systems (qq) and $(\bar{q}\bar{q})$ between the quark and antiquark.

These systems are expected to be very massive (of order 2M

$\gtrsim$ 10 GeV) and can give rise only to forces of exceedingly

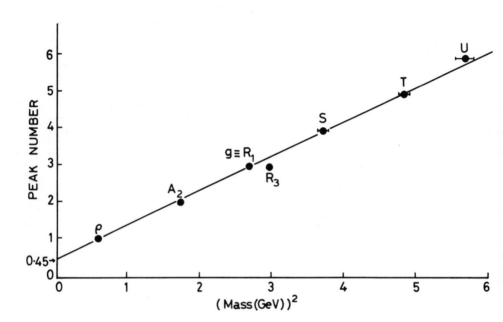

Figure 1. A plot of (mass)^2 for the prominent MM peaks in the reaction $\pi^- p \rightarrow p(MM)^-$, as found by Focacci et al.[15], against their order in this sequence. The line is interpreted as giving the (coincident) ρ^- and A2- Regge trajectories, the ordinate being the spin J. For J = 3, the point shown on the line corresponds to the g-(or R_1-) meson, the point off the line to R_3(1750); the state for which spin (3-) seems now established is ρ(1700), roughly midway between.

short range (which might affect $L = 0$ states a little, but $L \geq 1$ states not appreciably).

(iii) The straight line passing through ρ and A_2 has intercept $+0.45$ at $(mass)^2 = 0$. This is in good accord with the values (typically $+0.55$) obtained[17] for the intercept $\alpha\rho(0)$ of the ρ-trajectory from observations on scattering and reaction processes in the physical region, corresponding to $(mass)^2 \leq 0$ on Fig. 1.

(iv) The widths observed for the high-lying resonance states are surprisingly small; for example, the width quoted by Focacci et al.[15] for the T-meson is $\Gamma(T) \leq 13$ MeV, despite its high mass value of 2195 MeV. With these high spin values for the high-mass mesons ($J=5$ for the T-meson), it is quite possible to understand such narrow widths as a consequence of the high centrifugal barriers to be penetrated by the outgoing particles which result from decay of the mesonic state[9,10,18]. We know of no other interpretation for such narrow widths.

The fact that the Regge-trajectory is linear can also be given a simple interpretation. However, this depends on the choice of a suitable wave-equation for the $\bar{q}$-q system. The equation we shall adopt is as follows:

$$(E^2/4)\,\psi \;=\; (M^2 + \frac{3}{2}p^2 + MV)\,\psi .$$

This equation was originally derived[9,10,19] as an approximation
to the Bethe-Salpeter equation, appropriate for a static potential
(as seen in the $\bar{q}$-q rest frame) and for non-relativistic internal
motion. It has often been assumed in the literature that non-
relativistic internal motion implies that the Schrodinger wave-
equation must be used to describe this motion. Here we emphasize that there are at least two conditions which must be satisfied
before one can conclude that the Schrodinger equation should
necessarily hold;

(i)   non-relativistic momenta, $p \ll M$,

(ii) small binding energy, $(2M-E) \ll 2M$.

We may note that Eq. (1.6) does happen to reduce to a Schrodinger
form in the latter limit.* The equation (1.6) leads naturally to
mass relation-found physically appropriate (for example, in the
use of the Gell-Mann-Okubo mass formula for mesons). Also,
this equation has a physically sensible behavior in the limit of
small E (cf. p. 217 of ref. 9). At least, the use of this equation
provides a simple model with physically sensible properties.

---

*The Blankenbecler-Sugar equation[20], obtained from the Bethe-
Salpeter equation for two spinless particles with the same mass
M and interacting through a static potential V, has the form

$$(E^2/4 - p^2 - M^2)\psi = \frac{M^2}{\sqrt{(M^2 + p^2)}} \, V \, \psi \qquad \text{(i)}$$

*(Contd.)

Eq. (1.6) results from (i), when the approximations $E^2 \ll M^2$ and $p^2 \ll M^2$ are made; the factor $\frac{3}{2}$ in ships which hold for $(\text{mass})^2 = E^2$, as has been Eq. (1.6) arises when the square root factor is brought over to the left hand side of Eq. (i) and expanded in powers of p^2/M^2. For the case of weak binding, when $-\epsilon = (2M-E) \ll M$, the left hand factor in Eq. (i) reduces to $(M_\epsilon -p^2)$ and the square root factor becomes simply M; with these reductions Eq. (i) takes the usual Schrodinger form, as expected. It is clearly not correct to take the weak binding limit for Eq. (1.6), since the contrary assumption $E^2 \ll 4M^2$ has already been made in its derivation.

We do not mean to imply here that the Bethe-Salpeter equation, the Blankenbecler-Sugar equation, or its non-relativistic limit (1.6), are necessarily the correct equation to use for the $\bar{q}$-q system. It is simply that the Bethe-Salpeter equation is fully relativistic, and well known in its covariant form; it offers a convenient and familiar starting point for the derivation of an equation different from the Schrodinger equation, appropriate to tight-binding, and quadratic in E (as the meson mass formula requires). We could just as well replace Eq. (i) with another equation of ad. hoc. form in the c.m. frame, such as

$$(E^2/4 - p^2 - M^2)\, \psi \;=\; MV\, \psi \qquad\qquad \text{(ii)}$$

With Eq. (1.6), a smooth flat-bottomed potential can be well approximated by

$$V(r) = V(0) + \frac{1}{2} M\omega^2 r^2 \tag{1.7}$$

and leads to the eigenvalues

$$E^2(n, L) = E_0^2 + (4\sqrt{3} \, M\omega)(2n + L - 2). \tag{1.8}$$

These natural assumptions (cf. refs. 9,19 and 21) therefore lead directly to the linear dependence of E^2 on L found empirically. In expression (1.8), E_0^2 denotes the quantity

$$E_0^2 = 4M^2 + 4MV(0) + 6\sqrt{3}M\omega, \tag{1.9}$$

n denotes the principal (radial) quantum number, and L is the orbital angular momentum. The corresponding eigenfunctions (properly normalized) are the harmonic oscillator wave functions[22],

$$\psi_m(n, L) = \left(\frac{M\omega/\sqrt{3}}{\Gamma(n+L+\frac{1}{2})}\right)^{\frac{3}{2}} \left(\frac{\Gamma(n)}{4n+2L-1}\right)^{\frac{1}{2}} \left(\frac{M\omega r^2}{\sqrt{3}}\right)^{\frac{1}{2}}$$

$$L_{n-1}^{L+\frac{1}{2}} \left(\frac{M\omega r^2}{\sqrt{3}}\right) \exp\left(-\frac{M\omega r^2}{2\sqrt{3}}\right) Y_L^m (\theta, \phi), \tag{1.10}$$

where m denotes the magnetic quantum number, Y_L^m $(\theta, \emptyset)$ denotes the spherical harmonic, normalized to unity, and the L_ν^α (z) are the Laguerre polynomials (tabulated in ref. 22).

The parameter $(\sqrt{3}e\, M\omega)$ is given by the slope

$$(4\sqrt{3}\, M\omega)^{1/2} = 1.01 \text{ GeV} \tag{1.11}$$

With wavefunction (1.10) for n=1, L=0, the r.m.s. radius for the π and ρ mesons is given by

$$\langle r^2 \rangle^{\frac{1}{2}} = \frac{1}{2} (3\sqrt{3}/2M\omega)^{\frac{1}{2}} = 0.42 \text{ fm} \tag{1.12}$$

The r.m.s. momentum of the quarks in this state is then given by

$$\langle p^2 \rangle^{\frac{1}{2}} = (\sqrt{3}M\omega/2)^{\frac{1}{2}} = 0.36 \text{ GeV/c}, \tag{1.13}$$

so that the requirement of non-relativistic motion in this state is well satisfied, for the parameters physically appropriate.

We note that the r.m.s. radius (1.11) is much smaller than the values which have been quoted in the literature for the charge radius of the pion[23,24]. This situation is also that found for the proton[19], where the charge and magnetic moment radii are reliably known. In both cases, we must suppose that the quarks themselves have an intrinsic charge and magnetic structure with r.m.s. radii R_Q and R_M, and that the corresponding hadron radius measured is then given by $(R^2 + \langle r^2 \rangle)^{1/2}$. Since the measured radii are all about 0.8 fm, we have to conclude that the quark has a diffuse charge and magnetic moment structure,

and that the hadronic r.m.s. radii observed are primarily due to
the electromagnetic size of the quarks themselves. With this
picture, the assumption of a rigid charge and magnetic moment
structure for the quarks does not appear very plausible; it would
be most reasonable to expect this quark structure to be severely
distorted by the superstrong interactions of the other quarks present since these all lie well within the charge and magnetic moment distribution of the quark being considered. This would
complicate the interpretation of the electromagnetic form factors
for the hadrons, but would leave the qualitative picture much as
just discussed above, that the spatial distributions of the charge
and magnetic moment in hadrons do not depend sensitively on the
size and shape of the quark distribution within them.

With non-relativistic internal motion for the quarks and
antiquarks within the hadronic states, Pauli spin is appropriate
for the quarks and antiquarks; the total Pauli spin in the $\bar{q}q$ system
can then be $S=0$ or $S=1$. In this situation, SU(6) symmetry can
hold approximately for the low-lying hadronic states; if this is
the case, then the $\bar{q}q$ interaction must be limited to the form:

$$\bar{U}(r) = \bar{U}(\underline{35}) + \bar{U}_1 (1 - \underline{\sigma} \cdot \bar{\underline{\sigma}}) \ (1 - F \cdot \bar{F})/36, \qquad (1.14)$$

where the interaction $\bar{U}(\underline{35})$ holds for all the sub-states of the
SU(6) $\underline{35}$-representation, for the octet and singlet states with
$S=1$ and the octet state with $S=0$, and the interaction $\bar{U}(\underline{1}) =$
$(\bar{U}(\underline{35}) + U_1)$ holds in the SU(6) singlet state, the unitary singlet
state with $S=0$. The $S=1$ states then form an ideal nonet, the

octet and singlet states being governed by the same SU(6)-
invariant interaction and therefore having the same mass and the
same spatial wavefunction. For S=0, the octet and singlet states
are governed by different interactions and can be widely separate
in mass value. For the n=1, L=0 configurations, the octet and
singlet states with S=0 (approximately given by $\eta(548)$ and $\eta'(969)$)
do lie relatively close in mass (on the scale M). This could be
somewhat fortuitous, the interactions $\overline{U}_0$ and $\overline{U}_1$ could have quite
different shapes, and the spatial wavefunctions $\emptyset(\underline{35})$ and $\emptyset(\underline{1})$
appropriate to the S=0 octet and singlet states, respectively,
could well be quite different in form. However, with the assumption of potentials of harmonic form, the simplest expectation
would be that the form of the spatial wavefunction is governed
primarily by the mass (for given n and L), although it is still
possible in principle that the spring constants could be different
for $\overline{U}(\underline{35})$ and $\overline{U}(\underline{1})$. It is not known yet whether or not the S=0
octet and singlet masses also lie relatively close for the higher
configurations (n, L), as this simplest expectation would suggest.

A particularly attractive hypothesis is that the super-
strong coupling with the quarks q_i and $\overline{q}_i$ is independent of the type
of quark and so does not depend on the suffix i. In this case, the
interaction $\overline{U}$ would have no dependence on the unitary spin and
the octet and singlet configuration for given (n, L, S) would be
governed by the same forces and therefore have the same wavefunctions, even for S=0. However, in general, we must note
here that the S=0 nonets could well be on quite a different footing
from that for the S=1 nonets.

Nonet States	Unitary Spin Wavefunction
$V(I=1,\ Y=0)$	$V^+ = \bar{n}p$
	$V^0 = (\bar{p}p - \bar{n}n)/\sqrt{2}$
	$V^- = \bar{p}n$
$K(I=\frac{1}{2},\ Y=+1)$	$K^+ = \bar{\lambda}p,\ K^0 = \bar{\lambda}n$
$\bar{K}(I=\frac{1}{2},\ Y=-1)$	$K^- = \bar{p}\lambda,\ \bar{K}^0 = \bar{n}\lambda$
$S_8(I=0,\ Y=0)$	$S_8 = (\bar{p}p + \bar{n}n - 2\bar{\lambda}\lambda)/\sqrt{6}$
$S_1\ (I=0,\ Y=0)$	$S_1 = (\bar{p}p + \bar{n}n + \bar{\lambda}\lambda)/\sqrt{3}$

Table I. The unitary-spin wavefunctions for the substates
of a mesonic nonet.

The SU(6)-breaking interactions can be of several different
kinds:

(i) terms depending on $\underline{\sigma}\cdot\bar{\underline{\sigma}}$ or $F\cdot\bar{F}$, other than the
SU(6)-invariant form (1.13). The $\underline{\sigma}\cdot\bar{\underline{\sigma}}$ terms separate the $S=0$
and $S=1$ states for given (n, L); the $F\cdot\bar{F}$ terms separate the octet
and singlet states for a given nonet, for both $S=0$ and $S=1$. With
these interactions, the singlet mass m_1 will generally differ
from the octet mass m_8, for any nonet (n, L, S), even for $S=1$.

(ii) non-central interactions, which may be of spin-orbit form,

$$\bar{U}_{SO} = (1 + \lambda \ F \cdot \bar{F}) \ (\underline{\sigma} + \bar{\underline{\sigma}}) \cdot \underline{L} \ w(r), \qquad (1.15a)$$

or of tensor form

$$\bar{U}_{T} = (1 + \nu \ F \cdot \bar{F}) \ (\underline{\sigma} \cdot r \ \bar{\underline{\sigma}} \cdot r - \frac{1}{3} \underline{\sigma} \cdot \bar{\underline{\sigma}} r^2) \ w_{T}(r). \qquad (1.15b)$$

These interactions clearly violate SU(6) symmetry since the SU(6) operations transform the spin (and unitary spin) variables but not the ordinary space variables, so that they cannot leave the non-central forms (1.15) invariant. As we shall see later, the empirical evidence indicates that the dominant non-central interactions are of the spin-orbit form (1.15a).

With these non-central terms, the mass of an $S=1$ configuration now depends on total angular momentum J, and the octet and singlet masses must now be written m_8 (n, L, S, J) and m_1 (n, L, S, J), respectively. We note that the non-central terms (1.15) generally depend on unitary spin. For example, with the particular model of SU(6) invariant forces discussed by Radicati[25], the vector meson exchanges generate a spin orbit force of the form (1.15a) with $\lambda = -1$; since this spin-orbit interaction vanishes for octet states, this example does not fit the empirical observation that there is a spin-orbit splitting observed for the $I=1$ states of the $n=1$, $L=1$ - nonets. However, this dependence of Eqs. (1.15) on unitary spin means that for given n, L, and $S=1$, that m_8 and m_1 could have different dependences on J.

The SU(6)-breaking interactions which also break SU(3) symmetry, are assumed to transform like the I=0, Y=0 component of an octet (in tensor notation, like the component T_3^3 of a traceless tensor T_j^i), as required for the validity of the Gell-Mann-Okubo mass formula. These interactions satisfy isospin symmetry, of course, and are of two types:

(iii) <u>one-body terms.</u> These contribute an addition of Δ to the (mass)^2 for the system for each λ (or $\bar{\lambda}$) quark present (each weighted according to its intensity in the state considered).

In the octet states (cf. Table I), the one-body terms contribute amount Δ to (mass)^2 for the $(I = \frac{1}{2}, Y = \pm 1)$ states, and amount $4\Delta/3$ for the $(I = 0, Y = 0)$ state, (mass)^2 for the $(I = 1, Y = 0)$ state being left unaffected; (mass)^2 for a singlet state receives the contribution $2\Delta/3$. These terms also contribute a cross-term connecting the $(I = 0, Y = 0)$ states for the octet and singlet, in amount

$$m^2(1,8) \;=\; -\,\frac{2\sqrt{2}}{3}\,\Delta\, 1_{18}, \tag{1.16}$$

where 1_{18} denotes the overlap integral between the octet and singlet wavefunctions.

(iv) two-body terms. Here we consider the most general form for a central potential which transforms like T_3^3. For a given spin S, this potential may be written schematically as a second-quantized interaction,

$$v_3^3 = \left(\int q^3(1)q_3(1)u(12)q^i(2)q_i(2)d\tau_1 d\tau_2 + \int q^3(1)q_i(1)v(12)q^i(2)q_3(2)d\tau_1 d\tau_2 \right) /M$$

$$(1.17)$$

This expression is not traceless, but it differs from a traceless tensor by a unitary singlet term; in fact, we may characterize the form (1.17) by the statement that it is chosen to give zero contribution for the I=1, Y=0 state and for the I=0, Y=0 state which has no $\overline{\lambda}\lambda$ component (cf. Table I). Together with the one-body terms, these potentials contribute to $(mass)^2$ for the meson states of a given nonet $(n^{(2S+1}L_J)$, to give the following final expressions:

I=1, Y=0. m_8^2 (1.18a)

$I=\frac{1}{2}$, Y=±1 $m_8^2 + \Delta + u_{88}$ (1.18b)

$$\underline{I=0, \ Y=0} \quad (\text{mass})^2 \text{ matrix} =$$

$$\begin{pmatrix} m_8^2 + \dfrac{4}{3}(\Delta + u_{88}) & \dfrac{-2\sqrt{2}}{3}(\Delta 1_{18} + u_{18}) - \sqrt{2}v_{18} \\[3mm] \dfrac{-2\sqrt{2}}{3}(\Delta 1_{81} + u_{81}) - \sqrt{2}v_{18} & m_1^2 + \dfrac{2}{3}(\Delta + u_{11}) + 2v_{11} \end{pmatrix}$$

$$(1.18c)$$

Here the notations $u_{\alpha\beta}$, $v_{\alpha\beta}$ refer to the matrix-elements of u and v between the space wavefunctions for the SU(3) states $\{\alpha\}$, $\{\beta\}$ specified, where α and β may each refer to either octet or singlet.

For an ideal nonet, such that $\phi(\{1\}) = \phi(\{8\})$ for the space wavefunctions, these expressions simplify. First, the matrix-elements u_{88}, u_{81} and u_{11} are then all equal, with value $\bar{u}$, say, and the matrix-elements v_{88}, v_{81} and v_{11} are all equal, with value $\bar{v}$, say; also 1_{18} is simply unity. We may redefine the terms as follows:

$$\Delta' = \Delta + \bar{u}, \tag{1.19a}$$

$$\mathcal{I}\Delta' = \Delta' + \frac{3}{2}\bar{v}, \tag{1.19b}$$

$$m(1)^2 = m_1^2 + 2\bar{v}, \tag{1.19c}$$

$$m(8)^2 = m_8^2. \tag{1.19d}$$

The $(\text{mass})^2$ matrix (1.18c) then takes the form appropriate to the Schwinger treatment of an ideal nonet[1,26]:

$$(M(I=0,\ Y=0))^2 = \begin{pmatrix} m(8)^2 + \dfrac{4}{3}\Delta' & -\dfrac{2\sqrt{2}}{3}\Delta' \\[3ex] -\dfrac{2\sqrt{2}}{3}\Delta' & m(1)^2 + \dfrac{2}{3}\Delta' \end{pmatrix}$$

(1.20a)

$$(m(I=1,\ Y=0))^2 = m(8)^2,$$

(1.20b)

$$\left(m\left(I=\tfrac{1}{2},\ Y=\pm 1\right)\right)^2 = m(8)^2 + \Delta'$$

(1.20c)

However, the physical interpretation of the symbols is now different from that appropriate to the Schwinger treatment. Δ' can now vary from nonet to nonet, since it includes the expectation value of the potential u(r). The parameter $\mathfrak{g}$ no longer has the simple interpretation as 1_{18}, the overlap integral, and it is no longer restricted to have modulus less than unity; it is related to the potentials by the equation

$$\mathfrak{g} = 1 + \frac{3}{2}\ \frac{\bar{v}}{(\Delta + \bar{u})}$$

(1.21)

There are now four masses for the nonet sub-states, which we will characterize in future by V(for isovector), K(hypercharge + 1), S and S' (for isoscalar), the S' state being that which receives the greater contribution from the unitary singlet state. There are also four parameters m(8), m(1), Δ'

and $\mathcal{I}$. However, there is one further quantity available empirically, the mixing angle θ; this is defined by the following equations,

$$|S') = \cos \theta |S_1) + \sin \theta |S_8), \qquad (1.22a)$$

$$|S) = -\sin \theta |S_1) + \cos \theta |S_8) . \qquad (1.22b)$$

The following procedures have been proposed for the determination of the mixing angle θ for a given nonet:

(i) decay processes which involve a one-quark interaction do not allow any transition from $\bar{\lambda}\lambda$ to $\bar{p}p$ or $\bar{n}n$. From Table I, the $\bar{\lambda}\lambda$ state may be written

$$-|\bar{\lambda}\lambda) = (-|S_1) + \sqrt{2}|S_8))/\sqrt{3}, \qquad (1.23)$$

which corresponds to a state (1.22b) with a mixing angle θ_0 given by

$$\tan \theta_0 = 1/\sqrt{2}, \qquad (1.24)$$

that is $\theta_0 = 35.3°$. Expressing S_1 and S_8 in terms of the particle states S and S', by means of Eqs. (1.22), we have

$$-|\bar{\lambda}\lambda) = (-\sin \theta_0 |S_1) + \cos \theta_0 |S_8))$$

$$= \sin (\theta-\theta_0)|S') + \cos (\theta-\theta_0)|S). \qquad (1.25)$$

The transitions of most interest are those to the final states V, which involve only (p, n) quarks and ($\bar{p}, \bar{n}$) antiquarks. Since these transitions are forbidden for one-quark transitions, we have for the corresponding amplitudes A

$$-A(\bar{\lambda}\lambda \to V) = 0$$
$$= \sin(\theta-\theta_o)A(S' \to V)+\cos(\theta-\theta_o)A(S \to V),$$

$$(1.26)$$

leading to the ratio

$$A(S \to V)/A(S' \to V) = - \tan(\theta-\theta_o).$$ (1.27)

Hence, after allowance for the difference in phase-space and in centrifugal barrier effects for the two transitions, the ratio of the absolute rates for the transitions leads to a determination of θ.

The two situations of particular interest are the transitions involving γ or π emission, (when the latter process is described by the model interactions $q \to q + \pi$ and $\bar{q} \to \bar{q} + \pi$). This procedure has been applied by Glashow and Socolow[27] to the case of vector meson decay; the appropriate expression (1.26) leads to the relationship

$$\Gamma(\emptyset \to \rho\pi) = 17 \tan^2(\theta-\theta_o) \Gamma(\omega \to \rho\pi).$$ (1.28)

The empirical values for these widths lead to the solution $\theta = 39\pm1^o$, which agrees well with the value $|\theta| = 40^o$ obtained from a phenomenological analysis of the masses (there is a second solution from Eq. (1.28), $\theta = 31\pm4^o$, which is rejected for this reason). The same discussion could be made for the comparison of the γ decays, $\emptyset \to \pi\gamma$ and $\omega \to \pi\gamma$. However, this relation could be deduced from (1. 28) on the basis of the ρ-dominance model for γ-transitions; also there are no data on the process $\emptyset \rightarrow \pi^0\gamma$, which is quite a difficult process to observe (especially so, as the transition $\emptyset \rightarrow \eta\gamma$ is expected to be rather strong).

(ii) Essentially the same argument has been given by Alexander et al. [28] for strong reaction processes of the type,

$$\text{meson+nucleon} \rightarrow (N^* \text{ or } \Delta^*) + S, \text{ and } (N^* \text{ or } \Delta^*) + S'.$$

$$(1. 29)$$

Here the assumption is again that this reaction process involves interaction with only one quark in the mesonic system. This assumption is particularly plausible for processes of peripheral character, which are dominated by some simple meson exchange; also, it is a particular application of the "additivity assumption" that the complete reaction amplitude is given by the sum of the reaction amplitudes for each quark in the incident and target systems, which has been very successful in describing the relationships between high-energy collision cross-sections. [29-31] The statement that the amplitude for $\pi N \rightarrow (N^* \text{ or } \Delta^*) + (\bar{\lambda}\lambda)$ is zero leads to relationships analogous to (1. 27). Some preliminary determinations have been reported for the L=0 cases by Benson et al. [32] and by Lai and Schumann[33].

(iii) For the vector meson states, a determination of θ is possible[34,35] from measurements of the absolute decay rates for $\emptyset \to e^+e^-$ and $\omega \to e^+e^-$. This depends on the natural expectation that these processes arise through the direct electromagnetic couplings $\emptyset \to \gamma$ and $\omega \to \gamma$, followed by internal pair conversion. It depends on the SU(3) requirement that there should be no coupling $\omega_1 \to \gamma$ for the unitary singlet ω_1; with Eq. (1.22) (ω corresponds to S', $\emptyset$ to S), this leads to the expectation for the amplitudes

$$f(\omega \to \gamma)/f(\emptyset \to \gamma) = \tan \theta. \tag{1.30}$$

We note that the rate comparison involves $\tan^2 \theta$, so that only $|\theta|$ can be determined. There are now a number of preliminary measurements for these rates[36,37], but these allow only an exceedingly rough estimate for $|\theta|$.

For an ideal nonet, the parameters are related to the observed masses, as follows:

$$m(8)^2 = V^2, \tag{1.31}$$

$$\Delta' = K^2 - V^2, \tag{1.32}$$

where the symbols K, V, .. for the mesonic states are used here to denote the masses appropriate to these states. Since the eigenvalues of the matrix (1.20a) are S^2 and S'^2, we have

$$m(8)^2 + m(1)^2 + 2\Delta' = S^2 + S'^2. \tag{1.33}$$

With Eqs. (1.31) and (1.32), this equation leads to

$$m(1)^2 - m(8)^2 = S^2 + S'^2 - 2K^2. \tag{1.34}$$

Finally, we have the modified Schwinger relation[26], which is essentially an expression for $\mathcal{J}$ in terms of the observed meson masses,

$$(S'^2-V^2)\ (S^2-V^2)-\frac{4}{3}\ (K^2-V^2)\ (S^2+S'^2-2K^2)$$

$$=\frac{8}{9}\ (K^2-V^2)^2\ (1-\mathcal{J}^2) \tag{1.35}$$

From the fact that the states (1.22) diagonalize the (mass)^2 matrix (1.20a), we deduce a further expression for $\mathcal{J}$ in terms of the mixing angle θ,

$$\mathcal{J} = \frac{3}{4\sqrt{2}}\ .\ \ \sin 2\theta.\ \ \frac{S^2 - S'^2}{K^2 - V^2}\ . \tag{1.36}$$

The compatibility of Eqs. (1.35) and (1.36) for $\mathcal{J}$ provides the only constraint predicted for the observable properties of the mesons belonging to a given ideal nonet.

For a non-ideal nonet, exemplified perhaps by the S=0 nonets, where the space wavefunctions $\emptyset\ (\{1\})$ and $\emptyset\ (\{8\})$ can be quite different, the general (mass)^2 expressions (1.18) include a large number of unknown terms. With such a general model for SU(3)-breaking in the $\bar{q}q$ systems, no useful analysis is possible. However, we have emphasized above the possibility that the relation $\emptyset\,(\,\{8\})\approx\emptyset\,(\,\{\;1\,\})$ might well hold even for the case S=0, if the octet and singlet masses are sufficiently close, and it will always be worthwhile to consider the analysis of the observed properties of an S=0 nonet first on the assumption that the states represent an ideal nonet.

The simplest of all possibilities is the case discussed by many workers in the past, which we may refer to as an "SU(6)-nonet", where the unitary spin-dependent interactions are neglected, and the only SU(3)-breaking interaction considered is that due to the one-body operator Δ. Then we have $m(8) = m(1)$ and $\mathfrak{g} = 1$. The (mass)^2 eigenvalues for (1.20) are then $m(8)^2$ and $m(8)^2 + 2\Delta$, which correspond to the states S' and S, respectively. For this SU(6)-nonet case, these eigenstates have the form

$$|S') = (\bar{p}p + \bar{n}n)/\,2, \tag{1.37a}$$

$$|S) = \bar{\lambda}\lambda. \tag{1.37b}$$

As mentioned above, following Eq. (1.23), these eigenstates have the forms (1.22) with mixing angle θ_0, given by Eq. (1.23). These eigenvalues correspond to the SU(6) mass relations given by Schwinger[26] and others,

$$S'^2 = V^2, \tag{1.38a}$$

$$S^2 + S'^2 = 2K^2 . \tag{1.38b}$$

We should mention here one important distinction between these
states S and S', which follows from the discussion about
transition amplitudes given above, just after Eq. (1.22). The
S state (1.37b) does not allow any π-emission decay transition,
both because the π-meson does not couple to a λ quark, and
because this transition can lead only to a final state $\pi + V$,
which would involve a two-quark interaction $(\bar{\lambda}\lambda) \rightarrow V$. Decay
processes leading to the states $\bar{K}K$ (if the parity P satisfies
the relation $P = (-1)^J$), $\bar{K}K^*$ and $K\bar{K}^*$, are the natural
expectation for the S state (1.37b); decay processes of the
form $\pi\pi$, πV, or ρV are expected to occur for the S state
only through its deviation from the SU(6) form (1.37b). On the
other hand, the decay modes $\pi + V$ and $\rho + V$ are the modes
naturally expected to be prominent for the S' state (1.37a),
although decay modes of the form $K\bar{K}$, $K\bar{K}^*$, $K^*\bar{K}$, etc.
can also occur from this state. We shall see below that the
low-lying nonet of vector mesons provides an example of an
"SU(6)-nonet", to a good first approximation. For this nonet,
the ϕ meson represents the S state (1.37b), and illustrates
the above remarks quite nicely. The dominant decay mode
for the ϕ meson is $K\bar{K}$, but the decay mode $\pi\rho$ is also
observed to occur owing to the deviation of the mixing angle θ
from the value θ_o appropriate to an SU(6) nonet.

2.   THE OBSERVED MESONIC NONETS.

The L=0+ States.   The isospin submultiplets of the vector meson and pseudoscalar meson nonets, corresponding to the n=1 configurations $^3S_1$ and $^1S_0$ are well known, as listed in Table II.

The vector meson nonet has the structure of an SU(6)-nonet, as expected.   The singlet and octet (mass)^2 values are 0.643 and 0.585 (GeV)^2, quite comparable in magnitude. The conventional mass values[38] do not quite fit the Schwinger mass equality (but there is uncertainty what mass values to use, for resonances as broad as the ρ-meson); they require $\mathcal{J}$ = 1.04, strikingly close to unity.   The mixing angle θ obtained from the mass values is 39.4°, close to the SU(6)-nonet value θ_0 and in good agreement with the value obtained above from the comparison of the rates $\emptyset \rightarrow \rho\pi$ and $\omega \rightarrow 3\pi$. The ρ and ω mass values differ by only 2%, in good agreement with Eq. (1.38a), and the relation (1.38b) is satisfied to 4% accuracy.

The pseudoscalar mesons do not form an SU(6)-nonet. For this case, the singlet and octet (mass)^2 values differ widely, being 0.75 and 0.02 (GeV)^2, respectively.   The parameter $\mathcal{J}$ differs significantly from unity, with value about 0.5, and the mixing angle has magnitude 10° only (note that the sign of θ cannot be determined from the mass values;   the negative sign given on Table IV is that required by the quark model). This contrast with the $^3S_1$ case is certainly of the kind expected with SU(6)-invariant superstrong interactions. What is surprising, from this standpoint, is the substantial (mass)^2 difference between the S=0 and S=1 octet states; the SU(6)-singlet state η' has mass much closer to the mean mass of the $^3S_1$ nonet, than does the $^1S_0$ octet state. This π-ρ mass difference requires that there be moderate SU(6)-breaking spin-spin forces with just such σ- and F-dependence as to pull the $^1S_0$ octet mass down while leaving the $^1S_0$ singlet mass close to that characteristic of the SU(6) 35-representation with L=0+.

We note that the SU(3)-breaking interaction specified by Δ' has essentially the same value for the S=0 and S=1 configurations, the equality

$$K^2 - \pi^2 = K^{*2} - \rho^2 \qquad\qquad (2.1)$$

being satisfied, to about 7% accuracy. We conclude that there is no real indication for spin-dependence in the SU(3)-breaking interactions, a conclusion that would follow automatically from dominance of the one-body terms.

A tenth pseudoscalar meson has become strongly identified in the past year, the E(1424) meson, especially from the work of Montanet et al.[39]. The E-meson is produced in the reaction $\bar{p}p \to \pi^+\pi^- E$, and it is seen rather strongly in the decay mode $E \rightarrow K_1^0 K_1^0 \pi^0$, which implies $C = +1$ for the E-meson, as is appropriate for the configuration $^1S_0$. There is clearly some question whether this E-meson might be the ninth pseudoscalar meson, rather than η' (958). The strongest argument for η' (958) to be (0-) comes from the observation of the angular correlation $\sin^2 \theta$ for the ρ decay relative to the photon in the decay process $\eta' \rightarrow \rho\gamma$. However, it has been pointed out by Ogievetsky and Zaslavsky[40] that, with spin 1+ for η' (a possibility pointed out in ref. 2), this radiative transition could occur by E1 and M2 transitions; the M2 transition automatically leads to a $\sin^2 \theta$ distribution, so that the observed distribution would follow for η' spin (1+) if the M2 transition were dominant. This is a serious possibility, even though we are accustomed to think of the M2 transition as forbidden relative to an E1 transition, since the quarks are required to have a large anomalous magnetic moment (in order to account for the proton magnetic moment in the qqq model for the baryons). This possibility needs to be looked into more quantitatively. On the other hand, the simplest interpretation of the energy distributions for the decay process $\eta' \rightarrow \eta\pi\pi$ leads directly to the assignment (0-) for the η' meson, although it may be possible to obtain the observed distributions also for η' spin (1+) if the $\pi\pi$ interaction at low energies had a suitable energy dependence (cf. ref. 41). Although the most probable interpretation for these η' decay data is that η' is pseudoscalar, it is worth remarking here that this lingering possibility of spin (1+) for η' would be finally excluded by any observation of the decay process,

$$\eta' \; (958) \; \to \; \gamma + \gamma \; . \tag{2.2}$$

Quite generally, this decay process is forbidden for any meson with spin J=1, by the constraints imposed by conservation of angular momentum and parity and by Bose statistics for photons[42]. If η' (958) is the ninth pseudoscalar meson, then the decay process (2.2) is expected to have quite a strong rate[43], the calculated branching ratio being $\Gamma(\eta' \to \gamma\gamma)/\Gamma(\eta') \approx 2\%$. Direct observation of this $\gamma\gamma$ process for η' (958) would therefore be of much value at this point, to rule out decisively the possibility of spin (1+) for this meson.

The only interpretation available for the tenth pseudoscalar meson is that it belongs to the first (n=2) radial excitation for the $^1S_0$ nonet. With a harmonic $\bar{q}q$ potential, the n=2 S-states would be expected to occur at the same mass as the L=2+ nonets, in the region of the R-meson cluster, about 1600-1700 MeV. It is quite possible that an I=0 state of the n=2 $^1S_0$ nonet could lie as low as 1400 MeV, but there are

Config.	$(J, P)^C$	V	K	S'	S
$^3S_1$	$(1-)^-$	$\rho(765)$	$K^*(893)$	$\omega(783)$	$\phi(1019)$
$^1S_0$	$(0-)^+$	$\pi(138)$	$K(496)$	$\eta'(958)$	$\eta(549)$
$^3P_2$	$(2+)^+$	$A_{2u}(1319)$	$K^*(1419)$	$f(1263)$	$f'(1514)$
$^3P_1$	$(1+)^+$	$A_1(1070)$	$K^*(1230)$	$D'(?)$	$D(1285)$
$^3P_0$	$(0+)^+$	$\delta(962)$	$K\pi(\approx 1100)$	?	$S^*(1060)$
$^1P_1$	$(1+)^-$	$B(1220)$	$K^*(1320)$	?	?
Outstanding		$A_{1.5}(1170)$			$E(1424)$
States		$A_{2\ell}(1295)$			

Table II. Each of the established mesons, with mass below about 1500 MeV, is assigned to the nonet appropriate to the evidence on its spin-parity. Four states in the L=0+ and L=1- nonets lack any candidates in the empirical data. Three outstanding states in this mass region are also listed, for which there is no definite nonet assignment yet.

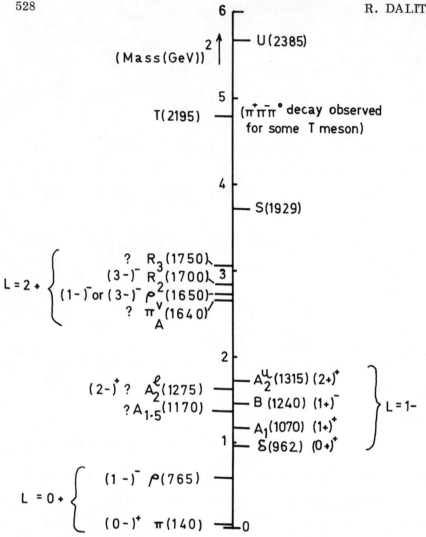

Fig. 2. (Mass)^2 is plotted for all the I=1, Y=0 mesonic states for which there is good evidence. The meson parameters (JP)^C are given where known. Negative-parity states are placed on the left, positive-parity states on the right; where parity is unknown, the state is placed as expected from the quark model. The plot shows some indication for bands of mesonic states which alternate in parity with increasing (mass)^2.

no indications yet for other $^1S_0$ mesons in this mass region, although there are a number of outstanding levels not yet identified (see Table II).

The L=1- States.   Here the S=1 states are expected to be split into three nonets, corresponding to the configurations $^3P_2$, $^3P_1$ and $^3P_0$, by the non-central interactions.   SU(6) symmetry requires also an S=0 octet, with the possibility of an SU(6) singlet state with configuration $^1P_1$ to make a further nonet.   The mesonic states which are believed to have these spin-parity values are listed together in Table II.

We begin by considering the I=1 state from each nonet.   These states give directly the octet mass m(8) for each nonet, and hence a direct indication of the nature of the octet non-central interaction.   The contributions to (mass)^2 for the configurations $^{(2S+1)}L_J$ are given in Table III for spin-orbit and tensor interactions.   The first question is which I=1 states to accept.

Configuration	$^3L_{L-1}$	^3L_L	^1L_L	$^3L_{L+1}$
Spin-orbit	-(L+1)	-1	0	+L
Tensor	(L+1)/(2L-1)	-1	0	L/(2L+3)

Table III.   The coefficients of the contribution to (mass)^2 for non-central interactions of spin-orbit and tensor form are tabulated for the configurations $^{(2S+1)}L_J$.

The A_2 meson has been found by Chikovani et al.[44]
to consist of two peaks, the $A_{2\mu}$ at 1319 MeV and $A_{2\ell}$ at
1290 MeV, and this result has now been confirmed in
another missing-mass spectrometer experiment by Baud
et al.[45] and in a bubble-chamber experiment by Crennell
et al.[46]. Also, Morrison[47] has considered the momentum-
transfer and energy dependence of the cross section for
$\rho\pi$ (1300) production, and compared it with that for the
corresponding $K\pi$ (1420) production. The flatness of the
$\rho\pi$ (1300) production as function of p_L (like $p_L^{-0.5}$) suggests that this state is produced diffractively and therefore
has spin-parity in the series (0-), (1+), (2-),.. ; on the other
hand, the decay mode $A_2 \rightarrow K\overline{K}$ (especially $K_1^0 K_1^0$) is well-
known (and allows only spin-parity in the series (0+), (2+),
(4+)...) and the $K\pi$ (1420) production cross section falls
rapidly with p_L (like $p_L^{-2.2}$). Spin-parity analyses for
the $\rho\pi$ (1300) state have indicated the possibility (2+),
and the possibility (2-) or (1+) (the data do exclude (0-)),
under different production conditions. These conclusions fit
together if there are two $\rho\pi$ resonances near 1300 MeV,
one with spin-parity (2+) (corresponding to the mode $K_1^0 K_1^0$,
and to the K*(1420) $\rightarrow$ $K\pi$ mode) produced prominently at
high momentum transfer (and with σ_{tot} falling rapidly with
p_L) and the other with spin-parity (2-) or (1+), produced
most prominently for small momentum transfer at high
energies, as appropriate for a diffractive process.

Since the mode $K_1^0 K_1^0$ appears to be associated with a higher mean mass than that for the $\rho\pi(1300)$ bump, we shall identify the upper A_2 peak, $A_{2\mu}$ (1319), with the (2+) nonet.

The B-meson has recently been shown very clearly in the reaction

$$\pi^- p \rightarrow p \pi^- \omega, \qquad\qquad (2.3)$$

studied at 5 GeV/c by Ascoli et al.[48]. Its observed characteristics fit well the assignment (1+) (but also fit (2+), (3-), etc.); with this assignment, the decay $B \rightarrow \pi\omega$ involves both s- and d-wave pion emission, since the angular correlation between the pion direction and the normal to the ω decay plane was found to be $\sin^2\chi$ (although isotropy disagrees only by 2.7 standard deviations). The $A_1(1070)$ meson is now considered established, most probably with spin-parity (1+), as is compatible with the diffractive nature of its production process (the feature which has given so much confusion with the diffractive Deck mechanism for production of a final $\rho\pi$ state in πp interactions at high energy). However, one of the experiments which shows the A_1 meson most clearly also shows a peak at 1170 MeV[49], which has become named $A_{1.5}$. It seems probable that $A_{1.5} \rightarrow \rho\pi$ is a strong decay mode for this meson, but otherwise very little is known of its properties. For the present, we shall have to omit this meson from consideration; there appears no direct place for it.

The $\underline{\delta(962) \text{ meson}}$ was discovered in the missing

mass experiments of Kienzle et al. [14]. It has recently been

detected also in K^-p reactions at 6 GeV/c by the BNL-

Syracuse group [50], who conclude that it has the decay mode

$\delta \rightarrow \eta\pi$, but that this is not the only decay mode (another

possible decay mode is $\delta^- \rightarrow \rho^-\gamma$). However, this is

sufficient to establish its spin-parity as in the series (0+),

(1-), (2+) . . . , and it is clear that the assignment (0+) is

the only possible assignment consistent with the quark model.

There has also been evidence given by Astier et al. [51] for an

I=1, s-wave enhancement in the $K\overline{K}$ system near threshold.

This can be interpreted as either (i) a $K\overline{K}(1016)$ resonance

with spin-parity (0+) and G = -1, or (ii) as a threshold

scattering effect associated with strong coupling of the $K\overline{K}$

system to the I=1 resonance $\delta(962)$. With the latter inter-

pretation, the scattering length required by the data is given

by ReA = -2.3 fm and ImA = $0^{+0.5}_{-0.0}$ fm; these parameters are

consistent with the existence of an s-wave virtual bound state

at 975^{+15}_{-10} MeV, with narrow width ($\Gamma < 5$ MeV, empirically),

features which are consistent with the resonance $\delta(962)$. For

economy, we shall identify the $K\overline{K}$ enhancement with the

δ-meson and assign these to spin-parity (0+).

From the parameters listed in Table IV, we see the $(mass)^2$-splitting for the L=1- octet states is as follows:

$$(m^2(^3P_2)-m^2(^3P_1))/(m^2(^3P_1)-m^2(^3P_0)) = 2.7, \qquad (2.4)$$

to be compared with the expected values (cf. Table III) of +2 for spin-orbit, and -2/5 for tensor interaction. We conclude that the octet non-central interaction is dominantly of spin-orbit form.

We note that the B-meson, assigned to the $^1P_1$ configuration, lies roughly mid way between $A_{2\mu}$ and A_1, as would be the case with SU(6)-symmetry, broken only by an SU(3)-invariant spin-orbit interaction and spin-independent SU(3)-breaking effects. This is in contrast with the situation for L=0+, where the S=0 octet state lies 0.56 $(GeV)^2$ lower in $(mass)^2$ than the S=1 octet state. However it is conceivable that this spin-spin interaction may be of short range and therefore ineffective in configurations with L ≥ 1.

The attractive picture which emerges from the above remarks is that SU(6) symmetry may hold for the L=1 states, to a very good approximation. In this approximation, the ^3P nonets and the ^1P octet would be degenerate in mass (with an SU(6) singlet $^1P_1$ state whose mass value might not be far different), apart from the effects of the spin-orbit interactions

and the SU(3)-breaking interactions. The spin-orbit
interactions will generally depend on the unitary spin F^2, so that

$$m^2 (\{\alpha\}) = m_0^2(\{\alpha\}) + a(\{\alpha\})\underline{L}.\underline{S} \qquad (2.5)$$

where m_0^2 is independent of J (and independent of α in the
SU(6) approximation), and the coefficient $a(\{\alpha\})$ may be
expected to be different for the octet and singlet states. This
assumes that no tensor interaction is effective in the unitary
singlet states. We must now enquire the extent to which the
empirical data now on the L=1- nonets gives support to this
simple picture.

The (2+) Nonet states are listed on Table II, and the nonet
parameters are given in Table IV. Their conventional mass
values[38] do not satisfy the Schwinger equality (1.35) with
$\mathcal{J}^2 = 1$. They actually require $\mathcal{J} = 1.2$, a value possible only
if there are SU(3)-breaking $\bar{q}q$ potentials; however, the value
for $\mathcal{J}$ is sensitive to the mass values used ($\mathcal{J} = 1.02$ holds if
the A_2 mass is taken as 1305 MeV, for example). The
mixing angle θ is not sensitive to the mass values, and lies
quite close to the SU(6)-nonet value. The value of Δ' is about
20% larger than that for L=0+, which again points to $\bar{q}q$
SU(3)-breaking potentials. The singlet and octet masses lie
quite close, with $m^2(8) = 1.74$ and $m^2(1) = 1.60$; the
f(1263) meson lies close in mass with $A_2(1319)$, and the
f'(1514) mass is quite well given by the SU(6)-nonet

Nonet parameters	$m(8)^2$ $(\text{GeV})^2$	$m(1)^2$ $(\text{GeV})^2$	Δ' $(\text{GeV})^2$	$\mathcal{I}$	θ°
$^3S_1$	0.585	0.643	0.212	1.04	39.4°
$^1S_0$	0.019	0.916 (1.86)	0.227	0.52 (0.87)	-10.5° (-6.2°)
$^3P_2$	1.740 (1.703)	1.603	0.272 (0.309)	1.2 (1.02)	31.5° (30.3)
$^3P_1$	1.145	(1.01?)	(0.272)	1.0	(29°)
$^3P_0$	0.925	1.66?	(0.272)	1.23?	24°?
$^1P_1$	1.513	?	0.28	?	–

Table IV. The parameters $m(8), m(1), \Delta', \mathcal{I}$ and θ for each of the L=0+ and L=1- nonets. The bracketed entries for $^1S_0$ correspond to the assumption that the ninth meson is E(1420). The bracketed entries for the $^3P_2$ configuration correspond to the use of the mean mass for the two A_2 peaks, 1305 MeV, as the A_2 mass. The underlined entries are assumed values. For the $^3P_1$ nonet, the bracketed entries correspond to the assumptions $\Delta' = 0.272 (\text{GeV})^2$ and the Schwinger equality for $\mathcal{I}^2 = 1$. For the $^3P_0$ nonet, the queried entries correspond to the assumption that the ninth $(1+)^+$ meson has mass 1410 MeV.

relation (1. 38b). Glashow and Socolow examined the partial decay
rates for all the (2+) nonet mesons several years ago[1,27],
and found that the overall fit to the relationships required by
SU(3)-symmetry for a nonet was good.   There was one outstanding feature of these decay processes, that the SU(3)-
parameters appeared accidentally to be just such that the
amplitude (f' → $\pi\pi$) was very small.   We now understand that
this was not an accidental cancellation, but an expression of
the SU(6)-nonet structure for the (2+) states; the state f' is
quite well given by the form (1. 37b).

The (0+) Nonet states are listed on Table II.   The K-state
has been identified with the $K\pi$ resonance in the region 1000-
1200 MeV conjectured by Schlein[52] on the basis of a phase-shift
analysis of $K\pi$ elastic scattering deduced from data on
peripheral processes involving the one-pion-exchange transition K → $K\pi$; the indications for this broad K resonance are
weak and we include this state here only because it does bear
a reasonable mass relationship with δ (962).   The S*(1070)
meson is known mainly in the mode $K_1^0 K_1^0$.   Evidence for a $\pi\pi$
resonance at 1080 MeV has recently been reported by
Whitehead et al.[53], and it appears reasonable to identify this
also with the S* meson (although the authors consider this
unlikely); the $\pi\pi/K\bar{K}$ branching ratio is not really known, but
the general opinion is that this is certainly less than 2.

We consider now where the nonet model would predict the ninth scalar meson to lie. We adopt the value $(K^2-V^2) = 0.272$ $(GeV)^2$, as holds for the $^3P_2$ nonet; this would place the (0+) K-state at 1095 MeV. We note that $S*(1070)$ lies below $((4K^2-V^2)/3)^{1/2} = 1135$ MeV, so that the second S state is required to lie high in mass. The Schwinger relation (1.35) requires its mass to be given by

$$S^2 = V^2 + \frac{4}{3} \Delta' - \frac{8}{9} \Delta'^2 \, \mathfrak{f}^2/(S*^2 - V^2 - \frac{4}{3} \Delta'). \qquad (2.6)$$

With $\mathfrak{f}^2=1$, this expression leads to the mass value 1325 MeV. It is of interest to note that there has been some evidence, put forward by Bettini et al.[54], for the existence of an I=0 (0+) meson at 1410 MeV (width $\Gamma \approx 90$ MeV), with decay mode $\rho\rho$. If we assume this state to be the ninth scalar meson, then we would conclude $\mathfrak{f} = 1.23$ and mixing angle $\theta = 24^o$. We should note that this interpretation would mean that the meson $S(1410)$ would have $\bar{\lambda}\lambda$ structure, so that its dominant decay mode would be predicted to be $(K*(891) \bar{K}*(891))$; with a mixing angle so far from the value θ_o, the decay mode $\rho\rho$ could be quite strong, although far from dominant. It would therefore be of much interest to look for this $S(1410)$ resonance in the systems $K_1^0 K_1^0 \pi^+ \pi^-$ and $K^+ K^- \pi^+ \pi^-$, following reactions such as $\bar{p}n \rightarrow K\bar{K}\pi\pi$.

There has been much discussion in recent years of the possibility of an I=0 scalar σ-meson, with s-wave decay mode $\sigma \to \pi\pi$ and with mass which has been estimated to lie at various values between 350 MeV to 900 MeV from the analyses of a wide variety of experimental data. The only comment about this meson is that the σ-meson and the S*(1070) can only be fitted in the same nonet by a very gross deviation from the nonet regularities, as observed to date and as expected from SU(6)-symmetry; even with a high mass value, say $m(\sigma) = 700$ MeV, which is the most favorable situation, this nonet identification would require a value for Δ' as low as $0.14(\text{GeV})^2$, and $m^2(1) = 0.44(\text{GeV})^2$.

The (1+) Nonets correspond to the $^3P_1$ and $^1P_1$ states. These have opposite charge conjugation parities, C= +1 for $^3P_1$ and C= -1 for $^1P_1$. This means that there is no mixing between these nonets for the non-strange submultiplets; this is forbidden by C-parity conservation for the I=0 states, and by G-parity conservations for the I=1 states. However, the two K* states can undergo mixing by SU(3)-breaking interactions[56-58]; the simplest C-invariant $\bar{q}q$ potential which can mix these states is an antisymmetric spin-orbit term

$$b_{S0} = Y(\underline{\sigma} - \underline{\bar{\sigma}}). \, Ly(r), \qquad (2.7)$$

where Y denotes the total hypercharge of the $\bar{q}q$ state considered. If K_A and K_B denote the masses of the $^3P_1$ and $^1P_1$ K* states, then the mixed physical states will have masses given by

$$K^2 = \frac{1}{2}\left\{K_A^2 + K_B^2 \pm \left(K_A^2 - K_B^2\right)^2 + 4\epsilon^2\right)^{\frac{1}{2}}\right\}, \qquad (2.8)$$

where ϵ is the matrix-element for the (mass)^2 operator between the states K_A and K_B. The physical effects of such K* mixing have been discussed in detail by Goldhaber[57]; we shall not consider these further here, except to remark that interference between these two states in their decay to $K\pi\pi$, and between them and the diffractive K*π background, is the likely cause of the confusion which exists at present concerning the mass values for the K resonances in the mass region 1100–1400 MeV.

   If we take the value $\Delta' = 0.27(\text{GeV})^2$ obtained from the $^3P_2$ nonet as a guide for the $^3P_1$ and $^1P_1$ nonets (this involves supposing that the SU(3)-breaking potentials have no large non-central component), then the K* states (denoted by K_A and K_B, respectively) corresponding to the A_1 and B mesons would be expected to lie at masses 1190 and 1336 MeV, respectively. Any K_A-K_B mixing would push these two mass values further apart, as indicated by Eq. (2.8). The physical mass values are generally estimated[38] as being in the range

1230-1260 MeV for K_A (in agreement with the C-meson mass, as reported from $\bar{p}p \to \bar{K}K\pi\pi$ studies for some years) and 1320-1360 MeV for K_B.

The ninth (D') state is not known for the $^3P_1$ nonet. If we assume an ideal nonet structure, with $\Delta' = 0.272$ $(GeV)^2$ as for the $^3P_2$ nonet and $\mathcal{g}^2=1$, then the Schwinger equality (2.6) predicts that the D'-meson mass should be at 1025 MeV. With this ninth state, the $(1+)^+$ mesons have the appearance of an SU(6)-nonet, since the A_1 and D' masses then lie quite close together. Also, the D-state does decay strongly into strange particles, as expected for the upper isospin singlet of an SU(6)-nonet. The D-meson has width 32 ± 8 MeV, with dominant decay modes $K\bar{K}^*$ and $\bar{K}K^*$ (actually the D mass lies below the $K\bar{K}^*$ threshold (1380 MeV), but it is clear that the decay involves a p-wave $K\pi$ system, effectively the tail of the K^* resonance). A D'(1025) meson would lie far below all the thresholds for the modes (pseudoscalar-meson + vector-meson) allowed by the selection rules. The only three-body decay mode allowed by energy conservation and selection rules is $D' \to \eta\,\pi\pi$; the threshold for $\rho\pi\pi$ is at 1045 MeV, but the ρ-meson could still influence strongly a decay mode $D' \to 4\pi$, allowed by the selection rules. Otherwise, there is the possibility of radiative decay; with the selection rules for electro-magnetic transitions, as discussed by Feinberg and Pais[59], the decay processes allowed are

$D' \to \rho\gamma$ and $\omega\gamma$. In fact, the decay processes permitted are very like those observed for $X°(958)$, and this has led to the question whether $X°(958)$ might not be the missing D' meson[2], as mentioned briefly in our discussion above about the identification of the X^O as the $\eta'(958)$ meson. As we concluded there, the most direct interpretations for the decay modes observed for $X^O(958)$ do point to spin-parity $(0-)$. However, the possibility of a $(1+)^+$ meson in this mass region, with rather similar decay properties, could cause some confusion and so needs to be kept in mind. If the D' meson did have mass 958 MeV, this would lead to $\mathcal{f} = 1.14$, mixing angle $\theta = 27.5°$, and $m(1)^2 = 0.880(\text{GeV})^2$, still quite close to an SU(6)-nonet structure.

The $I=Y=0$ states (H and H') for the $^1P_1$ nonet are not yet known. If the $^1P_1$ states were actually an octet, the Gell-Mann-Okubo mass formula would indicate mass about 1370 MeV for the eighth state (which we shall name H' here); its strong decay modes would be $\pi\rho$ and $K\overline{K}^*$ (and $\overline{K}K^*$). The only evidence for such a resonance in this mass region is for the $K\overline{K}\pi$ mode, the $E(1424)$ meson. This possibility for the E-meson has been considered carefully by Baillon et al.[39] who concluded that spin-parity $(1+)$ gives a very poor fit to the data. They consider that the main decay mode is $E \to \delta(962)\pi$, which implies $G = +1$ for $E(1424)$ - this

is also required by their observation of the decay mode
$E \rightarrow K_1^0 K_1^0 \pi^0$, which implies $C = +1$- however, the $^1P_1$ assignment
would require $C = G = -1$. The meson H(990) for which evidence
has been reported by a number of groups in the past, would have
the appropriate quantum numbers, as the decay mode reported
was $\pi\rho$ and the decay distribution was consistent with spin (1+);
however, Barbaro-Galtieri and Soding[60] have discounted much of
this evidence, owing to the possibility of confusion with the decay
process $\eta' \rightarrow \rho\gamma$. If there <u>were</u> an H-meson at 990 MeV, then the
Schwinger equality (2.6) would require the H' meson to lie a little
higher in mass, at about 1400 MeV (with $\delta^2 = 0$ instead of $\delta^2 = 1$,
this mass falls only to the GMO value, 1370 MeV); the mixing
angle θ would then be 16° (for $\delta^2 = 1$, falling to 0° for $\delta^2 = 0$).
In this case, the nonet would differ a great deal from an SU(6)-
nonet, since $m(1)^2 \approx 0.87 (GeV)^2$ is quite far from $m(8)^2 = 1.51$
$(GeV)^2$ (which would be in marked contrast with the L=0+ SU(6)
singlet, where m(1) lies well above m(8)), and θ is quite far from
the SU(6)-nonet value $\theta_0 = 35.3°$.

Our hope was that the unitary singlet masses m(1) should
show a J-dependence appropriate to a spin-orbit coupling. At
present, the estimates given above for $m(1)^2$ assuming the nonet
for each spin-parity to follow an ideal-nonet structure are as
follows:

$(JP)^C$	$(2+)^+$	$(1+)^-$	$(1+)^+$	$(0+)^+$	
$m(1)^2 =$	1.60	(0.87?)	(1.01)	(1.66)	$(GeV)^2$
$m(8)^2 =$	1.74	1.49	1.15	0.92	$(GeV)^2$

The $m(1)^2$ entry for $(1+)^-$ is completely speculative; those for $(1+)^+$ and $(0+)^+$ depend on the use of the Schwinger equality (2.6) (with $\mathcal{J}^2 = 1$). The $m(1)^2$ values given do not suggest any simple interpretation, such as a unitary singlet spin-orbit force. We can only conclude that at present we have too little information about the I=Y=0 members of these nonets; from our present point of view, there must exist a $(1+)^+$ D'-meson, a $(1+)^-$ H'-meson (and probably H-meson, also), and another $(0+)^+$ S-meson, still to be established uniquely. The I=Y=0 states are clearly more difficult to detect and study than the I=1, Y=0 states plotted on Fig. 2. There are expected to be twice as many I=Y=0 mesonic resonances as I=1, Y=0 resonances, and the production reactions convenient for the I=Y=0 mesons (such as $\pi^+ n \to pM^0$) also produce the $I_3=0$ component of each I=1, Y=0 resonance. There is need for far more investigation of the I=Y=0 mesonic systems at the present stage.

Decay Widths for the L=1- Mesons. It is convenient to adopt a
crude model for the calculation of the partial decay widths for
the mesons, in which the outgoing pseudoscalar meson P is treated as an external field coupled to the quarks. This coupling may
be written in the form

$$f_q \sum_i (\bar{q} \underline{\sigma} F_i q) \cdot \underline{p}_\pi \phi_i, \tag{2.9}$$

where the sum i is over the octet of pseudo-scalar mesons, with
F_i denoting the unitary spin operator. This model really just
provides an explicit means for the calculation of the Clebsch-
Gordan coefficients which relate the various decay amplitudes;
it has been pointed out by Lipkin[61] that these Clebsch-Gordan
coefficients are just those of the $SU(6)_W$ group. The transitions
we have to consider here correspond to amplitudes of the form

$$(P \mid (\underline{\sigma} \cdot \underline{k} e^{i\underline{k} \cdot \underline{r}/2} \pm \underline{\bar{\sigma}} \cdot \underline{k} e^{-i\underline{k} \cdot \underline{r}/2}) \mid S), \tag{2.10}$$

where $\underline{\sigma}$ and $\underline{\bar{\sigma}}$ are the q and $\bar{q}$ spins, respectively, $\underline{r}$ denotes the
position vector from $\bar{q}$ to q, and $\underline{k}$ denotes the outgoing meson
momentum. P and S denote the L = 1- and 0+ orbital angular
momentum states, respectively. It is clear that the only part of
$\exp(i\underline{k} \cdot \underline{r}/2)$ which contributes is the part with orbital form $Y_1^m(\underline{r})$,
i.e. $i \underline{k} \cdot \underline{r} (j_1(kr)/2kr)$ - if the mesonic radius is sufficiently small,
the last factor may be replaced by 1/2. We see that all the

amplitudes are therefore proportional to k^2. The usual expectation is that, provided k is sufficiently small (such that $(kR)^2 <$
$(4L+6)$), a transition amplitude is proportional to k^L, where L is
the orbital angular momentum in the final two-body state and R
denotes a typical radius for the initial state. When the transition allows two values L_1 and L_2 for L, the two amplitudes are
generally proportional to $(kR)^{L_1}$ and $(kR)^{L_2}$, respectively, so
that the final state with the lower L is expected to dominate the
transition, at least if (kR) is sufficiently small. Hence, a k^2
dependence is natural for the (2+) decays, such as $A_2 \rightarrow K\overline{K}$,
since the final state is d-wave. For the (1+) decays, such as
$B \rightarrow \pi\omega$, the final L may be 0 or 2, and the natural expectation
would be that the L = 0 wave should be dominant. The (0+) de-
cays, such as $\delta \rightarrow \eta\pi$, are necessarily s-wave, and it is anomalous that their amplitudes should have k^2 dependence. The origin
of this anomalous behavior lies in the fact that these states have
internal angular momentum, whose contribution to the balance
of the orbital angular momentum leads to special constraints on
the forms possible for the transition amplitudes.

The coefficient f_q of the interaction (2.9) can be estimated by comparing the ρ-meson width with the value calculated with this interaction. This brings us to face with a general

difficulty with the quark model at present.   Consider the decay
process $\rho^+ \to \pi^+ \pi^0$.   This may be considered either as the emission of a π^+ quantum in the $^3S_1 \to {}^1S_0$ transition $\rho^+ \to \pi^0$, or as
the emission of a π^0 quantum in the transition $\rho^+ \to \pi^+$.   There
is an asymmetry in the treatment of the two pions which reflects
the static nature of the quark model; in fact, both pions recoil
with relativistic velocity, and neither picture of the decay process
describes the physical situation correctly.   At present, we do
not know to make quantitative allowance for the effects of recoil.
However, the asymmetry still exists even for a decay process
where the recoil is not so large.   For example, the process
$B \to \pi \omega$ may be regarded as the emission of a π quantum in the
$^1P_1 \to {}^3S_1$ transition $B \to \omega$, for which the static approximation is not completely unrealistic; however we can also intro-
duce a coupling $f_\omega (\bar{q} \gamma_\mu q) \omega_\mu$ and regard this decay process
as an ω-quantum emission in the $^1P_1 \to {}^1S_0$ transition $B^i \to \pi$.
Weisskopf and van Royen[62] and Becchi and Morpurgo[63] have
adopted the average of the two prescriptions as a reasonable
compromise estimate for the amplitude in their discussion of
$\rho \to \pi \pi$ decay, and Uretsky[7] has proposed that the prescription
should be adopted quite generally.

With this interaction (2.9) and f_q determined from
ρ -decay, the decay widths for the (2+) mesons may be calculated,
as done by Uretsky.   This depends on a radial integral of the
form $(P \mid \underline{r} \mid S)$, from Eq. (2.10).   When this is chosen to fit the
$f \rightarrow 2\pi$ width (Γ = 120 MeV), the calculation leads to reasonable widths for decay of the (2+) mesons to two pseudoscalar
mesons; for example, Uretsky then finds 3.7 MeV for $\Gamma (A_2 \rightarrow \overline{K}K)$,
to be compared with the experimental value 3 ± 1 MeV.   If we
next consider the (0+) decays, all the parameters are fixed; with
a k^5 dependence for the widths, it is not surprising that the
δ -width should be so small $(\Gamma (\delta) < 5$ MeV), since $k \approx 300$ MeV
for $\delta \rightarrow \eta \pi$ decay compared with $k \approx 600$ MeV for $f \rightarrow \pi\pi$ decay.
The S^* width (≈ 80 MeV) is not unreasonable, since $k \approx 500$ MeV
for $S^* \rightarrow \pi\pi$; however it is surprising that the $K\overline{K}$ mode should be
so strong (partial width > 25 MeV) since only $k \approx 200$ MeV holds
for this.   The $K^* \rightarrow K \pi$ width would be expected to be quite
small,   certainly less than 25 MeV, in contrast with the very
broad resonance (width of order 200 MeV) reported by Schlein[52].

The interaction (2.9) is not the only form possible for
the quark-pseudoscalar meson coupling. In fact, the requirement of Galilean invariance for this interaction would require
that it be supplemented by a term of the form

$$-f_q \sum_i (\overline{q} \, \underline{\sigma} \, F_i \, q) \cdot \frac{\omega \pi}{2M} \, (\underline{p} + \underline{p}') P_i, \qquad (2.11)$$

where $\underline{p}$ and $\underline{p}'$ denote the initial and final momenta for the quark emitting the meson.   This term allows the emission of an s-wave pion in the $\bar{q}q$ transitions $P \rightarrow S$ with an amplitude which approaches a finite limit as the pion momentum $\underline{k} = \underline{p}-\underline{p}'$ approaches zero.   The factor $(\underline{p}+\underline{p}')/2M$ is just the average velocity for the emitting quark, and the indications for non-relativistic internal motion for the quarks within the meson states would suggest that this correction term should be correspondingly small.   The interaction (2.11) would then have a relatively minor effect on the partial width calculations.   Lipkin[64] has recently questioned this conclusion.   The form (2.11) is appropriate for free quarks or for lightly bound quarks, but not necessarily for tightly bound quarks.   For the latter situation, there are arguments which make it appear more reasonable to replace the quark mass by the quark energy; for the mesonic systems this would mean replacing M by $E/2$, where E is the meson mass.   This correction would increase the amplitudes for this s-wave emission by a rather large factor.   The effect of this correction term on the (0+) partial widths has not yet been considered in detail.

For the decay processes leading to "pseudoscalar-meson + vector-meson", it is necessary to introduce further coupling parameters to describe the vector-meson interaction with the quarks; these interactions generally involve two

independent couplings, one corresponding in form to an electric
coupling, the other to a magnetic coupling. We shall not give
details of these calculations (cf. ref. 7). The ρ coupling may be
adjusted to fit $\Gamma(A_2 \rightarrow \rho\pi)$, and the ω coupling to fit $\Gamma(B \rightarrow \omega\pi)$.
These interactions may then be used to calculate the width
$\Gamma(A_1 \rightarrow \rho\pi)$; the result obtained by Uretsky is 8MeV, far below
the experimental estimate of 80 ± 35 MeV; again, the reason
for the small width is its k^5 - dependence ($k \approx 250$ MeV/c for
$A_1 \rightarrow \rho\pi$, compared with $k \approx 400$ MeV/c for $A_2 \rightarrow \rho\pi$).

Uretsky[7] and Lipkin [61] have pointed out that the quark
interaction (2.9) and the internal spin structure specific to the A_1
and B mesons imply that their decay processes should show some
characteristic angular correlation effects. For example, the
amplitude (2.10) appropriate to B $\rightarrow \pi\omega$ has the form
$(^1P_1 \, | \, (\sigma - \bar{\sigma}) \cdot \underline{k} \, \underline{k} \cdot \underline{r} \, | \, ^3S_1)$, which leads directly to a transition
amplitude such that

$$\underline{B} \rightarrow \underline{k} \, \underline{k} \cdot \underline{\omega}. \qquad\qquad (2.12)$$

The ω-decay interaction has the form $\underline{\omega} \rightarrow \underline{n}$, where $\underline{n}$ denotes
the vector normal to the plane of the $\omega \rightarrow 3\pi$ decay. Hence, for
B $\rightarrow \pi\omega$ decay, the interaction (2.9) leads to the prediction that
the angular correlation between the outgoing pion direction and
the ω decay plane should have the form $\cos^2 \chi$. We note that the
final state (2.12) may be re-written

$$B_i \rightarrow (k_i k_j - \frac{1}{3}k^2 \delta_{ij}) \, \omega_j + \frac{1}{3} k^2 \, \omega_i. \tag{2.13}$$

The second term describes s-wave pion emission, the first term describes d-wave pion emission; the interaction (2.12) obtained from expression (2.10) therefore corresponds to a definite relation between the s- and d-amplitudes. The corresponding prediction for A_1 decay is

$$A_{1i} \rightarrow \rho_i k^2 - k_i \underline{k} \cdot \underline{\rho} = - (k_i k_j - \frac{1}{3} k^2 \delta_{ij}) \, \rho_j + \frac{2}{3} k^2 \, \rho_i, \tag{2.14}$$

leading to distribution $\sin^2\theta$ for the angle θ between the $\rho \rightarrow 2\pi$ decay direction and the direction of the first pion in the $A_1 \rightarrow \pi \rho$ decay. In the A_1 decay, there are the complications involved in the requirement of Bose statistics for the final pions in the overall $A_1 \rightarrow 3\pi$ decay; The A_1 mass value is such, and the ρ-meson is so broad, that the two ρ-bands overlap strongly in the $A_1 \rightarrow 3\pi$ phase-space plot, and the resulting interference effects distort this angular correlation. However, these complications could be handled in a fairly well-defined way; for the A_1 decay, the real problem is the difficulty of obtaining a clean sample of $A_1 \rightarrow \rho\pi$ decay events, because of the strong $\pi\rho$ background arising from the Deck mechanism.

For B-meson decay, the physical situation is relatively clean; the ω meson is quite narrow in width and the interference effects due to Bose statistics are rather unimportant, in consequence. Recent data reported by Ascoli et al.[48] gives a strong B-meson peak, relatively free from background; the decay angular distribution found for the B-meson was very well fitted by the form $\sin^2 \chi$, in complete contradiction to the prediction $\cos^2 \chi$ discussed above. These authors report that an isotropic fit to this angular distribution is barely tolerable, being off by 2.7 standard deviations. It is possible that the Galilean interaction (2.11) (with 2M replaced by E) may increase the s-amplitude in expression (2.12) quite strongly; this could bring the predicted distribution closer towards isotropy (or beyond) to fit the data. If this s-amplitude were to add a term $\alpha \underline{\omega}$ to expression (2.12), the calculated angular distribution would become

$$\left| \alpha + k^2 \right|^2 - (2k^2 \mathrm{Re}\alpha + k^4) \sin^2 \chi. \tag{2.15}$$

This distribution can agree with the data, but only for a rather limited range for α, in the neighborhood $\alpha \approx -k^2$. As for the total width, the inclusion of this s-emission term would simply mean a re-adjustment of the coupling constant for ω-quark coupling.

For A_1-meson decay, the addition of an s-wave amplitude $\beta \rho_i$ to expression (2.12) would lead to angular distribution

$$\left| \beta + k^2 \right|^2 - (k^4 + 2k^2 \mathrm{Re}\,\beta)\cos^2\chi. \qquad (2.16)$$

Here the π-quark and ρ-quark couplings are fixed from consideration of other decays. A large s-wave amplitude β would increase the calculated width $\Gamma(A_1)$, as required by the data, and would bring the angular distribution (2.16) closer to isotropy. Experimentally, the angular distribution for $A_1 \to \rho\pi$ is not really known, but the experiments which have led to the spin-parity assignment (1+) have generally done so on the basis that the angular distribution is consistent with isotropy.

There are still two outstanding I=1 states in this mass region, as shown on Fig. 2, the $A_{1.5}$-meson at 1170 MeV and $A_{2\ell}$ at 1290 MeV. Both of these states undergo 3π decay, mostly in the $\rho\pi$ configuration. There is a possibility that two negative parity nonets could lie in this mass region, corresponding to the (n=2) $^3S_1$ and (n=2) $^1S_0$ configurations, although they would be expected to occur in the R-meson region, 1600-1700 MeV. Only the $^1S_0$ state can undergo 3π decay, since the I=1 $^3S_1$ states has G = +1. Almost nothing is known about the spin-parity for $A_{1.5}$; Morrison's A_2 studies[47] allow (2-) (or (1+), but the (1+) states available in the quark model are already filled) for the state $A_{2\ell}$, but exclude the possibility (0-). We recall that the E(1424) meson has already been assigned to the (n=2) $^1S_0$ nonet. The spin-parity (0-) is therefore a particularly attractive hypothesis for $A_{2\ell}$, especially as their mass relationship is very appropriate to the S=0 octet expected from SU(6) symmetry (as is found to be the case for the (n=1) $^1S_0$ states), corresponding to the reasonable value

$$\Delta' = \frac{3}{4} (E^2 - A_{2\ell}^2) = 0.27 \ (GeV),^2 \qquad (2.17)$$

so that the exclusion of spin-parity (0-) for $A_{2\ell}$ should be made as firm as possible. The favored possibility of spin-parity (2-) for $A_{2\ell}$ (1290) would indicate assignment to the lowest $^1D_2$ configuration, since the $A_2 \to \rho\pi$ decay observed requires G = -1 and therefore excludes any ^3D configuration. We shall comment on this possibility again in the next chapter.

   With the above situation, the only $\bar{q}q$ state available for the $A_{1.5}$(1170) meson is the I=1 member of the (n=2) $^1S_0$ octet. There is no positive evidence for this, so confirmation of the $A_{1.5}$ state and information on its decay distributions will be of much interest.

   We should add that there is no empirical evidence for any (n=2) $^3S_1$ states in this mass region. The I=0 mesons and the I_3=0 substate for the I=1 meson are all expected to couple directly to the photon (interaction meson $\to \gamma$) quite strongly. In the naive picture, the corresponding amplitude f_n is proportional to $\psi_n(0)$ for the $\bar{q}q$ wavefunction describing the radial excitation n, since the $\bar{q}$ and q must annihilate to give the virtual photon. The amplitude f_n vanishes for $L \geq 1$; for L=0, it is finite, with the following dependence on n:

$$f_n = C \left(\frac{\Gamma(n + \frac{1}{2})}{(4n-1)\, \Gamma(n)} \right)^{1/2} , \qquad (2.18)$$

so that $f_2/f_1 = \sqrt{(9/10)}$. Such states have been sought through the study of the mass spectrum for $\mu^+ \mu^-$ pair production both by photons and pions interacting with complex nuclei[65]. Although the known vector mesons appear clearly in the $\mu^+ \mu^-$ mass spectrum (except for the $\phi(1019)$, which has a small production cross section), no further peaks are found below mass 1500 MeV. Of course, it is not known whether the radially-excited vector mesons are actually produced with appreciable cross section in these collision processes, so that these negative experiments do not exclude the possibility of further vector mesons in this mass region.

3.   HIGHER MESONIC STATES

On Fig. 2, we see a noticeable gap in the $(\text{mass})^2$ spectrum for I=1, Y=0 mesons after the L=1- nonets. The next band of states (the R-meson region) starts at about 2.6 $(\text{GeV})^2$; these states are expected to correspond to the two-quantum excitations, the L=2+ states with n=1 and the L=0+ states with n=2. This requires all the nonets in this band to have negative parity. The nonets which can be expected to occur are as follows:

	$^3D_3$	$^3D_2$	$^3D_1$	$^1D_2$	$2\,^3S_1$	$2\,^1S_0$
$(JP)^C$	$(3-)^-$	$(2-)^-$	$(1-)^-$	$(2-)^+$	$(1-)^-$	$(0-)^+$
G(I=1 state)	+	+	+	−	+	−
Spin-orbit coefficient	+2	−1	−3	0		

Most of our information is about the I=1, Y=0 member of each nonet; the little information we have concerning I=Y=0 states and K* states in this region will be mentioned at the end of this chapter.

The following states appear to be well established in detail:

(i)   g-meson $\equiv \rho_V(1650)$.

This was first seen in the reactions[66] $\pi^\pm p \to pg^\pm$; its decay mode is $g \to \pi\pi$, its total width about 120 MeV. Its spin-parity

value is limited to the series (1-), (3-),.. The $g \to \pi\pi$ angular
distribution does not agree well with any of these possibilities
(probably because of background events); from the narrow width
of the forward peak in $d\sigma/d\Omega$, the authors favour spin-parity
(3-), but (1-) does not appear to be completely excluded.

(ii) π_A(1640) meson.

This meson (total width about 100 MeV) is observed in the 3π
states for the reactions $\pi^{\pm} p \to p \pi^{\pm} \pi^{+} \pi^{-}$. Its total production
cross section does not fall with increasing pion momentum up
to 20 GeV/c; this suggests that it is produced by a diffractive
process, hence that its spin-parity is limited to the series
(0-), (1+), (2-),.. (this is the meaning of the suffix A, which
stands for the "abnormal parity" series). Just two of the
states listed above have G=-1 and "abnormal parity", the $^{1}D_{2}$
and the $(n=2)^{1}S_{0}$ states. It is believed that the decay mode

$$\pi_A(1640) \to f\pi \tag{3.1}$$

is quite strong, with branching ratio $40 \pm 20\%$ relative to all
$\pi^{\pm} \pi^{+} \pi^{-}$ modes. This high branching ratio can readily be
understood if π_A(1640) has spin-parity (2-), since the transition (3.1) can then occur with s-wave pion emission (spin-parity
(0-) would require d-wave pion emission and the c.m. momentum for this decay is only 300 MeV/c).

(iii) $\rho(1700)$ meson.

This meson (total width about 110 MeV) is seen in the 4π final
states of the reactions

$$\pi^{\pm}p \to p\pi^{\pm}\pi^{-}\pi^{0} \qquad\qquad (3.2)$$

It appears very clearly in the final state $\pi^{\pm}\omega$, which represents
about 20% of this 4π decay rate. Johnson et al.[16] have
examined the angular correlations in the $\pi\omega$ system in detail.
The Treiman-Yang distribution is isotropic. Johnson et al.
have assumed that the $\rho(1700)$ production process is due to
a one-pion-exchange (OPE) process (this assumes that its
spin-parity is limited to the series (1-), (3-), (5-),..) and,
in fact, this gives an excellent fit to the data. The ω angular
distribution (in the $\rho(1700)$ frame) is strongly non-isotropic
relative to the incident pion; it requires orbital angular momentum $\ell \geq 2$ for the $\pi\omega$ system. This excludes the possibility (1-). For the possibility spin-parity (3-), parity
conservation requires $\ell=3$. OPE and J=(3-), $\ell=3$ for the
$\pi\omega$ decay require angular distribution

$$\sin^{2}\theta \, (5\cos^{2}\theta - 1)^{2}, \qquad\qquad (3.3)$$

which fits the observed distribution well. In the $\rho(1700) \to \pi\omega$
decay, these parameters require distribution $\sin^{2}\chi$ for the
angle between the normal $\underline{n}$ to the ω decay plane (in its rest

frame) and the direction of the decay pion (in the same frame)
and the data fit this well (although they are compatible with
isotropy); the $\sin^2 \phi'$ distribution expected for the azimuthal
angle for $\underline{n}$ (measured from the $\omega-\pi$ (incident) plane) also
fits the data well. The data of Johnson et al.[16] make a
strong case for spin-parity (3-) for $\rho(1700)$; they place the
mass value at 1675 ± 10 MeV. In a compilation of all the
4π - data from reaction (3.2), Ferbel[67] gives 1700 MeV as
the mean mass value for this state.

This is also a peak at this mass value for the
state $\rho^- \rho^0$. This could come from the same state, although
this is not necessarily the case. The distributions show
some evidence for $\ell_{\rho\rho}=1$ for the $\rho\rho$ system. The symmetries
of the possible isospin and spin states are as follows, with
$\underline{J} = \underline{\ell}_{\rho\rho} + \underline{S}_{\rho\rho}$,

	I-spin	Spin $S_{\rho\rho}$	$\ell_{\rho\rho}$
Symmetric	2, 0	2, 0	even
Antisymmetric	1	1	odd

With I=1 for this state, and $\ell_{\rho\rho}=1$, Bose statistics for the
ρ-mesons requires $S_{\rho\rho}=$ 0 or 2. There is observed a strong
azimuthal angular correlation between the spins of the two

ρ-mesons (i. e. between the vectors $\underline{q}^- = (\underline{p}(\pi_1^-) - \underline{p}(\pi^0)$ for the ρ^- meson (in its c. m. frame) and $\underline{q}^0 = (\underline{p}(\pi^+) - \underline{p}(\pi_2^-))$) for the ρ^0 meson (in its rest frame), with the $\rho\rho$ relative momentum $\underline{p}_{\rho\rho}$ as axis); this excludes $S_{\rho\rho} = 0$, for this gives the correlation $(q \cdot q^0)^2$ which does not depend on azimuth (since it does not involve the direction $\underline{p}_{\rho\rho}$), and therefore $S_{\rho\rho} = 2$. This situation can occur for total spin-parity (1-), (2-) or (3-), and so it is possible that this $\rho^-\rho^0$ decay mode comes from the (3-) state which gives the $\omega\pi$ decay. It is of interest to note that the neutral (4π) states do not show any $\rho^0\rho^0$ mode: this is forbidden if I=1, but would be allowed if I=2 (or 0) held, so that its absence serves as a check on the isospin assignment. The decay modes for these neutral substates are $\pi^0\omega$ and $\rho^+\rho^-$, respectively; both of these modes involve two π^0 mesons (together with a neutron, when they come from π^-p collisions) and are therefore not available for analysis.

With I=1 and spin-parity (3-), a 2π decay would be possible for this mesonic state. It is not clear whether this has or has not been observed. Johnson et al.[16] actually identify these two 4π- states with the 2π- state known as the g-meson (called ρ_v(1650) above); the mass 1675 MeV they quote is a mean mass for all three modes. However, the masses obtained for the 2π- states by other workers are almost all lower than this mass, and those obtained for the 4π- state are almost all well above this mass. It is quite possible that there are two 2π- states, $\rho_V(1650)$ with spin-parity (1-) and $\rho(1700)$ with spin-parity (3-), whose production cross sections vary in relative magnitude from one incident energy to another. Ferbel[67] gives the overall estimate $(\pi\pi)/(4\pi) < 0.10$ for $\rho^{\pm}(1700)$.

The relationship of the R-mesons reported from "missing mass spectrometer" work by Dubal et al.[68], the $R_1(1630)$, $R_2(1700)$ and $R_3(1750)$ (and possibly $R_4(1830)$), and the mesonic states just described is far from clear at present. It is possible that R_1 corresponds to a mixture of $\rho_V(1650)$ and $\pi_A(1640)$, and that R_2 corresponds with $\rho(1700)$. One puzzle is that Dubal et al. give rather narrow widths for the R-meson states, comparable with the experimental width Γ_{exp} =30MeV, whereas the widths obtained from bubble chamber work are all of order 100 MeV. There has not yet been any resonance near 1750 MeV reported from bubble chamber work.

Other non-strange states reported in this region are:

(a) $\omega\rho^0(1689)$, reported by Danysz et al.[69]. The G parity is opposite that for ρ (1700). Also, the two G=-1 states allowed by the quark model, namely $^1D_2$ and $^1S_0$, have already been assigned, most probably to the $\pi_A(1640)$ and $A_{2\ell}(1290)$ mesons, respectively. The evidence that this decay mode involves a ρ meson is not strong; it could just as well represent an $\omega \pi^+ \pi^-$ state with I=0, the $\pi^+ \pi^-$ system having ℓ=0+ or 2+. In this case, this state could belong to any of the ^3D nonets.

(b) $\rho^0 \pi^+ \pi^-$ (1704), reported by Danysz et al.[69] This has G-parity which suggests it could be identified with ρ(1700); however the final state $\rho^0 \rho^0$ is forbidden for the decay of ρ^0(1700), by isospin conservation (any state $U^0 V^0$ for isovectors U, V can have only I=0 or 2). If this state is assigned to I=0, its G-parity permits it only to belong to the $^1D_2$ configuration.

(c) $\rho \pi$ (1636), reported by Armenise et al.[70] The evidence that this peak includes $\rho^0 \pi^0$ decay is quite clear and indicates I=0 for this state (I=2 is excluded by lack of any evidence in the corresponding $\rho^- \pi^-$ state in previous $\pi^- d$ work at the same energy by the same group). This state has G=-1, which is consistent with its being an I=0 state for any of the ^3D nonets. It seems most natural that it should be the I=0 counterpart of ρ_v(1650), but no angular correlation data are available to test this assignment yet. We should conclude this discussion by pointing out that none of the I=0 mesons included in the six nonets allowed by the $\bar{q}q$ model allows 2π- decay.

K* States. There is now a well-established K* resonance (with I=1/2) at 1781 MeV (width 72±24 MeV), known as the L-meson and reported by many groups[71]. A typical set of branching ratio values are those of the ABCLV collaboration[71,72,58]:

Mode	K*(891) π	Kρ(765)	K$\pi\pi$ (other)
Branching ratio	24 ± 8%	10 ± 6	44 ± 15%

Mode	Kω	K*(1400)π	K*(891)η	Kπ
Branching ratio	5 ± 2%	16±8%	0±3%	< 2%

Kane[58] has discussed the branching ratios to be expected for the K-member of a nonet; in the absence of K-mixing between nonets with the same JP but opposite C, there are characteristic branching ratios which correspond to the two possible values C=±1 and which reflect the appropriateness of D- or F-type coupling between the initial octet and the final two octets, as given in Table V. Decay of the L-meson to two pseudo-scalar particles is not seen, so that the first line of Table V is not relevant here. With the quark model, the last line gives no discrimination between the two values for C; the data agree with the value predicted. C**=+1 would require that K*(891)η should have a much greater rate (factor 2, including the other K*π charge state) than K*(891)π; corrections due to phase space and centrifugal barriers will act against the η mode, but these corrections will not reduce the (K*(891)η)/(K*(891)π) below unity. Since the

Branching ratio	$C^{**} = +1$	$C^{**} = -1$
$(K^{**+} \to K^+ \pi^0)/(K^{**+} \to K^+ \eta)$	3	1/3
$(K^{**+} \to K^{*+} \pi^0)/(K^{**+} \to K^{*+} \eta)$	1/3	3
$(K^{**+} \to K^+ \rho^0)/(K^{**+} \to K^+ \omega)$	1	9(1)

Table V   Branching ratios predicted for various K^{**+} decay processes, with neglect of K^{**} mixing, as function of the charge-conjugation parity C^{**} (equal to the charge-conjugation parity of the $I_3 = 0$ members of the nonet) of the nonet to which it belongs. Kane's value 9 on the last line corresponds to his assumption[58] that the transition $K^{**} \to K\omega_1$ has vanishing amplitude for a final unitary singlet state ω_1. This assumption appears quite unreasonable in the context of the quark model. The quark model does forbid the transition

$$(\bar{\lambda}p) \to K^+ + (\bar{n}n),$$

since this requires a two-quark transition. The entry in brackets is the value predicted by the quark model. Corrections due to differences in phase space and centrifugal barriers depend on the spin-parity and are not included in these entries.

$K^*(891)\eta$ mode certainly has a much smaller branching ratio than 24%, we must conclude $C^{**} = -1$; this requires at most branching ratio $3\pm1\%$ for the $K^*(891)\eta$, and this is compatible with the data. This C^{**} value is compatible with any of the ^3D configurations, or

with the $(n=2)^3S_1$ configuration. It has usually been argued that the
absence of decay to two pseudoscalar mesons implies that only the
spin-parity series (1+), (2-), (3+), ... need be considered; the
only configuration in this series is $^3D_2$, so that the quark model
would only allow the (2-) assignment. However, it is not excluded
that the decay to two pseudoscalar mesons may simply be weak,
for other reasons; this means that the spin-parities (1-), (2+),
(3-) should also be considered. The $\rho_V(1650)$ decays strongly to
two pseudoscalar mesons, so that the L-meson does not correspond to this state; the π_A (1640) state is excluded since this nonet
has C=+1. The only established non-strange state to which it
could belong is $\rho(1700)$, which also has C=-1. We note that, for
these two states,

$$\Delta' = (1.781)^2 - (1.700)^2 = 0.282\pm0.08 \text{ (GeV)}^2, \qquad (3.4)$$

in good accord with the entries in Table IV for L=0+ and 1-. The
L-meson has a strong branching ratio (40%) for "pseudoscalar
meson + vector meson" states, just as $\pi\omega$ is a strong decay mode
for $\rho(1700)$. $\rho(1700)$ decay to two pseudoscalar mesons has not
been established; there is a very strong limit on the branching
ratio for L→Kπ. The decay $\rho(1700)\rightarrow\rho\rho$ is strong (if we accept
identification of the latter mode as corresponding to spin-parity
(3-)— the possibility (2-) is still open). This suggests that decay

processes of the type $K^*\rho$ and $K^*\omega$ should be strong for the L-meson; although they have low Q-values, (the $K^*\varphi$ threshold is above the L-mass), they would involve only $\ell = 1$ centrifugal barriers. Study of these more complicated modes (especially $K^*\omega$) would be very helpful in settling the situation. With this assignment to the $^3D_3$ configuration, the study of the angular correlations in the $K^*(1400)\pi$ system would be of much interest; this would require $\ell_\pi = 2+$ for the pion emitted (and therefore strong angular correlations) whereas the assignment $^3D_2$ (which is also possible, as mentioned just above) would allow $\ell_\pi = 0+$ and would give isotropy.

Some evidence has recently been reported by Jobes et al[73] for a K^* resonance at 1660 MeV (width $\Gamma = 60$ MeV), with definite decay modes $K^*(1420)\pi$ and $K^*(891)\pi$. In view of the low Q-values for the $K^*(1420)\pi$ mode, the prominence of this mode would suggest that the pion emitted must have $\ell_\pi = 0$. This would lead to the assignment (2-) for this $K^*(1660)$; negative parity would be expected to be the case for any K^* meson in this mass region, and any other such assignment would require $\ell_\pi \geq 2$, which would strongly disfavour the decay mode $K^*(1420)\pi$. However, in view of the systematics between K and V states in the same nonet (as expressed in Table IV and Eq. (3.4)), it is surprising to find a K^* resonance at such a low mass value, since

no I≠1 mesonic resonances have been reported for the corresponding mass range 1550-1600 MeV. This state has not yet been
confirmed by other groups, apart from an indication for a
$\bar{K}\omega$ (1660) peak in the study of the reaction $K^-p \rightarrow K^-p\omega$ by Carmony
et al.[74]

    Dubal et al.[75] have searched for $\bar{K}^*$ resonances in the
"Missing-Mass" distribution for the reaction $K^-p \rightarrow p\,(MM)^-$ at 7
and 12 GeV/c. Besides $\bar{K}^*$(1400), they found a small peak at
1850 MeV, with width about 85 MeV. This state has not yet been
confirmed by other groups. It could be the $\bar{K}^*$ state corresponding
to the I=1, Y=0 peak R_3 (1750) found by the same group; this
would correspond with a value $\Delta' = 0.375 \pm 0.06 (GeV)^2$, compatible
with the value (3.4) found for the L and ρ(1700) mesons.

    The spin-orbit coupling pattern is far from clear for
the two-quantum excited mesonic nonets. Not all of the I=1
states expected have yet been seen, and not all the states seen
have yet been assigned to definite spin-parity values. We identify
ρ (1700) with the $^3D_3$ state; it is then necessary to assign
ρ_V (1650) to spin(1-) and to identify it with the $^3D_1$ configuration
(although it could then be just as well identified with the
$(n=2)^3S_1$ state). The most plausible identifications for the other
states are that $A_{2\varrho}$ (1290) represents the $(n=2)^1S_0$ state, and that
π_A (1640) represents the $^1D_2$ state. This is contrary to the

experimental data at present. The evidence excludes (0-) for
$A_{2\ell}(1290)$ and favours (2-); in this case, $\pi_A(1640)$ would have to
be assigned to spin-parity (0-), corresponding to the $(n=2)^1S_0$
configuration, and there is no evidence to exclude this possibility.
There is no candidate for the configuration $(n=2)^3S_1$, nor for the
configuration $^3D_2$. On the basis of these assignments, and
assuming a spin-orbit interaction (cf. Table III), the $^3D_2$ state
would be expected to lie two-fifths of the way between $\rho_V(1650)$
and ρ (1700), at about mass 1670 MeV. This state could have
decay processes such as $\rho\rho$, $\pi\omega$, $\pi\phi$, $K\bar{K}^*$ (and $\bar{K}K^*$) and πA_{2u};
the latter mode would be especially significant since it is allowed
for $\ell_\pi = 0$ for the $^3D_2$ state, whereas $\ell_\pi = 2$ would be required for
the $^3D_1$ or $^3D_3$ initial states. Since the $\rho\rho$ and $\pi\omega$ modes
already occur for $\rho(1700)$ (and possibly for $\rho_V(1650)$), it may
well be quite difficult to identify all of the resonant states which
contribute to the phenomena observed in this mass region
(unless decay modes are found which are characteristic of one
particular state, as might be the case for a mode πA_{2u}); it is
not excluded that the $\rho\rho$ and $\pi\omega$ modes observed in this region
could result from two different parent states.

  We conclude discussion of the two-quantum excited
states with two remarks:

  (i) the transition (meson$\rightarrow\gamma$) is not expected to be
strong for the $^3D_1$ state. The reason is that this transition

corresponds to a radiative annihilation $\bar{q}q \to \gamma$ for the quark-antiquark system, and that this amplitude will be proportional (at least to a good first approximation) to $\psi(0)$, which vanishes for $L \neq 0$. Hence, even if the $^3D_1$ state (here identified with $\rho_V(1650)$) is strongly produced in some π- or γ-induced reaction, this state is not expected to show up strongly in the $\mu^+\mu^-$ spectrum observed for this reaction. As pointed out earlier, the $(n=2)^3S_1$ state is expected to show up strongly in this spectrum, if it is produced at all in these reactions. There is, of course, the possibility of mixing between the $(n=2)^3S_1$ and the $^3D_1$ states; if this occurred, then both of the resulting mesonic states would be expected to appear in this spectrum. However, mixing between these states requires the presence of a $\bar{q}q$ tensor interaction. We have already argued, on the basis of the $L=1$- nonets, that there is no significant contribution to the diagonal terms of the mass matrix from a tensor interaction, but we should recognize that, if the two-quantum excited states $(n=2)^3S_1$ and $^3D_1$ lie close in mass value in first approximation, then rather strong mixing could be produced between these two states by quite a weak tensor interaction.

(ii) On the ρ-trajectory shown on Fig. 1, the mass which corresponds to $N=3$ is 1630 GeV, corresponding to $(mass)^2 = 2.67$. $(Mass)^2$ for ρ (1700), which we have actually assigned to spin $J = (3-)$, is 2.89, significantly off the linear trajectory.   The second point shown on Fig. 1 is actually for $R_3(1750)$, for which $(\text{mass})^2 = 3.07$.   It is not clear whether any significance should be given to any of these agreements or disagreements with the linear trajectory.   Although we began on the basis of a linear trajectory, we must remember that small effects, such as the spin-orbit splittings and the SU(3)-breaking interactions, give corrections which are not likely to have linear dependence on L, even for the sequence of states $^3L_{L+1}$.

Next, we consider briefly the S-region (~1930 MeV), corresponding to three-quantum excitations.   There are eight nonets to be expected, all with positive parity.   The only mesonic resonance reported from bubble chamber analyses near this mass value is $\pi^+\pi^0$(1900), first reported by Deutschmann et al.[76], but for which the weight of evidence has continually diminished[71].   We note that an I=1 $\pi\pi$ resonance necessarily has odd parity, so that there are no resonances of this type included in the three-quantum $\bar{q}q$ states.

There are two or three other resonances reported in the mass range 1800-1850 MeV, which might perhaps be associated with the (n=2)P configurations.   Danysz et al.[77] have reported a $(4\pi)^0$ resonance at 1832 MeV (width 40 MeV), with quite strong evidence, which might be related with the small R_4 peak reported by Dubal et al.[68].   It seems rather probable

Confign.	$(JP)^C$	G (for I = 1 state)	Spin–orbit term
$^3F_4$	$(4+)^+$	-1	$3a$
$^3F_3$	$(3+)^+$	-1	$-a$
$^3F_2$	$(2+)^+$	-1	$-4a$
$^1F_3$	$(3+)^-$	$+1$	0
$2\,^3P_2$	$(2+)^+$	-1	b
$2\,^3P_1$	$(1+)^+$	-1	$-b$
$2\,^3P_0$	$(0+)^+$	-1	$-2b$
$2\,^1P_1$	$(1+)^-$	$+1$	0

that this $(4\pi)^0$ state is dominantly $\rho^0\pi^+\pi^-$, and perhaps even $\rho^0\rho^0$. The latter mode would exclude the possibility I = 1 but, until data on the decay angular correlations becomes available, this mode is quite compatible with decay from any of the I = 0 states from the $2\,^3P$ nonets. Danysz et al.[69] have also reported an $\omega\pi^+\pi^-$ resonance at 1848 MeV (width 67 MeV), which may be of the form $\omega\rho^0$. The latter mode requires I = 1 and C = +1, and is compatible with any of the ^3F or $2\,^3P$ nonets; the former mode could have I = 0 (which would require C = -1) and is then compatible with either $^1F_3$ or 2^1P_1 nonets.

Very little is known of the higher mesons in this rotational sequence. Alles-Borrelli et al.[78] have reported a striking
$\pi^+\pi^-\pi^0$ peak at 2207 MeV (width 62±50 MeV), close to the
T⁼meson mass, 2195±15 MeV, from their analysis of the reac-
tions $\bar{p}p \to 2\pi^+2\pi^-\pi^0$ at 5.7 GeV/c. Abrams et al.[79] have found
evidence for I≈0 and 1 resonances in the $\overline{N}N$ system, from their
studies of the total cross sections for $\bar{p}p$ and $\bar{p}d$ collisions. These
resonances appear to be quite well correlated with the T⁻ and U⁻
meson peaks reported by Focacci et al.[15] but their widths are
very much greater than those reported from the missing mass
spectrometer studies. We may hope that more detailed studies
of the $\bar{p}p$ and $\bar{p}d$ reactions will soon give us more detailed
information about the parameters for these higher mesonic
resonances, to test the spin and parity assignments which are
suggested by the $\bar{q}q$ model for mesonic resonances described
briefly here.

4.   CONCLUSION

Our progress on the discovery and identification of new
mesonic resonance states has been quite slow over the past few
years, despite the enormous effort which has been devoted to
this study, the fruits of which we have heard reviewed and
discussed at this meeting. Even three years ago[2], it was clear
from SU(3)- symmetry alone that there must exist quite a number
of mesonic resonance states, simply to fill out the octets

required by the established $I = 1$, $Y = 0$ mesonic states. In
several cases, enough states of the octet are known for the prediction of the mass of the missing $I = 0$, $Y = 0$ state and of its
decay modes, but no empirical evidence for these states has yet
become available; the simplest explanation for this discrepancy
is distortion of the octet structure by the presence of a unitary
singlet state with the same spin-parity which mixes strongly with
the $I = 0$, $Y = 0$ state of the octet through SU(3)- breaking interactions, in other words that the mesonic states generally occur
as nonets, as the $\bar{q}q$ model for these states suggests. At present,
then, our greatest need is for an intensive study of the $I = Y = 0$
mesonic systems. It is urgent that these missing states should
be found, especially for the $L = 1-$ (positive-parity) nonets in the
mass range 1000-1500 MeV, and that their $(JP)^C$ values be
firmly established.   Until this is achieved, we theoreticians
shall have to mark time in our study of the spectroscopy of
mesonic states, for we shall not know how secure are the
indications of the quark model, which has been unexpectedly
successful so far.   There could well be unpleasant surprises
ahead; a much wider mixing between mesonic nonets with a
given spin-parity might occur, resulting from the existence
of an infinite series of radially excited states (e. g. the possibility of $(n = 2)$ $^3S_1$ and $^3D_1$ mixing).

The quark model really provides only a theoretical framework for the interpretation of the mesonic states observed. We have no fundamental theory for the origin of the various $\bar{q}q$ forces which appear to play a significant role. For the present, our approach has to be semi-phenomenological; we examine the data in order to learn what features such $\bar{q}q$ forces should have in order to account for the states observed. From the distribution of the mean masses for the various supermultiplets, we hope to learn about the super-strong forces. The patterns of mass splitting within each supermultiplet will give us rather direct indications about the strong SU(6)- breaking forces, the spin-orbit interaction terms, and the moderately-strong SU(3)- breaking interactions.

At the present stage, we need much more detailed and more accurate information on the mesonic resonances and their decay processes. Information about the decay angular correlations are obviously very important and the quark model often predicts that the decay amplitudes are not of the simplest possible form consistent with the requirements of $(JP)^C$ conservation. The systematics of the partial decay widths provide a test of the $(JP)^C$ and SU(3) assignments for the mesonic states, and of the detailed methods used for the discussion of the transitions between these mesonic states. Radiative decay amplitudes are of particular importance, since one feels that the calculational methods used for those amplitudes may be on a more secure footing.

It is important to stress the value and importance of this work. It is not just a question of collecting new resonances and of classifying them, in the spirit of zoology; in order to recognize and to establish firmly the patterns of these mesonic states and of the phenomena involving their interactions, we need to know the picture completely. Together with the corresponding work with baryons, these empirical studies offer the clearest route to an understanding of the internal structures of the hadrons and of the nature of the super-strong interactions which gave rise to them. At present, there is rather little in the data on mesonic resonances which is necessarily inconsistent with the naive quark model. This does not mean just that this model is sufficiently flexible to fit the data. In fact, the opposite situation holds; one spin-parity determination in firm disagreement with the expected patterns would be sufficient to remove the quark model from the domain of interesting hypotheses. It is by no means trivial that it has been possible to fit so much of the data concerning hadrons into the framework provided by the quark model, and it is of much importance to search for areas of mesonic phenomena which test the relevance of this framework more severely.

References

1. R. Dalitz, Quark Models for the Elementary Particles, chapter in High Energy Physics (Gordon and Breach, New York, 1966) p. 253

2. R. Dalitz, in Proc. Oxford Intl. Conf. on Elementary Particles (Rutherford High-Energy Laboratory, Chilton, January 1966) p. 157

3. S. Ishida, Progr. Theor. Phys. (Kyoto) $\underline{32}$ (1964) 922; $\underline{34}$ (1965) 64

4. J. Iizuka, Progr. Theor. Phys. (Kyoto) 35 (1966) 117 and 309

5. O. Sinanoglu, Phys. Rev. Letters $\underline{16}$ (1966) 207

6. O. Sinanoglu, Hadron Spectroscopy, Dynamical Groups and and Mass Formulas, Lectures presented at the Istanbul NATO Advanced Study Institute on Symmetry Principles at High Energy (August, 1966) unpublished

7. T. Uretsky, On the Bosons of Zero Baryon Number as Bound States of Quark-Antiquark Pairs, in High Energy Theoretical Physics (ed. H. Aly, Univ. of Beirut, 1967)

8. N. Bogoliubov, B. Struminsky, and A. Tavkhelidze, J. I. N. R. preprint D-1968 (Dubna, 1965). A convenient review of the work of the Dubna group has been given by A. Tavkhelidze in "High Energy Physics and Elementary Particles" (Intl. Atomic Energy Agency, Vienna, 1965) p. 753 and p. 763

9. R. Dalitz, Proc. XIII Intl. Conf. on High-Energy Physics (Univ. California Press, Berkeley and Los Angeles, 1967) p. 215

10.   R. Dalitz, Quark Substructure for Mesonic and Baryonic
       States, chapter in 1966 Tokyo Summer Lectures in
       Theoretical Physics - II Elementary Particle Physics
       (ed. G. Takeda and A. Fujii, Syokabo, Tokyo and
       Benjamin Inc., New York, 1967) p.56

11.   M. Gell-Mann, Phys. Letters $\underline{8}$ (1964) 214; G. Zweig, An
       SU(3) Model for Strong Interaction Symmetry and its
       Breaking, CERN preprint 8419/TH.412 February, 1964).
       See also G. Zweig, in Symmetries in Elementary
       Particle Physics (ed. A. Zichichi, Academic Press, New
       York, 1965) p.192

12.   A. Rosenfeld, Are There any Far-Out Mesons or Baryons,
       Lawrence Radiation Lab. Rept. UCRL-18266 (May, 1968)

13.   D. Dorfan, J. Eades, L. Lederman, W. Lee, and C. Ting,
       Phys. Rev. Letters $\underline{14}$ (1965) 999

14.   W. Kienzle, B. Maglic, B. Levrat, F. Lefebvres, D.
       Freytag and H. Blieden, Phys. Letters $\underline{19}$ (1965) 438

15.   M. Focacci, W. Kienzle, B. Levrat, B. Maglic, and M.
       Martin, Phys. Rev. Letters $\underline{17}$ (1966) 890

16.   T. Johnston, J. Prentice, N. Steenberg, T. Yoon, A.
       Garfinkel, R. Morse, B. Oh, and W. Walker, Phys. Rev.
       Letters $\underline{20}$ (1968) 1414

17.   L. van Hove, Proc. XIII Intl. Conf. on High-Energy Physics
       (Univ. California Press, Berkeley and Los Angeles, 1967)
       p.255

18.   D. Sutherland, Nuclear Physics, B2 (1967) 157

19.   R. Dalitz, Proc. Second Hawaii Topical Conf. in Particle
      Physics (Univ. Hawaii Press, Honolulu, 1968) p. 325

20.   R. Blankenbecker, and R. Sugar, Phys. Rev. $\underline{142}$ (1966)
      1051

21.   P. Freund, Phys. Rev. $\underline{157}$ (1967) 1412

22.   P. Morse and H. Feshbach, Methods of Theoretical Physics
      (McGraw-Hill Inc., New York 1953)

23.   C. Akerlof, W. Ash, K. Berkelman, C. Lichtenstein, A.
      Ramananskas, and R. Seeman, Phys. Rev. $\underline{163}$ (1967)
      1482

24.   M. Block, Phys. Letters 25B (1967) 604

25.   L. Radicati, in 1965 Cargese Lectures in Theoretical
      Physics (ed. M. Levy, Benjamin Inc., 1966)

26.   J. Schwinger, Phys. Rev. $\underline{135}$ (1964) B816

27.   S. Glashow and R. Socolow, Phys. Rev. Letters $\underline{15}$ (1965)
      329. This question has been discussed again recently by
      D. Bassano, M. Goldberg, B. Goz, G. Pertile, V. Barnes,
      D. Dornan, G. Kalbfleisch, N. Samios, I. Skillicorn and
      J. Leitner, Phys. Rev. Letters $\underline{19}$ (1967) 968

28.   G. Alexander, H. Lipkin, and F. Scheck, Phys. Rev.
      Letters $\underline{17}$ (1966) 412

29.   E. Levin and L. Frankfurt, JETP Letters $\underline{2}$ (1965) 65

30.   H. Lipkin and F. Scheck, Phys. Rev. Letters $\underline{16}$ (1966) 71

31.   H. Lipkin, in High Energy Physics and Nuclear Structure
       (ed. G. Alexander, North-Holland, Amsterdam, 1967)
       p. 363

32.   G. Benson, L. Lovell, C. Murphy, B. Roe, D. Sinclair,
       and J. Van der Velde, Production Cross Sections for
       $\eta, \omega, \eta', \phi$ and f^o mesons in π^+d Collisions at 3. 65 GeV/c
       (Univ. Michigan preprint, August 1966), unpublished

33.   K. Lai and T. Schumann, A New Experimental Determination
       of the Mixing Angles of Meson Nonets Using a Recent
       Quark Model Prediction, Brookhaven National Labora-
       tory preprint, BNLA-155(BC) (August 1966) unpublished

34.   R. Dashen and D. Sharp, Phys. Rev. $\underline{133}$ (1964) B1585

35.   R. Dalitz, in Proc. Sienna Intl. Conf. on Elementary
       Particles (Italian Phys. Soc., Bologna, 1963) p. 171

36.   S. Ting, Proc. 1967 Intl. Symposium on Electron and
       Photon Interactions at High Energies (U.S. Dept.
       Commerce, Springfield, Virginia, September 1967)
       p. 452

37.   D. Binnie, A. Duane, A. Faruqi, P. Horsey, W. Jones,
       M. Kay, D. Mason, P. Nicolson, I. Rahman, J. Walters,
       J. Wilson, and P. Palit, Measurement of the Partial
       Width of the Decay $\phi \rightarrow e^+ + e^-$, Rutherford Laboratory
       Preprint RPP/H/41 (May, 1968), unpublished

38. A. Rosenfeld, N. Barash-Schmidt, A. Barbaro-Galtieri,
     L. Price, M. Roos, P. Soding, W. Willis, and C. Wohl,
     Rev. Modern Phys. 40 (1968) 77

39. P. Baillon, D. Edwards, B. Marechal, L. Montanet,
     M. Tomas, Ch. d'Andlau, A. Astier, J. Cohen-Ganouna,
     M. Della Negra, S. Wojcicki, M. Baubillier, J. Duboc,
     F. James, and F. Levy, Nuovo Cimento 50 (1967) 393

40. A. Zaslavsky, V. Ogievetsky, and W. Tybor, The Broken
     SU(6)$_W$ Symmetry and the Ninth Pseudoscalar Meson,
     Joint Institute for Nuclear Research preprint P2.3391
     (Dubna, 1967)

41. G. Kalbfleisch, O. Dahl, and A. Rittenberg, Phys. Rev.
     Letters 13 (1964) 349a; see also A. Rittenberg, quoted
     by G. Goldhaber in Proc. XIII Intl. Conf. on High Energy
     Physics (Univ. California Press, Berkeley and Los
     Angeles, 1967) p. 105

42. C. Yang, Phys. Rev. 77 (1950) 242

43. R. Dalitz and D. Sutherland, Nuovo Cimento 37 (1965) 1777

44. G. Chikovani, M. Focacci, W. Kienzle, C. Lechanoine,
     B. Levrat, B. Maglic, M. Martin, P. Schubelin,
     L. Dubal, M. Fischer, P. Grieder, H. Neal, and
     C. Nef, Phys. Letters 25B (1967) 44

45. R. Baud, H. Benz, B. Bosniakovic, G. Damgaard,
    M. Focacci, W. Kienzle, M. Klauner, C.
    Lechanoine, M. Martin, C. Nef, P. Schubelin, and
    A. Weitsch, Confirmation of a Two-peak Structure
    in the A_2 Meson produced in $\pi^- p \to p A_2^-$ at 2. 65 GeV/c, in-
    vited paper presented at the Topical Conference on Meson
    Spectroscopy (Philadelphia, May 1968).

46. D. Crennell, U. Karshon, K. Lai, J. Scarr, and I.
    Skillicorn, Phys. Rev. Letters 20 (1968) 1318

47. D. Morrison, Phys. Letters 25B (1967) 238

48. G. Ascoli, H. Crawley, D. Mortara, and A. Shapiro,
    Phys. Rev. Letters 20 (1968) 1411

49. G. Ascoli, H. Crawley, U. Kruse, D. Mortara, E.
    Schafer, A. Shapiro, and B. Terreault, Phys. Rev.
    Letters 21 (1968) 113

50. N. Samios, The X^0 and δ Mesons, invited paper at the
    Topical Conf. on Meson Spectroscopy (Philadelphia,
    May 1968)

51. A. Astier, J. Cohen-Ganouna, M. Della Negra, B.
    Marechal, L. Montanet, M. Tomas, M. Baubillier,
    and J. Duboc, Phys. Letters 25B (1967) 294

52. P. Schlein, The $K\pi$ Interaction, invited paper at the Topical
    Conf. on Meson Spectroscopy (Philadelphia, May 1968),
    unpublished.

53.   C. Whitehead, J. McEwen, R. Ott, D. Aitken, G. Bennett,
      and R. Jennings, Observation of an Enhancement in the
      I=O $\pi^+\pi^-$ System at 1085 MeV, Rutherford Lab. Rept.
      RPP/H/33 (Chilton, 1968).

54.   A. Bettini, M. Cresti, S. Limentani, A. Loria, L. Peruzzo,
      R. Santangelo, L. Bertanza, A. Bigi, R. Carrara,
      R. Casali, E. Hart, and P. Lariccia, Nuovo Cimento
      42 (1966) 695

55.   W. Selove, The $\pi\pi$ Interaction, invited paper at the
      Topical Conf. on Meson Spectroscopy (Philadelphia,
      May 1968), unpublished

56.   R. Gatto, L. Maiani, and G. Preparata, Phys. Rev. 140
      (1965) B1579

57.   G. Goldhaber, Phys. Rev. Letters 19 (1967) 976

58.   G. Kane, Phys. Rev. 156 (1967) 1739

59.   G. Feinberg and A. Pais, Phys. Rev. Letters 9 (1962) 45

60.   A. Barbaro-Galtieri and P. Soding, Is There Evidence
      for an H Meson? (Is it just the η'?). Lawrence
      Radiation Laboratory Rept. UCRL-18271
      (April, 1968)

61.   H. Lipkin, Phys. Rev. 159 (1967) 1303

62.   V. Weisskopf and R. van Royen, Nuovo Cimento
      50 (1967) 617

63.   C. Becchi and G. Morpurgo, Phys. Rev. 149 (1966) 1284

64.   H. Lipkin, private communication (September, 1967)

65.   A. Wehmann, E. Engels, C. Hoffman, P. Innocenti, R.
      Wilson, W. Blanpied, D. Drickey, L. Hand, and
      G. Stairs, quoted by S. Ting, in Proc. 1967 Intl.
      Symposium on Electron and Photon Interactions at High
      Energies (U.S. Dept. Commerce, Springfield, Virginia,
      1967) p. 459

66.   D. Crennell, P. Hough, G. Kalbfleisch, K. Lai, J. Scarr,
      T. Schumann, I. Skillicorn, R. Strand, M. Webster,
      P. Baumel, A. Bachman, and R. Lea, Phys. Rev.
      Letters 18 (1967) 323
      The g-meson has been reported (and as early as 1965)
      by many groups. We shall not attempt to give a complete
      list of references on this topic, but refer the reader to
      the report given by Ferbel[67].

67.   T. Ferbel, invited paper on 4π decay modes at the Topical
      Conf. Meson Spectroscopy (Philadelphia, May 1968),
      unpublished

68.   L. Dubal, M. Focacci, W. Kienzle, C. Lechanoine, B.
      Levrat, B. Maglic, M. Martin, G. Chikovani,
      M. Fischer, H. Neal, C. Nef, and P. Schubelin,
      Experimental Confirmation of R-meson Structure, CERN
      preprint 67/987/5

69.   J. Danysz, B. French, and V. Simak, Nuovo Cimento
      51A (1967) 801

70. N. Armenise, B. Ghidini, V. Picciarelli, A. Romano, A.
     Forino, R. Gessaroli, L. Lendinara, G. Quareni,
     A. Quareni-Vignudelli, A. Cartacci, M. Dagliana,
     G. di Caporiacco, G. Parrini, M. Barrier, J.
     Laberrigue-Frolow, and J. Quinquard, Phys. Letters
     <u>26B</u> (1968) 336

71. I. Butterworth, Proc. Heidelberg Conf. on Elementary
     Particles (ed. H. Filthuth, North-Holland, Amsterdam
     1968) p. 11

72. J. Bartsch, M. Deutschmann, E. Keppel, G. Kraus, R.
     Speth, C. Grote, J. Klugow, D. Pose, H. Schiller,
     H. Vogt, M. Bardadin-Otwinowska, V. Cocconi, P.
     Dalpiaz, E. Flaminio, J. Hansen, H. Horomadnik,
     G. Kellner, D. Morrison, S. Nowak, N. Barford,
     D. Dallman, S. Goldsack, M. Mermikedes, N. Mukerjee,
     A. Frohlich, G. Otter, I. Wacek, and H. Wahl, Phys.
     Letters <u>22</u> (1966) 357

73. M. Jobes, W. Matt, G. Bassompierre, Y. Goldschmidt-
     Clermont, A. Grant, V. Henri, I. Hughes, B. Jongejans,
     R. Lander, D. Linglin, F. Muller, J. Perreau, I.
     Saitov, R. Sekulin, G. Wolf, W. de Baere, J. Debaiseux,
     P. Dufour, F. Grard, J. Heughebaert, L. Pape, P.
     Peeters, F. Verbeure, and R. Windmolders, Phys.
     Letters <u>26B</u> (1967) 49

74. D. Carmony, T. Hendricks, and R. Lander, Phys. Rev.
     Letters <u>18</u> (1967) 615

75. L. Dubal, P. Bareyre, C. Bricman, G. Chikovani, M. Focacci, W. Kienzle, B. Levrat, B. Maglic, M. Martin, and J. Seguinot, Spectrum of Strange Bosons in the Mass Region 1300 to 2200 MeV Observed by Missing-Mass Spectrometer, CERN preprint 66/1060/5, (July 1966)

76. M. Deutschmann, R. Schulte, R. Steinberg, H. Weber, W. Woischnig, C. Grote, J. Klugow, W. Meyer, S. Nowak, S. Brandt, V. Cocconi, O. Czyzewski, P. Dalpiaz, E. Flaminio, G. Kellner, and D. Morrison, Phys. Letters 18 (1965) 351

77. J. Danysz, B. French, J. Kinson, V. Simak, J. Clayton, P. Mason, H. Muirhead, and P. Renton, Phys. Letters 24B (1967) 309

78. V. Alles-Borelli, B. French, A. Frisk, L. Michejda, and E. Paul, Nuovo Cimento 50A (1967) 776

79. R. Abrams, R. Cool, E. Giacomelli, T. Kycia, B. Leontic, K. Lai, and D. Michael, Phys. Rev. Letters 18 (1967) 1209

TABLE OF MESON PROPERTIES

BY

N. Barash-Schmidt, A. Barbaro-Galtieri,
L. R. Price, Matts, Roos, A. H. Rosenfeld,
Paul Söding, C. G. Wohl

See following pages.

Table S: STABLE PARTICLES. August, 1968.
(Closing date for data: July 1, 1968)

From Review of Particle Properties, UCRL-8030.
N. Barash-Schmidt, A. Barbaro-Galtieri, L. R. Price, Matts Roos, A. H. Rosenfeld, Paul Söding, C. G. Wohl
Quantities in italics have changed by more than one (old) standard deviation since January, 1967

	$I^G(J^P)C$	Mass (MeV)	Mass difference (MeV)	Mean life (sec) $c\tau$(cm)	Mass² (GeV)²	Decays Partial mode	Decays Fraction	Q(MeV)	p or p_{max} (MeV/c)
γ	$0, 1(1^-)^-$	$0\ (<2.\times10^{21}\ \text{MeV})$		stable	0	stable			
ν	$\nu_e / \nu_\mu\ J=\frac{1}{2}$	$0(<0.2\,\text{keV})$ / $0(<1.6\text{MeV})$		stable	0	stable			
e	$J=\frac{1}{2}$	$0.511006 \pm.000002$		stable $(>2\times10^{21}\text{y})$	0.000	stable	$\mu_e = 1.001159557 \pm.000000030\ \frac{e\hbar}{2m_e c}$		
μ	$J=\frac{1}{2}$	$105.659 \pm.002$		$2.1983\times10^{-6} \pm.0008$, $c\tau=6.592\times10^4$	0.011	$ev\bar{\nu}$	100	105	53
	$\mu_\mu=1.00116645 \pm.00000033\ \frac{e\hbar}{2m_\mu c}$					$e\gamma\gamma$	$(<1.6)10^{-5}$	105	53
						$3e$	$(<1.3)10^{-7}$	104	53
						$e\gamma$	$(<6)10^{-9}$	105	53
			$-33.919 \pm.013$						
$\pi^\pm$	$1(0^-)$	$139.578 \pm.013$		$2.604\times10^{-8} \pm.007$, S=2.3*; $c\tau=781$; $(\tau^+-\tau^-)/\bar{\tau}=(.4\pm.2)\%$ (test of CPT)	0.019	$\mu\nu$	100 %	34	30
						ev	$(1.24\pm0.03)10^{-4}$	139	70
						$\mu\nu\gamma$	$(1.24\pm0.25)10^{-4}$	34	30
			$4.6041 \pm.0037$			$\pi^0 ev$	$(1.02\pm0.07)10^{-8}$	4	5
						$ev\gamma$	$(3\pm0.5)10^{-8}$	139	70
π^0	$1^-(0^-)^+$	$134.974 \pm.013$		c $0.89\times10^{-16} \pm.18$, S=1.6*; $\tau=2.67\times10^{-6}$	0.018	$\gamma\gamma$	$(98.83\pm0.04)\%$	135	67
						γe^+e^-	$(1.17\pm0.04)\%$	134	67
						$\gamma\gamma\gamma$	$(<5)10^{-6}$	135	67
						$e^+e^-e^+e^-$	b($3.47)10^{-5}$	133	67
$K^\pm$	$\frac{1}{2}(0^-)$	493.82 ± 0.11		$1.234\times10^{-8} \pm.004$ S=1.8*; $c\tau=370$; $(\tau^+-\tau^-)/\bar{\tau}=(.09\pm.12)\%$ (test of CPT) S=1.3*	0.244	$\mu\nu$	$(63.47\pm0.29)\%$ S=1.1*	388	236
						$\pi\pi^0$	$(20.84\pm0.28)\%$ S=1.1*	219	205
						$\pi\pi^-\pi^+$	$(5.54\pm0.04)\%$ S=1.1*	75	126
						$\pi^0\pi^0\pi^0$	$(1.69\pm0.05)\%$	84	133
						$\mu\pi^0\nu$	$(3.43\pm0.08)\%$	253	215
						$e\pi^0\nu$	$(5.02\pm0.08)\%$	358	228
			-3.94 ± 0.13			$\pi\pi^\pm e^\pm\nu$	$(3.8\pm0.8)10^{-5}$	214	203
						$\pi\pi^\pm e^\mp\nu$	$(<2)10^{-6}$	214	203
						$\pi\pi^\pm\mu^\pm\nu$	$(\leq1.4)10^{-5}$	109	151
						$\pi\pi^\pm\mu^\mp\nu$	$(<3)10^{-6}$	109	151
						ev	$(1.24\pm0.40)10^{-5}$	493	247
						$\pi^0\gamma$	$(2.2\pm0.7)10^{-4}$	219	205
						$\pi\pi^+\pi^-\gamma$	$(10\pm4)10^{-5}$	75	126
						$\pi ev\gamma$	$(6\pm4)10^{-4}$	354	227
						πe^+e^-	$(<1.1)10^{-6}$	353	227
						$\pi\mu^+\mu^-$	$(<2.4)10^{-6}$	143	172
						$\pi\gamma\gamma$	$(<1.1)10^{-4}$	354	227
K^0	$\frac{1}{2}(0^-)$	497.76 ± 0.16		50%K short, 50%K long					
K_S^0	$\frac{1}{2}(0^-)$	S=1.5*		$0.862\times10^{-10} \pm.006$ S=1.2*; $c\tau=2.59$	0.248	$\pi^+\pi^-$	$(68.4\pm1.1)\%$	219	206
			$-0.469\times\frac{1}{\tau_S} \pm.015$			$\pi^0\pi^0$	$(31.6\pm1.1)\%$	228	209
K_L^0	$\frac{1}{2}(0^-)$			$5.29\times10^{-8} \pm.15$; $c\tau=1587$; S=1.3*	0.248	$\pi^0\pi^0\pi^0$	$(25.5\pm2.4)\%$ S=1.3*	93	139
						$\pi^+\pi^-\pi^0$	$(12.1\pm0.5)\%$ S=1.1*	84	133
						$\pi\mu\nu$	$(27.3\pm1.4)\%$ S=1.2*	253	216
						πev	$(35.2\pm1.5)\%$ S=1.2*	358	229
						$\pi^+\pi^-$	$(0.149\pm0.006)\%$	219	206
						c)$\pi^0\pi^0$	still uncertain	228	209
						$\pi^+\pi^-\gamma$	$(<0.3)\%$	219	206
						c)$\gamma\gamma$	still uncertain	498	249
						$e\mu$	$(<0.6)10^{-5}$	392	238
						$\mu^+\mu^-$	$(<1.5)10^{-6}$	286	225
						e^+e^-	$(<1.7)10^{-5}$	497	249
η	$0^+(0^-)^+$	548.8 ± 0.6		$\Gamma=(2.3\pm0.5)$keV	Neutral decays 71.0%	$\gamma\gamma$	$(38.1\pm2.2)\%$	549	274
						$3\pi^0$	$(3.4\pm2.9)\%$ } S=1.3*	414	258
						$\pi^0\gamma\gamma$	$(29.4\pm2.8)\%$ (c)	144	179
					Charged decays 29.0%	$\pi^+\pi^-\pi^0$	$(23.4\pm1.1)\%$	135	174
						$\pi^+\pi^-\gamma$	$(5.5\pm0.5)\%$	269	236
						$\pi^0e^+e^-$	$(<0.01)\%$	413	258
						$\pi^+\pi^-e^+e^-$	$(0.1\pm0.1)\%$	268	236

The subscript N stands for "normal spin-parity series" ($J^P = 0^+, 1^-, 2^+, \ldots$), A for "abnormal" ($J^P = 0^-, 1^+, 2^-, \ldots$).

Quantities in italics have changed by more than one (old) standard deviation since January, 1967.

Symbol (J^P)	$I^G(J^P)C_n$ ⊢ estab. ? - guess	Mass M (MeV)	Width Γ (MeV)	$\pm\Gamma \cdot \frac{M^2}{M(a)}$ (GeV)^2	Partial decay modes Mode	Fraction %	Q (MeV)	p or p_{max}(b) (MeV/c)
$\pi^\pm$(140) π^0(135)	$\pi(0^-)$	$1^-(0^-)+$	139.58 134.97		0.019 0.018	See Table S			
η(549)	$\eta(0^-)$	$0^+(0^-)+$	548.8 ±0.6	2.3 kev ±.5 keV	0.301 ±.000	all neutral $\pi^+\pi^-\pi^0 + \pi^+\pi^-\gamma$	71 29 } See Table S		
$\rho^\pm$(765)	$\rho(1^-)$	$1^+(1^-)-$	755-770 (c)	110-150 (c)	0.585 ±.095	$\pi\pi$ $\pi^\pm\pi^+\pi^-\pi^0$ $\pi^+\pi^-\pi^+\pi^-$ $\pi^0\gamma$	≈ 100 < 0.2 < 0.15 < 0.4	491 212 212 630	359 247 247 372
ρ^0(765)			764±11	90-150 (c)	0.590 ±.090	$\eta\pi^\pm$ e^+e^- $\mu^+\mu^-$	< 0.8 .0056±.0006 (d) .0066±.0015 (e)	82 769 559	146 385 370
ω(783)	$\phi'(1^-)$	$0^-(1^-)-$	783.4 ±0.7 S=2.0*	12.2 ±1.3	0.614 ±.009	$\pi^+\pi^-\pi^0$ $\pi^+\pi^-$ $\pi^0\gamma$ $\eta+$neutral $\pi^+\pi^-\gamma$ $\pi^0\pi^0\gamma$ e^+e^- $\mu^+\mu^-$ $\pi^0\mu^+\mu^-$	≈ 90 seen (f) 9.3±0.8 < 1.5 < 5 < 1 0.02±.012 (g) < 0.10 < 0.2	369 504 648 234 504 513 782 572 437	328 366 380 199 366 368 392 377 350
η'(958) or X^0 See note (h), on name η'	$\eta'(0^-)$	$0^+(0^-)+$ ($J^P=1^+, 2^-$ not yet excluded)	958.3 ±0.8	<4	0.918 <.004	$\eta\pi\pi$ $\pi^+\pi^-\gamma$(incl. $\rho^0\gamma$) neutrals (excl. $\eta\pi\pi$) for upper limits see footnote (i)	67 ± 11 22 ± 3 11 ± 9	131 679	232 458
δ(962) Still needs confirmation	?( )	$\geqslant 1$ ( )	962 ±5	<5	0.927 <.005				
π_N(1016) → K$\bar{\text{K}}$	$\pi(0^+)$	$1^-(0^+)+$	1016 ← (if →, ²⁵ ±10 res.) ±⁵		1.032 ±.025	$K^\pm K^0$ $\eta\pi$	only mode seen < 80	24 328	110 342
Resonance, virtual bound state, or antibound state, still not distinguished.									
ϕ(1019)	$\phi(1^-)$	$0^-(1^-)-$	1019.5 ±0.6 S = 1.5*	3.4 ±0.8	1.039 ±.004	K^+K^- $K_L K_S$ $\pi^+\pi^-\pi^0$ (incl. $\rho\pi$) e^+e^- $\mu^+\mu^-$ for upper limits see footnote (j)	47.3±3.2 38.9±3.1 13.8±4.3 0.049±.016 0.035$^{+.035}_{-.018}$	32 24 605 1018 808	126 109 462 510 499

→ The following bumps, excluded above, are listed among the data cards: σ(410); ε(730); H(990); A1.5(1170); ρρ(1410); $K_S K_S$(1440); η(1600)↦4π; R$_{1-4}$(1630-1830); η or ρ(1830)→4π; φ or π(1830)→ωππ; S(1930); T(2200); NN$_{I=0}$(2380), U(2380); κ(725); K$_N$(1080); K$_{A(I=3/2)}$(1175); K$_{A(I=3/2)}$(1265); K$_{A(I=1/2)}$(1280); K$_{N(I=1/2)}$(1660); K*(2240) → ΥN

* Quoted error includes scale factor S = $\sqrt{\chi^2/(N-1)}$. See footnote to Table S.
† Square brackets indicate a subreaction of the previous (unbracketed) decay mode.
§ This is only an educated guess; the error given is larger than the error of the average of the published values (see listings for the latter).
(a) ΓM is the half-width of the resonance when plotted against M^2.
(b) For decay modes into ≥ 3 particles p_{max} is the maximum momentum that any of the particles in the final state can have. The momenta have been calculated using the averaged central mass values, without taking into account the widths of the resonances.
(c) Values reported for M(ρ) and Γ(ρ) fluctuate so widely that we cannot give averaged values with meaningful errors. The ranges given in the main table show where we believe the final values are most likely to fall. Contrast the results tabulated in this note.

	M	Γ	
ρ^0	764±11	93±15	from e^+e^- colliding beams
ρ^0	767± 2	151± 4	from ππ phase shift anal.
ρ^-	764± 2	147± 4	from πN→ρN, fits in phys. region
ρ^-	755± 5	110± 9	from πN→ρN, Chew-Low extrap.

(d) The quoted value of the rate $\rho^0 \to e^+e^-$ is the average from two $e^+e^- \to \pi^+\pi^-$ experiments (which alone give an average of (0.0054±0.0007)%) and one photoproduction experiment of high mass resolution. Interference effects with ω decay are hoped to be small.
(e) Warning: The values given in the literature, and in our table, for the rate $\rho^0 \to \mu^+\mu^-$ may be somewhat too high, due to possible interference with ω decay.
(f) Reported values range between 1% and 10%, and depend on assumptions on ρ-ω interference.
(g) If one includes results from experiments that do not resolve ω from ρ and therefore assume a ratio $\Gamma(\omega \to e^+e^-)/\Gamma(\rho \to e^+e^-)$ from SU(3) and ωφ mixing, the average value of the rate $\omega \to e^+e^-$ becomes (0.0069±.0013)% (where the error does not include systematic uncertainties).
(h) This 0^- meson was named η' on discovery, when it looked as if it completed the 0^- nonet. With the recent evidence that the E(1420) is probably also 0^-, it is no longer clear whether η' or E or both are mixed in with the π, η, K octet; so the name η' may be misleading.
(i) Empirical limits on fractions for other decay modes of η' (958): $\pi^+\pi^-$ < 7%, 3π < 7%, 4π < 1%, 6π < 1%, $\pi^+\pi^-e^+e^-$ < 0.6%, $\pi^0e^+e^-$ < 1.3%, ηe^-e^- < 1.1%, $\pi^0\rho^0$ < 4%, $\pi^0\omega$ < 8%.
(j) Empirical limits on fractions for other decay modes of φ(1019): $\pi^+\pi^-$ < 20%, ηγ < 8%, η + neutrals < 13%, $\pi^+\pi^-\gamma$ < 4%, ωγ < 5%, ργ < 2%.

Name		J^P	Mass (MeV)	Width (MeV)		Decay mode	Fraction/limit		
$\eta_{0+}(1070)$ $\to K_S K_S$	$\eta(0^+)$	$0^+(0^+)+$	1069 ±20§ S=2.3*	~80 (?) see note (k)	1.14 ±.09	$\pi\pi$	< 70	793	516
(Some data still favor large scattering length)						$K\bar{K}$	> 30	76	198
A1(1070) Existence still in doubt	$\pi(1^+)$	$1^-(1^+)-$ ($J^P = 2^-$ not yet excluded)	1070 ±20§	80 ±35§	1.12	3π see note (ℓ)	≈ 100	651	488
						$K\bar{K}$	< 0.25, $G=(-1)^{\ell+I}$ forbids this		
B(1220) ? $J^P = 2^+, 3^-, \ldots$ still poss.	$\rho(A)$	$1^+(1^+)-$	1221 ±16 S=1.2*	123 ±16 S=1.3*	1.46 ±.14	$\omega\pi$	≈ 100	297	339
						$\pi\pi$	< 30 } suggests	950	600
						$K\bar{K}$	< 2 } J^P=Abnormal	240	360
						for upper limits see footnote (m)			
f(1260)	$\eta'(2^+)$	$0^+(2^+)+$	1264 ±10§	145 § ±25 S=2.7*	1.57 ±.15	$\pi\pi$	large	984	616
						$2\pi^+2\pi^-$	< 4	705	552
						$K\bar{K}$ indic. seen,< 2.5		267	388
D(1285) (J^P = 0^-, 1^+, 2^- with 1^+ favored)	$\eta'(A)$	$0^+(A)+$	1285 ±4	32 ±8	1.65 ±.04	$K\bar{K}\pi$ (mainly $\pi_N(1016)\pi$) only mode seen		154	304
						$K^*\bar{K}+\bar{K}^*K$		-100	
						$\pi\pi\rho$	not seen	256	356
A2$_L$(1270) see footnote(n)	$\pi(N)$	$1^-(N)+$	1269 ±5	26 ±7	1.61 ±.03	$\rho\pi$ (and π+neutrals) dominant		364	387
						$\eta\pi$ indication seen → J^P=N		580	504
						$K\bar{K}$, $\omega\pi$ not seen → $G(K\bar{K})=(-1)^{\ell+I}$ sugg. ℓ odd.			
A2$_H$(1315) see footnote(n)	$\pi(2^+)$	$1^-(2^+)+$	1315 ±3 S=1.3*	29 ±6 S=1.4*	1.73 ±.04	$\rho\pi$ (and π+neutrals) dominant		410	420
						$K\bar{K}$	seen	327	434
						$\eta\pi$	indication seen	626	532
E(1420) (J^P = 1^+ not yet excluded)	$\eta(A)$	$0^+(0^-)+$	1424 ±6	71 ±10 S=1.2*	2.03 ±.10	$K^*\bar{K}+\bar{K}^*K$	50 ±10	38	157
						$\pi_N(1016)\pi$	50 ±10	268	328
						$\pi\pi\pi$	< 88	596	569
						$\pi\pi\rho$	not seen	384	455
f'(1515)	$\eta(2^+)$	$0^+(2^+)+$	1514 ±5	73 ±23 S=1.8*	2.29 ±.11	$K\bar{K}$	72 ± 12 (o)	518	570
						$K^*\bar{K}+\bar{K}^*K$	10 ± 10 (o)	128	294
						$\pi\pi$	< 14	1235	744
						$\eta\pi\pi$	18 ± 10	686	624
						$\eta\eta$	< 40	417	522

(k) Width of $\eta_{0+}(1070) \to K_S K_S$: Average value from two bubble chamber experiments is $\Gamma = (72\pm13)$MeV; whereas two spark chamber experiments on $K_S K_S$ give $\Gamma \gtrsim 100$ MeV and another spark chamber experiment (observing what might be a $\pi^+\pi^-$ mode) yields $\Gamma < 25$ MeV. (For references, see data listings.)

(ℓ) $\rho\pi$ fraction of 3π mode difficult to distinguish because ρ bands cover most of the Dalitz plot.

(m) Empirical limits on fractions for decay modes of B(1220): $\pi\pi < 30\%$, $K\bar{K} < 2\%$, $4\pi < 50\%$, $\phi\pi < 1.5\%$, $\eta\pi < 25\%$, $(K\bar{K})^\pm \pi^0 < 8\%$, $K_S K_S \pi^\pm < 2\%$, $K_S K_L \pi^\pm < 6\%$.

(n) Although the splitting of the A2 needs further confirmation, we give the results from the two experiments that have observed a split A2; for M and Γ of A2$_H$ we have also used the values for the $K\bar{K}$ mode from other experiments. Since most experiments have only seen one rather wide, A2 enhancement, we here list its ("combined") properties: $I^G(J^P)C = 1^-(2^+)+$; M = 1297±10 MeV (S=1.9*) (§); Γ = 91±10 MeV (S=1.1*) (§); partial decay modes: $\rho\pi$ 85 ±3% , $K\bar{K}$ 2.5 ±0.5%, $\eta\pi$ 12 ±4%, $\eta'\pi$ 0.5±0.4% (S=1.9*).

(o) There is only a weak indication for a $K^*\bar{K} + \bar{K}^*K$ mode of the f'(1515). If this mode does not exist, the $K\bar{K}$ branching fraction will have to be reported as (80±13)% (rather than (72±12)% as given in the table).

(p) See the listings for many statistically weak Y = 0 bumps with M ≳ 1700 MeV, seen in bubble chambers. We tabulate here 9 statistically strong bumps seen with a missing mass spectrometer ($\pi^-p \to p(MM)^-$) or seen in counter experiments on the $\bar{p}N$ total cross section.

Name	I	M (MeV)	Γ(MeV)	Decay Modes Observed
R1(1630)	≥1	1630 ± 15	≤21	1/3/>3 charg. part. ≈.37/.59/.04 } (MMS)⁻
R2(1700)	≥1	1700 ± 15	≤30	1/3/>3 charg. part. ≈.43/.56/.01
R3(1750)	≥1	1748 ± 15	< 38	1/3/>3 charg. part. >.14/<.80/.15
S(1930)	≥1	1929 ± 14	< 35	1/3/>3 charg. part. ≈ 0/.92/ 0
? $\{$ N$\bar{N}$(2190)	≥1	2190 ± 10	≈85 }	structure in N$\bar{N}$ total cross section
T(2200)	≥1	2195 ± 15	≤13 }	(MM)⁻ → 3 charged particl. ≈94%
? $\{$ N$\bar{N}$(2345)	≥1	2345 ± 10	≈140 }	structure in N$\bar{N}$ total cross section
U(2380)	≥1	2382 ± 24	≤30 }	(MM)⁻ → 1/3/>3 chrgd part. ≈30/45/25
N$\bar{N}$(2380)	0	2380 ± 10	≈140	structure in N$\bar{N}$ total cross section

There is no evidence on the G, J, or P quantum numbers of these bumps, nor is there satisfactory agreement between them and the bubble chamber claims. Further, the N$\bar{N}$ bumps are broader than the (MM)⁻ bumps, and there is no evidence for or against their interpretation as resonances.

Name	Other	$I^G(J^P)C$	Mass (MeV)	Width (MeV)		Decay mode	Fraction (%)	p_1	p_2
$\pi_A(1640)$	$\pi(A)$	$1^-(A)+$	1633 ±9	93 ±24	2.73 ±.18	3π	dominant	1245	797
$\rightarrow 3\pi$	?	$\leftrightarrow$?	S=1.2*			$[\pi^\pm\rho^0/\text{all }\pi^\pm\pi^+\pi^-$	$<20]$	745	637
$[\underset{=}{?} R_1(1630)$ see note (p)]						$[\pi^\pm f(\rightarrow\pi^+\pi^-)/\text{all }\pi^\pm\pi^+\pi^-$	$35\pm20]$	252	320
Not yet a completely established						$\eta\eta$	<9	966	727
resonance						$K\bar{K}$	<40	654	658
						$\pi^\pm 2\pi^+ 2\pi^-$	<10	935	714

Name	Other	$I^G(J^P)C$	Mass (MeV)	Width (MeV)		Decay mode	Fraction (%)	p_1	p_2
$\rho_N(1650)$	$\rho(N)$	$1^+(N)-$	1650 (q) ±20	120 (q) ±30	2.72 ±.20	2π	dominant	1385	820
$g \rightarrow 2\pi$	$(J^P = 1^-, 3^-, \ldots$ with 3^- favored)					$K\bar{K}$ indication seen, <10		668	667
$[\underset{=}{?} R_1(1630)$ see note (p)]						(other possible modes see under $\rho(1700)$? below)			

Name	Other	$I^G(J^P)C$	Mass (MeV)	Width (MeV)		Decay mode	Fraction (%)	p_1	p_2
$\rho(1700)?$	$\rho(A)$	$1^+(A)-$	1700 (r) ±20	110 (r) ±25	2.89 ±.19	4π	dominant	1141	792
?		$\mapsto$? $\mapsto$				$[\pi^\pm A_2^0(\rightarrow\pi^+\pi^-\pi^0)/\text{all }\pi^\pm\pi^+\pi^-\pi^0$	$40\pm20]$	263	333
$[\underset{=}{?} R_2(1700)$ see note (p)]						$[\pi^\pm\omega(\rightarrow\pi^+\pi^-\pi^0)/\text{all }\pi^\pm\pi^+\pi^-\pi^0$	$25\pm10]$	777	661
Not yet clear whether this is just an alternative						$[\rho^\pm\rho^0$	seen$]$	170	371
mode of the $\rho_N(1650)$, or a different resonance.						$\pi^\pm\phi/\pi^\pm\pi^+\pi^-\pi^0$	<11	540	532
The branching ratios are therefore only						$\pi^\pm 2\pi^+ 2\pi^-\pi^0$	<15	862	699
tentative.						2π (if $\neq \rho_N(1650)$)	<10	1420	838

$\rightarrow$ There is no well-established $Y = 0$ meson resonance with $M > 1700$ MeV. For a list of some possible states
$\rightarrow$ see footnote (p).

Name	Other	$I(J^P)$	Mass (MeV)	Width (MeV)		Decay mode	Fraction (%)	p_1	p_2
$K^+(494)$	$K(0^-)$	$1/2(0^-)$	493.82		0.244	See Table S			
$K^0(498)$			497.76		0.248				

Name	Other	$I(J^P)$	Mass (MeV)	Width (MeV)		Decay mode	Fraction (%)	p_1	p_2
$K^*(890)$	$K(1^-)$	$1/2(1^-)$	891.4 ±0.6	49.7 ±1.1	0.797 ±.044	$K\pi$	≈ 100	259	289
$m_0 - m_\pm = 6.3 \pm 4.1$				$\hookrightarrow$ for charged K^*		$K\pi\pi$	<0.2	120	216

Name	Other	$I(J^P)$	Mass (MeV)	Width (MeV)		Decay mode	Fraction (%)		
$K_A(1230)$ or C	$K(A)$	$1/2(1^+)$	≈ 1240	≈ 60	1.54 ±.07	Q-Region $\Bigg\}$	$K\pi\pi$ dominant		
Still some doubt. 2^- still poss.							See footnote (r).		
$K_A(1320)$	$K(A)$	$1/2(1^+)$	≈ 1330	≈ 70	1.77 ±.09				
$J^P = 2^-$ not yet completely ruled out.									

Name	Other	$I(J^P)$	Mass (MeV)	Width (MeV)		Decay mode	Fraction (%)	p_1	p_2
$K_N(1420)$	$K(2^+)$	$1/2(2^+)$	1422 ±4	89 ±6	2.012 ±.126	$K\pi$	51 ± 4	787	615
			S=1.2*			$K^*\pi$	33 ± 4	388	413
						$K\rho$	11 ± 3 $\Big\}$ S=1.4*	156	318
						$K\omega$	3.4 ± 1	143	304
						$K\eta$	2.0 ± 1	378	482

Name	Other	$I(J^P)$	Mass (MeV)	Width (MeV)		Decay mode	Fraction (%)	p_1	p_2
$K_A(1780)$ or L	$K(A)$?	$1/2(A)$?	1775 ±12 S=1.3*	72 ±26 S=1.4*	3.17 ±.13	$K\bar{\pi}$	<2.3	1167	825
						$K^*\bar{\pi}$	24 ± 8	772	670
						$K_N(1420)\pi$	16 ± 8	245	317
						$K\rho$	10 ± 6	532	632
						Remaining $K\pi\pi$	45 ± 15	1032	807
						$K\omega$	4.8 ± 2	519	624
						$K\eta$	<1	754	732

(q) Taken from compilation by T. Ferbel, Proc. 1968 Philadelphia Conf. See the data listings for averages of the values given in the literature.

(r) See note in listings. Some investigators see a broad enhancement in mass ($K\pi\pi$) from 1200 - 1350 MeV, and others see structure. A further bump at 1280 MeV, $\Gamma = 80$ MeV, has been suggested. In light of this confusion, the masses, widths, quantum numbers, and branching ratios are at best tentative. For the mass region 1200 - 1350 MeV, the decay rate into $K^*(890)\pi$ is large, and a $K\rho$ decay is seen. The $K\eta$, $K\omega$ and $K\pi$ rates are less than a few percent (although for $K\pi$, there is some disagreement among experimenters).

Mixing angles from Quadratic SU(3) Mass Formula: 0^- nonet (π, K, η, η') $\theta = 10.4°\pm0.2°$; 0^- nonet (π, K, η, E) $\theta = 6.2°\pm0.1°$; 1^- nonet $(\rho(m=765\pm15$ MeV$), K^*, \phi, \omega)$ $\theta = 39.9\pm1.1°$; 2^+ nonet $(A2, K_V(1420), f', f)$ $\theta = 29.9°\pm2.2°$.